A Second Course
in
CALCULUS

This book is in the

ADDISON-WESLEY SERIES IN MATHEMATICS

———————————

LYNN H. LOOMIS

Consulting Editor

A Second Course
in
CALCULUS

SERGE LANG

Columbia University, New York, New York

Second Edition

ADDISON-WESLEY PUBLISHING COMPANY

Reading, Massachusetts · Menlo Park, California · London · Don Mills, Ontario

Foreword

This volume is a continuation of a *First Course in Calculus*, and deals principally with functions of several variables.

The first chapter deals with vectors in n-space. This chapter covers enough linear algebra to be applied to the next six chapters (up to and including Chapter VII). We then take up more of the basic linear algebra (vector spaces, matrices, linear maps, determinants) to be able to apply this material to functions of several variables, viewing the derivative as a linear map. The applications include the chain rule, and the implicit function theorem, whose proof is based on the inverse mapping theorem. A proof for the latter requires techniques which belong to a more advanced analysis course. We also apply the linear algebra to multiple integrals, discussing the determinant as area (in the 2-dimensional case) and as volume in the higher dimensional case. We then discuss orthogonality, showing how the theory of orthogonality in n-space has the same algebraic foundations as the theory of Fourier series.

We end the book with a first introduction to normed vector spaces, and the (ϵ, δ) language of limits in this context. Such an introduction will be especially useful to students who go on to an advanced calculus course (essentially a first course in analysis), because having seen the (ϵ, δ) previously makes it much easier to assimilate the basic routine of limits, and then go on to more interesting material.

At present, still few students have had linear algebra before the calculus. Hence we developed it systematically, but not exhaustively, to cover what was needed. More complete accounts are easily available. For use in the present book, the reader may omit the treatment of determinants other than in the 2×2- and 3×3- case.

SERGE LANG
New York, 1968

Contents

Chapter VI

Higher Derivatives

Chapter VII

Maximum and Minimum

Chapter VIII

Vector Spaces

Chapter IX

Linear Equations and Bases

Chapter X

Linear Mappings

Chapter XVI

Orthogonality and Fourier Series

Chapter XVII

ϵ and δ

Chapter I

Vectors

The concept of a vector is basic for the whole course. It provides geometric motivation for everything that follows. Hence the properties of vectors, both algebraic and geometric, will be discussed in full.

The cross product is included for the sake of completeness. It is almost never used in the rest of the book. It is the only aspect of the theory of vectors which is valid only in three-dimensional space (not 2, nor 4, nor n-dimensional space). One significant feature of almost all the statements and proofs of this book (except for those concerning the cross product), is that they are neither easier nor harder to prove in 3- or n-space than they are in 2-space.

§1. DEFINITION OF POINTS IN n-SPACE

We have seen that a number can be used to represent a point on a line, once a unit length is selected.

A pair of numbers (i.e. a couple of numbers) (x, y) can be used to represent a point in the plane.

We now observe that a triple of numbers (x, y, z) can be used to represent a point in space, that is 3-dimensional space, or 3-space. We simply introduce one more axis. The following picture illustrates this:

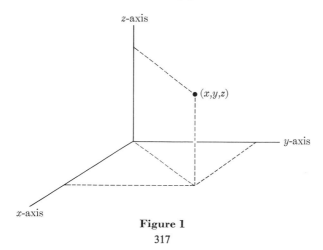

Figure 1

317

Instead of using x, y, z we could also use (x_1, x_2, x_3). The line could be called 1-space, and the plane could be called 2-space.

Thus we can say that a single number represents a point in 1-space. A couple represents a point in 2-space. A triple represents a point in 3-space.

Although we cannot draw a picture to go further, there is nothing to prevent us from considering a quadruple of numbers

$$(x_1, x_2, x_3, x_4)$$

and decreeing that this is a point in 4-space. A quintuple would be a point in 5-space, then would come a sextuple, septuple, octuple, ...

We let ourselves be carried away and *define a point in n-space* to be an n-tuple of numbers

$$(x_1, x_2, \ldots, x_n),$$

if n is a positive integer. We shall denote such an n-tuple by a capital letter X, and try to keep small letters for numbers and capital letters for points. We call the numbers $x_1, \ldots, x_n$ the *coordinates* of the point X.

Most of our examples will take place when $n = 2$ or $n = 3$. Thus the reader may visualize either of these two cases throughout the book. However, two comments must be made: First, practically no formula or theorem is simpler by making such assumptions on n. When we meet cases where a simplification occurs, we shall always treat these cases separately (e.g. in Taylor's formula for several variables). Second, the case $n = 4$ does occur in physics, and the case $n = n$ occurs often enough in practice or theory to warrant its treatment here. Furthermore, part of our purpose is in fact to show that the general case is always similar to the case when $n = 2$ or $n = 3$.

We shall now define how to add points. If A, B are two points, say

$$A = (a_1, \ldots, a_n), \qquad B = (b_1, \ldots, b_n),$$

then we define $A + B$ to be the point whose coordinates are

$$(a_1 + b_1, \ldots, a_n + b_n).$$

For example, in the plane, if $A = (1, 2)$ and $B = (-3, 5)$ then

$$A + B = (-2, 7).$$

In 3-space, if $A = (-1, \pi, 3)$ and $B = (\sqrt{2}, 7, -2)$ then

$$A + B = (\sqrt{2} - 1, \pi + 7, 1).$$

Furthermore, if c is any number, we *define* cA to be the point whose coordinates are

$$(ca_1, \ldots, ca_n).$$

If $A = (2, -1, 5)$ and $c = 7$ then $cA = (14, -7, 35)$.

We observe that the following rules are satisfied:

(1) $(A + B) + C = A + (B + C)$.

(2) $A + B = B + A$.

(3) $c(A + B) = cA + cB$.

(4) If c_1, c_2 are numbers, then

$$(c_1 + c_2)A = c_1A + c_2A \qquad \text{and} \qquad (c_1c_2)A = c_1(c_2A).$$

(5) If we let $O = (0, \ldots, 0)$ be the point all of whose coordinates are 0, then $O + A = A + O = A$ for all A.

(6) $1 \cdot A = A$, and if we denote by $-A$ the n-tuple $(-1)A$, then

$$A + (-A) = O.$$

[Instead of writing $A + (-B)$, we shall frequently write $A - B$.]

All these properties are very simple to prove, and we suggest that you verify them on some examples. We shall give in detail the proof of property (3). Let $A = (a_1, \ldots, a_n)$ and $B = (b_1, \ldots, b_n)$. Then

$$A + B = (a_1 + b_1, \ldots, a_n + b_n)$$

and

$$\begin{aligned} c(A + B) &= \big(c(a_1 + b_1), \ldots, c(a_n + b_n)\big) \\ &= (ca_1 + cb_1, \ldots, ca_n + cb_n) \\ &= cA + cB, \end{aligned}$$

this last step being true by definition of addition of n-tuples.

The other proofs are left as exercises.

Note. Do not confuse the number 0 and the n-tuple $(0, \ldots, 0)$. We usually denote this n-tuple by O, and also call it zero, because no difficulty can occur in practice.

We shall now interpret addition and multiplication by numbers geometrically in the plane (you can visualize simultaneously what happens in 3-space).

Take an example. Let $A = (2, 3)$ and $B = (-1, 1)$. Then

$$A + B = (1, 4).$$

The figure looks like a parallelogram (Fig. 2).

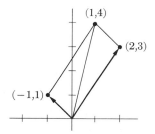

(1,4)

(2,3)

(−1,1)

Figure 2

Take another example. Let $A = (3, 1)$ and $B = (1, 2)$. Then

$$A + B = (4, 3).$$

We see again that the geometric representation of our addition looks like a parallelogram (Fig. 3).

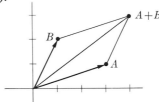

Figure 3

What is the representation of multiplication by a number? Let $A = (1, 2)$ and $c = 3$. Then $cA = (3, 6)$ (Fig. 4a).

Multiplication by 3 amounts to stretching A by 3. Similarly, $\frac{1}{2}A$ amounts to stretching A by $\frac{1}{2}$, i.e. shrinking A to half its size. In general, if t is a number, $t > 0$, we interpret tA as a point in the same direction as A from the origin, but t times the distance.

Multiplication by a negative number reverses the direction. Thus $-3A$ would be represented as in Fig. 4(b).

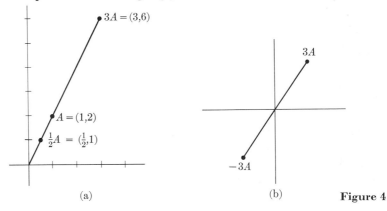

(a)   (b)   **Figure 4**

EXERCISES

Find $A + B$, $A - B$, $3A$, $-2B$ in each of the following cases.

1. $A = (2, -1)$, $B = (-1, 1)$ 2. $A = (-1, 3)$, $B = (0, 4)$

3. $A = (2, -1, 5)$, $B = (-1, 1, 1)$ 4. $A = (-1, -2, 3)$, $B = (-1, 3, -4)$

5. $A = (\pi, 3, -1)$, $B = (2\pi, -3, 7)$ 6. $A = (15, -2, 4)$, $B = (\pi, 3, -1)$

7. Draw the points of Exercises 1 through 4 on a sheet of graph paper.

8. Let A, B be as in Exercise 1. Draw the points $A + 2B$, $A + 3B$, $A - 2B$, $A - 3B$, $A + \frac{1}{2}B$ on a sheet of graph paper.

§2. VECTORS

We define a *located vector* to be an ordered pair of points which we write $\overrightarrow{AB}$. (This is *not* a product.) We visualize this as an arrow between A and B. We call A the *beginning point* and B the *end point* of the located vector (Fig. 5).

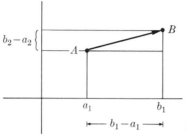

Figure 5

How are the coordinates of B obtained from those of A? We observe that in the plane,

$$b_1 = a_1 + (b_1 - a_1).$$

Similarly,

$$b_2 = a_2 + (b_2 - a_2).$$

This means that

$$B = A + (B - A).$$

Let $\overrightarrow{AB}$ and $\overrightarrow{CD}$ be two located vectors. We shall say that they are *equivalent* if $B - A = D - C$. Every located vector $\overrightarrow{AB}$ is equivalent to one whose beginning point is the origin, because $\overrightarrow{AB}$ is equivalent to $\overrightarrow{O(B - A)}$. Clearly this is the only located vector whose beginning point is the origin and which is equivalent to $\overrightarrow{AB}$. If you visualize the parallelogram law in the plane, then it is clear that equivalence of two located vectors can be interpreted geometrically by saying that the lengths of the line segments determined by the pair of points are equal, and that the "directions" in which they point are the same.

In the next figures, we have drawn the located vectors $\overrightarrow{O(B - A)}$, $\overrightarrow{AB}$, and $\overrightarrow{O(A - B)}$, $\overrightarrow{BA}$.

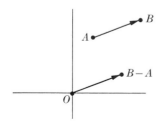

Figure 6

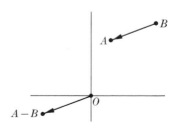

Figure 7

Given a located vector $\overrightarrow{OC}$ whose beginning point is the origin, we shall say that it is *located at the origin*. Given any located vector $\overrightarrow{AB}$, we shall say that it is *located at A*.

A located vector at the origin is entirely determined by its end point. In view of this, we shall call an n-tuple either a point or a vector, depending on the interpretation which we have in mind.

Two located vectors $\overrightarrow{AB}$ and $\overrightarrow{PQ}$ are said to be *parallel* if there is a number $c \neq 0$ such that $B - A = c(Q - P)$. They are said to have the *same direction* if there is a number $c > 0$ such that $B - A = c(Q - P)$, and to have *opposite direction* if there is a number $c < 0$ such that $B - A = c(Q - P)$. In a similar manner, any definition made concerning n-tuples can be carried over to located vectors. For instance, in the next section, we shall define what it means for n-tuples to be perpendicular. Then we can say that two located vectors $\overrightarrow{AB}$ and $\overrightarrow{PQ}$ are perpendicular if $B - A$ is perpendicular to $Q - P$. In the next figure, we have drawn a picture of such vectors in the plane.

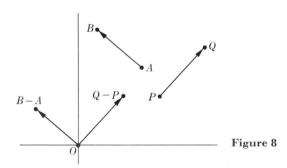

Figure 8

§3. SCALAR PRODUCT

It is understood that throughout a discussion we select vectors always in the same n-dimensional space.

Let $A = (a_1, \ldots, a_n)$ and $B = (b_1, \ldots, b_n)$ be two vectors. We define their *scalar* or *dot product* $A \cdot B$ to be

$$a_1 b_1 + \cdots + a_n b_n.$$

This product is a *number*. For instance, if

$$A = (1, 3, -2) \quad \text{and} \quad B = (-1, 4, -3)$$

then

$$A \cdot B = -1 + 12 + 6 = 17.$$

For the moment, we do not give a geometric interpretation to this scalar product. We shall do this later. We derive first some important properties. The basic ones are:

SP 1. *We have* $A \cdot B = B \cdot A$.

SP 2. *If A, B, C are three vectors then*

$$A \cdot (B + C) = A \cdot B + A \cdot C = (B + C) \cdot A.$$

SP 3. *If x is a number, then*

$$(xA) \cdot B = x(A \cdot B) \qquad \text{and} \qquad A \cdot (xB) = x(A \cdot B).$$

SP 4. *If $A = O$ is the zero vector, then $A \cdot A = 0$, and otherwise $A \cdot A > 0$.*

We shall now prove these properties.
Concerning the first, we have

$$a_1 b_1 + \cdots + a_n b_n = b_1 a_1 + \cdots + b_n a_n,$$

because for any two numbers a, b, we have $ab = ba$. This proves the first property.

For SP 2, let $C = (c_1, \ldots, c_n)$. Then

$$B + C = (b_1 + c_1, \ldots, b_n + c_n)$$

and

$$A \cdot (B + C) = a_1(b_1 + c_1) + \cdots + a_n(b_n + c_n)$$
$$= a_1 b_1 + a_1 c_1 + \cdots + a_n b_n + a_n c_n.$$

Reordering the terms yields

$$a_1 b_1 + \cdots + a_n b_n + a_1 c_1 + \cdots + a_n c_n,$$

which is none other than $A \cdot B + A \cdot C$. This proves what we wanted.

We leave property SP 3 as an exercise.

Finally, for SP 4, we observe that if one coordinate a_i of A is not equal to 0, then there is a term $a_i^2 \neq 0$ and $a_i^2 > 0$ in the scalar product

$$A \cdot A = a_1^2 + \cdots + a_n^2.$$

Since every term is $\geqq 0$, it follows that the sum is > 0, as was to be shown.

In much of the work which we shall do concerning vectors, we shall use only the ordinary properties of addition, multiplication by numbers, and the four properties of the scalar product. We shall give a formal discussion of these later. For the moment, observe that there are other objects with which you are familiar and which can be added, subtracted, and multiplied by numbers, for instance the continuous functions on an interval $[a, b]$ (cf. Exercise 5).

Instead of writing $A \cdot A$ for the scalar product of a vector with itself, it will be convenient to write also A^2. (This is the only instance when we allow ourselves such a notation. Thus A^3 has no meaning.) As an exercise, verify the following identities:

$$(A + B)^2 = A^2 + 2A \cdot B + B^2,$$
$$(A - B)^2 = A^2 - 2A \cdot B + B^2.$$

A dot product $A \cdot B$ may very well be equal to 0 without either A or B being the zero vector. For instance, let $A = (1, 2, 3)$ and $B = (2, 1, -\frac{4}{3})$. Then $A \cdot B = 0$.

We define two vectors A, B to be *perpendicular* (or as we shall also say, *orthogonal*) if $A \cdot B = 0$. For the moment, it is not clear that in the plane, this definition coincides with our intuitive geometric notion of perpendicularity. We shall convince you that it does in the next section.

EXERCISES

1. Find $A \cdot A$ for each one of the n-tuples of Exercises 1 through 6 of §1.
2. Find $A \cdot B$ for each one of the n-tuples as above.
3. Using only the four properties of the scalar product, verify in detail the identities given in the text for $(A + B)^2$ and $(A - B)^2$.
4. Which of the following pairs of vectors are perpendicular?
   (a) $(1, -1, 1)$ and $(2, 1, 5)$ (b) $(1, -1, 1)$ and $(2, 3, 1)$
   (c) $(-5, 2, 7)$ and $(3, -1, 2)$ (d) $(\pi, 2, 1)$ and $(2, -\pi, 0)$
5. Consider continuous functions on the interval $[-1, 1]$. Define the scalar product of two such functions f, g to be

$$\int_{-1}^{+1} f(x)g(x)\, dx.$$

We denote this integral also by $\langle f, g \rangle$. Verify that the four rules for a scalar product are satisfied, in other words, show that:

SP 1. $\langle f, g \rangle = \langle g, f \rangle$.

SP 2. $\langle f, g + h \rangle = \langle f, g \rangle + \langle f, h \rangle$.

SP 3. $\langle cf, g \rangle = c \langle f, g \rangle$.

SP 4. *If $f = 0$ then $\langle f, f \rangle = 0$ and if $f \neq 0$ then $\langle f, f \rangle > 0$.*

6. If $f(x) = x$ and $g(x) = x^2$, what are $\langle f, f \rangle$, $\langle g, g \rangle$, and $\langle f, g \rangle$?
7. Consider continuous functions on the interval $[-\pi, \pi]$. Define a scalar product similar to the above for this interval. Show that the functions $\sin nx$ and $\cos mx$ are orthogonal for this scalar product (m, n being integers).
8. Let A be a vector perpendicular to every vector X. Show that $A = O$.

§4. THE NORM OF A VECTOR

The following inequality is called the *Schwarz inequality* and is funda-mental in the theory of vectors.

Theorem 1. *Let A, B be two vectors. Then $(A \cdot B)^2 \leqq (A \cdot A)(B \cdot B)$.*

Proof. Let $x = B \cdot B$ and $y = -A \cdot B$. Then by SP 4 we have

$$0 \leqq (xA + yB) \cdot (xA + yB).$$

We multiply out the right-hand side of this inequality and get

$$0 \leqq x^2(A \cdot A) + 2xy(A \cdot B) + y^2(B \cdot B).$$

Substituting the values for x and y yields

$$0 \leqq (B \cdot B)^2(A \cdot A) - 2(B \cdot B)(A \cdot B)^2 + (A \cdot B)^2(B \cdot B).$$

If $B = O$ then the inequality of the theorem is obvious, both sides being equal to 0. If $B \neq O$, then $B \cdot B \neq 0$ and we can divide this last expres-sion by $B \cdot B$. We then obtain

$$0 \leqq (A \cdot A)(B \cdot B) - (A \cdot B)^2.$$

Transposing the term $-(A \cdot B)^2$ to the other side of the inequality con-cludes the proof.

We define the *norm*, or *length*, of a vector A, and denote by $\|A\|$, the number

$$\|A\| = \sqrt{A \cdot A}.$$

Since $A \cdot A \geqq 0$, we can take the square root. Furthermore, we note immediately that $\|A\| \neq 0$ if $A \neq O$.

In terms of coordinates, we see that

$$\|A\| = \sqrt{a_1^2 + \cdots + a_n^2},$$

and therefore that when $n = 2$ or $n = 3$, this coincides with our intuitive notion (derived from the Pythagoras theorem) of length. Indeed, when $n = 2$ and say $A = (a, b)$ then the norm of A is

$$\|A\| = \sqrt{a^2 + b^2},$$

as in the following picture.

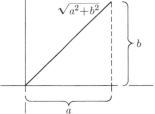

Figure 9

If $n = 3$, then the picture looks as follows, with $A = (x, y, z)$:

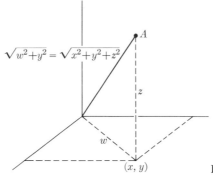

Figure 10

If we first look at the two components (x, y), then the length of the segment between $(0, 0)$ and (x, y) is equal to $w = \sqrt{x^2 + y^2}$, as indicated.
Then again the length of A by the Pythagoras theorem would be

$$\sqrt{w^2 + z^2} = \sqrt{x^2 + y^2 + z^2}.$$

Thus when $n = 3$, our definition of length is compatible with the geometry
of the Pythagoras theorem.

To take a numerical example, if $A = (1, 2, -3)$ then

$$\|A\| = \sqrt{1 + 4 + 9} = \sqrt{14}.$$

In view of our definition, we can rewrite the inequality of Theorem 1
in the form

$$|(A \cdot B)| \leq \|A\| \, \|B\|$$

by taking the square root of both sides. We shall use it in this form in
the proof of the next theorem.

Theorem 2. *Let A, B be vectors. Then*

$$\|A + B\| \leq \|A\| + \|B\|.$$

Proof. Both sides of this inequality are positive or 0. Hence it will
suffice to prove that their squares satisfy the desired inequality, in other
words,

$$(A + B) \cdot (A + B) \leq (\|A\| + \|B\|)^2.$$

To do this, we consider

$$(A + B) \cdot (A + B) = A \cdot A + 2A \cdot B + B \cdot B.$$

In view of our previous result, this satisfies the inequality

$$\leq \|A\|^2 + 2\|A\| \, \|B\| + \|B\|^2,$$

and the right-hand side is none other than

$$(\|A\| + \|B\|)^2.$$

Our theorem is proved.

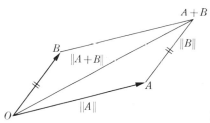

Figure 11

Theorem 2 is known as the *triangle inequality*. The reason for this is that if we draw a triangle as in Fig. 11, then Theorem 2 expresses the fact that the length of one side is $\leq$ the sum of the lengths of the other two sides. (Cf. Exercise 11.)

Theorem 3. *Let x be a number. Then*

$$\|xA\| = |x| \, \|A\|$$

(absolute value of x times the length of A).

Proof. By definition, we have

$$\|xA\|^2 - (xA) \cdot (xA),$$

which is equal to

$$x^2(A \cdot A)$$

by the properties of the scalar product. Taking the square root now yields what we want.

We shall say that a vector U is a *unit* vector if $\|U\| = 1$. Given any vector A, let $a = \|A\|$. If $a \neq 0$ then

$$\frac{1}{a} A$$

is a unit vector, because

$$\left\| \frac{1}{a} A \right\| = \frac{1}{a} a = 1.$$

We shall say that two vectors A, B (neither of which is O) have the *same direction* if there is a number $c > 0$ such that $cA = B$. In view of this definition, we see that the vector

$$\frac{1}{\|A\|} A$$

is a unit vector in the direction of A (provided $A \neq O$).

Example 1. Let $A = (1, 2, -3)$. Then $\|A\| = \sqrt{14}$. Hence the unit vector in the direction of A is the vector

$$U = \left(\frac{1}{\sqrt{14}}, \frac{2}{\sqrt{14}}, \frac{-3}{\sqrt{14}} \right).$$

We mention in passing that two vectors A, B (neither of which is O) have *opposite directions* if there is a number $c < 0$ such that $cA = B$.

Let A, B be two n-tuples. We define the *distance* between A and B to be $\|A - B\| = \sqrt{(A - B) \cdot (A - B)}$. This definition coincides with our geometric intuition when A, B are points in the plane (Fig. 12).

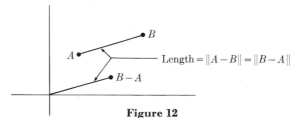

Figure 12

It is the same thing as the length of the located vector $\overrightarrow{AB}$ or the located vector $\overrightarrow{BA}$.

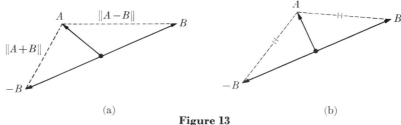

(a)   (b)

Figure 13

We are also in the position to justify our definition of perpendicularity. Given A, B in the plane, the condition that

$$\|A + B\| = \|A - B\|$$

(illustrated in Fig. 13b) coincides with the geometric property that A should be perpendicular to B.

Taking the square of each side, we see that this condition is equivalent with

$$(A + B) \cdot (A + B) = (A - B) \cdot (A - B)$$

and expanding out, this equality is equivalent with

$$A \cdot A + 2A \cdot B + B \cdot B = A \cdot A - 2A \cdot B + B \cdot B.$$

Making cancellations, we obtain the equivalent condition

$$4A \cdot B = 0$$

or

$$A \cdot B = 0.$$

This achieves what we wanted to show, namely that

$$\|A - B\| = \|A + B\| \qquad \text{if and only if} \qquad A \cdot B = 0.$$

We shall now use the notion of perpendicularity to derive the notion of projection, as on the following picture.

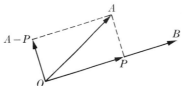

Figure 14

Let A, B be two vectors and $B \neq O$. We wish to define the projection of A along B, which will be a vector P as shown in the picture. We seek a vector P such that $A - P$ is perpendicular to B, and such that P can be written in the form $P = cB$ for some number c. Suppose that we can find such a number c, namely one satisfying

$$(A - cB) \cdot B = 0.$$

We then obtain

$$A \cdot B = cB \cdot B,$$

and therefore

$$c = \frac{A \cdot B}{B \cdot B}.$$

We see that such a number c is uniquely determined by our condition of perpendicularity. Conversely, if we let c have the above value, then we clearly have $(A - cB) \cdot B = 0$, as we see by multiplying out this dot product.

We now define the vector cB to be the *projection* of A along B, if c is the number

$$c = \frac{A \cdot B}{B \cdot B},$$

and we define c to be the *component* of A along B. *If B is a unit vector, then we have simply*

$$c = A \cdot B.$$

Example 2. Let $A = (1, 2, -3)$ and $B = (1, 1, 2)$. Then the component of A along B is the *number*

$$c = \frac{A \cdot B}{B \cdot B} = \frac{-3}{6} = -\frac{1}{2}.$$

Hence the projection of A along B is the *vector*

$$cB = (-\tfrac{1}{2}, -\tfrac{1}{2}, -1).$$

Our construction has an immediate interpretation in the plane, which gives us a geometric interpretation for the scalar product. Namely, assume $A \neq O$ and look at the angle θ between A and B (Fig. 15). Then from plane geometry we see that

$$\cos \theta = \frac{c\|B\|}{\|A\|},$$

or substituting the value for c obtained above,

$$\boxed{A \cdot B = \|A\| \, \|B\| \cos \theta.}$$

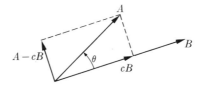

Figure 15

In view of Theorem 1, we know that in n-space, the number

$$\frac{A \cdot B}{\|A\| \, \|B\|}$$

has absolute value ≤ 1. Consequently,

$$-1 \leq \frac{A \cdot B}{\|A\| \, \|B\|} \leq 1,$$

and there exists a unique angle θ such that $0 \leq \theta \leq \pi$, and such that

$$\cos \theta = \frac{A \cdot B}{\|A\| \, \|B\|}.$$

We define this angle to be the *angle between A and B*.

In some treatments of vectors, one takes the relation

$$A \cdot B = \|A\| \, \|B\| \cos \theta$$

as definition of the scalar product. This is subject to the following disadvantages, not to say objections:

(a) The four properties of the scalar product SP 1 through SP 4 are then by no means obvious.

(b) Even in 3-space, one has to rely on geometric intuition to obtain the cosine of the angle between A and B, and this intuition is less clear than in the plane. In higher dimensional space, it fails even more.

(c) It is extremely hard to work with such a definition to obtain further properties of the scalar product.

Thus we prefer to lay obvious algebraic foundations, and then recover very simply all the properties. Aside from that, in analysis, one uses scalar products in the context of functions, where $\cos \theta$ becomes completely meaningless, for instance in Exercise 5 of §3, which is the starting point of the theory of Fourier series.

EXERCISES

1. Find the length of the vector A in Exercises 1 through 6 of §1.

2. Find the length of the vector B in Exercises 1 through 6 of §1.

3. Find the projection of A along B in Exercises 1 through 6 of §1.

4. Find the projection of B along A in these exercises.

5. In Exercise 6 of §3, find the projection of f along g and the projection of g along f, using the same definition of projection that has been given in the text (and did not refer to coordinates).

6. Find the norm of the functions $\sin 3x$ and $\cos x$, with respect to the scalar product on the interval $[-\pi, \pi]$ given by the integral.

7. Find the norm of the constant function 1 on the interval $[-\pi, \pi]$.

8. Find the norm of the constant function 1 on the interval $[-1, 1]$.

9. Let $A_1, \ldots, A_r$ be non-zero vectors which are mutually perpendicular, in other words $A_i \cdot A_j = 0$ if $i \neq j$. Let $c_1, \ldots, c_r$ be numbers such that

$$c_1 A_1 + \cdots + c_r A_r = 0.$$

Show that all $c_i = 0$.

10. Let A, B be two non-zero vectors in n-space. Let θ be the angle between them. If $\cos \theta = 1$, show that A and B have the same direction. If $\cos \theta = -1$, show that A and B have opposite direction.

11. If A, B are two vectors in n-space, denote by $d(A, B)$ the distance between A and B, i.e. $d(A, B) = \|B - A\|$. Show that $d(A, B) = d(B, A)$, and that for any three vectors A, B, C we have

$$d(A, B) \leqq d(A, C) + d(B, C).$$

12. For any vectors A, B in n-space, prove the following relations:

    (a) $\|A + B\|^2 + \|A - B\|^2 = 2\|A\|^2 + 2\|B\|^2$.

    (b) $\|A + B\|^2 = \|A\|^2 + \|B\|^2 + 2A \cdot B$.

    (c) $\|A + B\|^2 - \|A - B\|^2 = 4A \cdot B$.

    Interpret (a) as a "parallelogram law".

13. Determine the cosine of the angles of the triangle whose vertices are $(2, -1, 1)$, $(1, -3, -5)$, $(3, -4, -4)$.

14. Show that if θ is the angle between A and B, then

$$\|A - B\|^2 = \|A\|^2 + \|B\|^2 - 2\|A\|\,\|B\| \cos \theta.$$

15. Let A, B, C be three vectors, and $A \neq 0$. If $A \cdot B = A \cdot C$, show by an example that we do not necessarily have $B = C$.

16. Let A, B be non-zero vectors, mutually perpendicular. Show that for any number c we have $\|A + cB\| \geq \|A\|$.

17. Let A, B be non-zero vectors. Assume that $\|A + cB\| \geq \|A\|$ for all numbers c. Show that A, B are perpendicular. [*Hint:* Take c to be very large positive or negative.]

18. Let $B_1, \ldots, B_m$ be vectors of length 1 in n-space, and mutually perpendicular, that is $B_i \cdot B_j = 0$ if $i \neq j$. Let A be a vector in n-space, and let c_i be the component of A along B_i. Let $x_1, \ldots, x_m$ be numbers. Show that

$$\|A - (c_1 B_1 + \cdots + c_m B_m)\| \leq \|A - (x_1 B_1 + \cdots + x_m B_m)\|.$$

§5. LINES AND PLANES

We define the parametric equation of a straight line passing through a point P in the direction of a vector $A \neq O$ to be

$$X = P + tA,$$

where t runs through all numbers (Fig. 16).

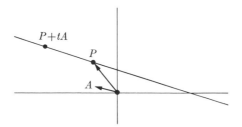

Figure 16

Suppose that we work in the plane, and write the coordinates of a point X as (x, y). Let $P = (p, q)$ and $A = (a, b)$. Then in terms of the coordinates, we can write

$$x = p + ta, \qquad y = q + tb.$$

We can then eliminate t and obtain the usual equation relating x and y.

For example, let $P = (2, 1)$ and $A = (-1, 5)$. Then the parametric equation of the line through P in the direction of A gives us

(*) $\qquad\qquad\qquad x = 2 - t, \qquad y = 1 + 5t.$

Multiplying the first equation by 5 and adding yields

(**) $\qquad\qquad\qquad 5x + y = 11,$

which is familiar.

This elimination of t shows that every pair (x, y) which satisfies the parametric equation (*) for some value of t also satisfies equation (**). Conversely, suppose we have a pair of numbers (x, y) satisfying (**). Let $t = 2 - x$. Then

$$y = 11 - 5x = 11 - 5(2 - t) = 1 + 5t.$$

Hence there exists some value of t which satisfies equation (*). Thus we have proved that the pairs (x, y) which are solutions of (**) are exactly the same pairs of numbers as those obtained by giving arbitrary values for t in (*). Thus the straight line can be described parametrically as in (*) or in terms of its usual equation (**). The same procedure works in general.

In higher dimensional space, we *cannot* eliminate t in this manner, and thus the parametric equation is the only one available to describe a straight line.

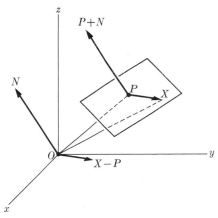

Figure 17

However, we can describe planes by an equation analogous to the single equation of the line. We proceed as follows.

Let P be a point, and consider a located vector $\overrightarrow{ON}$. We define the *hyperplane* passing through P perpendicular to $\overrightarrow{ON}$ to be the collection of all points X such that the located vector $\overrightarrow{PX}$ is perpendicular to $\overrightarrow{ON}$. According to our definitions, this amounts to the condition

$$(X - P) \cdot N = 0,$$

which can also be written as

$$X \cdot N = P \cdot N.$$

We shall also say that this hyperplane is the one perpendicular to N, and consists of all vectors X such that $X - P$ is perpendicular to N. We have drawn a typical situation in 3-space in Fig. 17.

Instead of saying that N is perpendicular to the plane, one also says that N is *normal* to the plane.

Let t be a number $\neq 0$. Then the set of points X such that

$$(X - P) \cdot N = 0$$

coincides with the set of points X such that

$$(X - P) \cdot tN = 0.$$

Thus we may say that our plane is the plane passing through P and perpendicular to the *line* in the direction of N. To find the equation of the plane, we could use any vector tN (with $t \neq 0$) instead of N.

In 3-space, we get an ordinary plane. For example, let $P = (2, 1, -1)$ and $N = (-1, 1, 3)$. Then the equation of the plane passing through P and perpendicular to N is

$$-x + y + 3z = -2 + 1 - 3$$

or

$$-x + y + 3z = -4.$$

Observe that in 2-space, with $X = (x, y)$, we are led to the equation of the line in the ordinary sense. For example, the equation of the line passing through $(4, -3)$ and perpendicular to $(-5, 2)$ is

$$-5x + 2y = -20 - 6 = -26.$$

We are now in position to interpret the coefficients $(-5, 2)$ of x and y in this equation. They give rise to a vector perpendicular to the line. In any equation

$$ax + by = c$$

the vector (a, b) is perpendicular to the line determined by the equation. Similarly, in 3-space, the vector (a, b, c) is perpendicular to the plane determined by the equation

$$ax + by + cz = d.$$

Two vectors A, B are said to be parallel if there exists a number $c \neq 0$ such that $cA = B$. Two lines are said to be *parallel* if, given two distinct points P_1, Q_1 on the first line and P_2, Q_2 on the second, the vectors

$$P_1 - Q_1$$

and

$$P_2 - Q_2$$

are parallel.

Two planes are said to be *parallel* (in 3-space) if their normal vectors are parallel. They are said to be *perpendicular* if their normal vectors are perpendicular. The *angle* between two planes is defined to be the angle between their normal vectors.

Example 1. Find the cosine of the angle between the planes

$$2x - y + z = 0,$$
$$x + 2y - z = 1.$$

This cosine is the cosine of the angle between the vectors

$$A = (2, -1, 1) \quad \text{and} \quad B = (1, 2, -1).$$

It is therefore equal to

$$\frac{A \cdot B}{\|A\| \, \|B\|} = -\frac{1}{6}.$$

Example 2. Let $Q = (1, 1, 1)$ and $P = (1, -1, 2)$. Let $N = (1, 2, 3)$. Find the point of intersection of the line through P in the direction of N, and the plane through Q perpendicular to N.

The parametric equation of the line through P in the direction of N is

(1) $$X = P + tN.$$

The equation of the plane through Q perpendicular to N is

(2) $$(X - Q) \cdot N = 0.$$

We must find the value of t such that the vector X in (1) also satisfies (2), that is

$$(P + tN - Q) \cdot N = 0,$$

or after using the rules of the dot product,

$$(P - Q) \cdot N + tN \cdot N = 0.$$

Solving for t yields

$$t = \frac{(Q - P) \cdot N}{N \cdot N} = \frac{1}{14}.$$

Thus the desired point of intersection is

$$P + tN = (1, -1, 2) + \tfrac{1}{14}(1, 2, 3) = (\tfrac{15}{14}, -\tfrac{12}{14}, \tfrac{31}{14}).$$

Example 3. Find the equation of the plane passing through the three points

$$P_1 = (1, 2, -1), \qquad P_2 = (-1, 1, 4), \qquad P_3 = (1, 3, -2).$$

We visualize schematically the three points as follows:

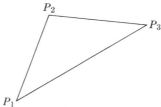

Figure 18

Then we find a vector N perpendicular to $\overrightarrow{P_1P_2}$ and $\overrightarrow{P_1P_3}$, or in other words, perpendicular to $P_2 - P_1$ and $P_3 - P_1$. We have

$$P_2 - P_1 = (-2, -1, +5),$$
$$P_3 - P_1 = (0, 1, -1).$$

Let $N = (a, b, c)$. We must solve:

$$-2a - b + 5c = 0,$$
$$b - c = 0.$$

We take $b = c = 1$ and solve for a, getting $a = 2$. Then

$$N = (2, 1, 1)$$

satisfies our requirements. The plane perpendicular to N, passing through P_1 is the desired plane. Its equation is therefore

$$2x + y + z = 2 + 2 - 1 = 3.$$

EXERCISES

Find a parametric equation for the line passing through the following points.

1. $(1, 1, -1)$ and $(-2, 1, 3)$ 2. $(-1, 5, 2)$ and $(3, -4, 1)$

Find the equation of the line in 2-space, perpendicular to A and passing through P, for the following values of A and P.

3. $A = (1, -1), P = (-5, 3)$ 4. $A = (-5, 4), P = (3, 2)$

5. Show that the lines

$$3x - 5y = 1, \qquad 2x + 3y = 5$$

are not perpendicular.

6. Which of the following pairs of lines are perpendicular?
   (a) $3x - 5y = 1$ and $2x + y = 2$
   (b) $2x + 7y = 1$ and $x - y = 5$
   (c) $3x - 5y = 1$ and $5x + 3y = 7$
   (d) $-x + y = 2$ and $x + y = 9$

7. Find the equation of the plane perpendicular to the given vector N and passing through the given point P.
   (a) $N = (1, -1, 3)$, $P = (4, 2, -1)$
   (b) $N = (-3, -2, 4)$, $P = (2, \pi, -5)$
   (c) $N = (-1, 0, 5)$, $P = (2, 3, 7)$

8. Find the equation of the plane passing through the following three points.
   (a) $(2, 1, 1)$, $(3, -1, 1)$, $(4, 1, -1)$
   (b) $(-2, 3, -1)$, $(2, 2, 3)$, $(-4, -1, 1)$
   (c) $(-5, -1, 2)$, $(1, 2, -1)$, $(3, -1, 2)$

9. Find a vector perpendicular to $(1, 2, -3)$ and $(2, -1, 3)$, and another vector perpendicular to $(-1, 3, 2)$ and $(2, 1, 1)$.

10. Let P be the point $(1, 2, 3, 4)$ and Q the point $(4, 3, 2, 1)$. Let A be the vector $(1, 1, 1, 1)$. Let L be the line passing through P and parallel to A.
    (a) Given a point X on the line L, compute the distance between Q and X (as a function of the parameter t).
    (b) Show that there is precisely one point X_0 on the line such that this distance achieves a minimum, and that this minimum is $2\sqrt{5}$.
    (c) Show that $X_0 - Q$ is perpendicular to the line.

11. Let P be the point $(1, -1, 3, 1)$ and Q the point $(1, 1, -1, 2)$. Let A be the vector $(1, -3, 2, 1)$. Solve the same questions as in the preceding problem, except that in this case the minimum distance is $\sqrt{146/15}$.

12. Find a vector parallel to the line of intersection of the two planes
$$2x - y + z = 1, \qquad 3x + y + z = 2.$$

13. Same question for the planes,
$$2x + y + 5z = 2, \qquad 3x - 2y + z = 3.$$

14. Find a parametric equation for the line of intersection of the planes of Exercises 12 and 13.

15. Find the cosine of the angle between the following planes:
   (a) $x + y + z = 1$ (b) $2x + 3y - z = 2$
       $x - y - z = 5$ $x - y + z = 1$
   (c) $x + 2y - z = 1$ (d) $2x + y + z = 3$
       $-x + 3y + z = 2$ $-x - y + z = \pi$

16. Let $X \cdot N = P \cdot N$ be the equation of a plane in 3-space. Let Q be a point not lying in the plane. Show that there is a unique number t such that $Q + tN$ lies in the plane (i.e. satisfies the equation of the plane). What is this value in terms of P, Q, and N?

17. Let $Q = (1, -1, 2)$, $P = (1, 3, -2)$, and $N = (1, 2, 2)$. Find the point of the intersection of the line through P in the direction of N, and the plane through Q perpendicular to N.

18. Let P, Q be two points and N a vector in 3-space. Let P' be the point of intersection of the line through P, in the direction of N, and the plane through Q, perpendicular to N. We define the *distance* from P to that plane to be the distance between P and P'. Find this distance when

$$P = (1, 3, 5), \qquad Q = (-1, 1, 7), \qquad N = (-1, 1, -1).$$

19. Let $P = (1, 3, 5)$ and $A = (-2, 1, 1)$. Find the intersection of the line through P in the direction of A, and the plane

$$2x + 3y - z = 1.$$

20. Find the distance between the point $(1, 1, 2)$ and the plane

$$3x + y - 5z = 2.$$

21. Let $P = (1, 3, -1)$ and $Q = (-4, 5, 2)$. Determine the coordinates of the following points: (a) The midpoint of the line segment between P and Q. (b) The two points on this line segment lying one-third and two-thirds of the way from P to Q.

22. If P, Q are two arbitrary points in n-space, give the general formula for the midpoint of the line segment between P and Q.

§6. THE CROSS PRODUCT

This section applies only in 3-space!

Let $A = (a_1, a_2, a_3)$ and $B = (b_1, b_2, b_3)$ be two vectors in 3-space. We define their *cross product*

$$A \times B = (a_2 b_3 - a_3 b_2, a_3 b_1 - a_1 b_3, a_1 b_2 - a_2 b_1).$$

We leave the following assertions as exercises:

CP 1. $A \times B = -(B \times A)$.

CP 2. $A \times (B + C) = (A \times B) + (A \times C),$ *and*

$$(B + C) \times A = B \times A + C \times A.$$

CP 3. *For any number a, we have*

$$(aA) \times B = a(A \times B) = A \times (aB).$$

CP 4. $(A \times B) \times C = (A \cdot C)B - (B \cdot C)A.$

CP 5. $A \times B$ *is perpendicular to both A and B.*

As an example, we carry out this computation. We have

$$A \cdot (A \times B) = a_1(a_2b_3 - a_3b_2) + a_2(a_3b_1 - a_1b_3) + a_3(a_1b_2 - a_2b_1)$$
$$= 0$$

because all terms cancel. Similarly for $B \cdot (A \times B)$. This perpendicularity may be drawn as follows.

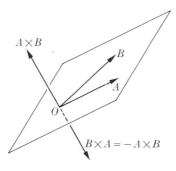

Figure 19

The vector $A \times B$ is perpendicular to the plane spanned by A and B. So is $B \times A$, but $B \times A$ points in the opposite direction.

Finally, as a last property, we have

CP 6. $(A \times B)^2 = (A \cdot A)(B \cdot B) - (A \cdot B)^2.$

Again, this can be verified by a computation on the coordinates. Namely, we have

$$(A \times B) \cdot (A \times B)$$
$$= (a_2b_3 - a_3b_2)^2 + (a_3b_1 - a_1b_3)^2 + (a_1b_2 - a_2b_1)^2,$$
$$(A \cdot A)(B \cdot B) - (A \cdot B)^2$$
$$= (a_1^2 + a_2^2 + a_3^2)(b_1^2 + b_2^2 + b_3^2) - (a_1b_1 + a_2b_2 + a_3b_3)^2.$$

Expanding everything out, we find that CP 6 drops out.

From our interpretation of the dot product, and the definition of the norm, we can rewrite CP 6 in the form

$$\|A \times B\|^2 = \|A\|^2\|B\|^2 - \|A\|^2\|B\|^2 \cos^2\theta,$$

where θ is the angle between A and B. Hence we obtain

$$\|A \times B\|^2 = \|A\|^2\|B\|^2 \sin^2\theta$$

or

$$\boxed{\|A \times B\| = \|A\| \, \|B\| \, |\sin\theta|.}$$

This is analogous to the formula which gave us the absolute value of $A \cdot B$.

EXERCISES

Find $A \times B$ for the following vectors.

1. $A = (1, -1, 1)$ and $B = (-2, 3, 1)$
2. $A = (-1, 1, 2)$ and $B = (1, 0, -1)$
3. $A = (1, 1, -3)$ and $B = (-1, -2, -3)$
4. Find $A \times A$ and $B \times B$, in Exercises 1 through 3.
5. Let $E_1 = (1, 0, 0)$, $E_2 = (0, 1, 0)$, and $E_3 = (0, 0, 1)$. Find $E_1 \times E_2$, $E_2 \times E_3$, $E_3 \times E_1$.
6. Show that for any vector A in 3-space we have $A \times A = O$.
7. Compute $E_1 \times (E_1 \times E_2)$ and $(E_1 \times E_1) \times E_2$. Are these vectors equal to each other?

Chapter II

Differentiation of Vectors

We begin to acquire the flavour of the mixture of algebra, geometry, and differentiation. Each gains in appeal from being mixed with the other two.

The chain rule especially leads into the classical theory of curves. As you will see, the chain rule in its various aspects occurs very frequently in this book, and forms almost as basic a tool as the algebra of vectors, with which it will in fact be intimately mixed.

§1. DERIVATIVE

Let I be an interval. A parametrized *curve* (defined on this interval) is an association which to each point of I associates a vector. If X denotes a curve defined on I, and t is a point of I, then $X(t)$ denotes the vector associated to t by X. We often write the association $t \mapsto X(t)$ as an arrow

$$X: I \to \mathbf{R}^n.$$

Each vector $X(t)$ can be written in terms of coordinates,

$$X(t) = \big(x_1(t), \ldots, x_n(t)\big),$$

each $x_i(t)$ being a function of t. We say that this curve is *differentiable* if each function $x_i(t)$ is a differentiable function of t.

For instance, the curve defined by

$$X(t) = (\cos t, \sin t, t)$$

is a spiral (Fig. 1). Here we have

$$x(t) = \cos t,$$

$$y(t) = \sin t,$$

$$z(t) = t.$$

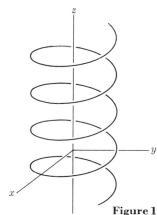

Figure 1

Remark. We take the intervals of definition for our curves to be open, closed, or also half open or half closed. When we define the derivative of a curve, it is understood that the interval of definition contains more than one point. In that case, at an end point the usual limit of

$$\frac{f(a + h) - f(a)}{h}$$

is taken for those h such that the quotient makes sense, i.e. $a + h$ lies in the interval. If a is a left end point, the quotient is considered only for $h > 0$. If a is a right end point, the quotient is considered only for $h < 0$. Then the usual rules for differentiation of functions are true in this greater generality, and thus Rules 1 through 4 below, and the chain rule of §2 remain true also. [An example of a statement which is not always true for curves defined over closed intervals is given in Exercise 11(b).]

Let us try to differentiate vectors using a Newton quotient. We consider

$$\frac{X(t + h) - X(t)}{h} = \left(\frac{x_1(t + h) - x_1(t)}{h}, \ldots, \frac{x_n(t + h) - x_n(t)}{h}\right)$$

and see that each component is a Newton quotient for the corresponding coordinate. If each $x_i(t)$ is differentiable, then each quotient

$$\frac{x_i(t + h) - x_i(t)}{h}$$

approaches the derivative dx_i/dt. For this reason, we define the *derivative* dX/dt to be

$$\frac{dX}{dt} = \left(\frac{dx_1}{dt}, \ldots, \frac{dx_n}{dt}\right).$$

In fact, we could also say that the vector

$$\left(\frac{dx_1}{dt}, \ldots, \frac{dx_n}{dt}\right)$$

is the limit of the Newton quotient

$$\frac{X(t + h) - X(t)}{h}$$

as h approaches 0. Indeed, as h approaches 0, each component

$$\frac{x_i(t + h) - x_i(t)}{h}$$

approaches dx_i/dt. Hence the Newton quotient approaches the vector

$$\left(\frac{dx_1}{dt}, \ldots, \frac{dx_n}{dt}\right).$$

For example, if $X(t) = (\cos t, \sin t, t)$ then

$$\frac{dX}{dt} = (-\sin t, \cos t, 1).$$

It will also be convenient to denote dX/dt by $\dot{X}$; thus in the previous example, we would also write

$$\dot{X}(t) = (-\sin t, \cos t, 1) = X'(t).$$

(The notation $\dot{X}$ is used by the physicists.)

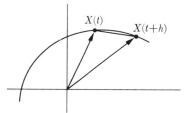

Figure 2

We define the *velocity vector* of the curve at time t to be the vector $X'(t)$. In our previous example, when

$$X(t) = (\cos t, \sin t, t),$$

the velocity vector at $t = \pi$ is

$$X'(\pi) = (0, -1, 1),$$

and for $t = \pi/4$ we get

$$X'(\pi/4) = (-1/\sqrt{2}, 1/\sqrt{2}, 1).$$

The velocity vector is located at the origin, but when we translate it to the point $X(t)$, then we visualize it as tangent to the curve, as in the next picture.

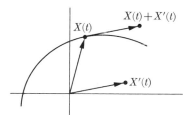

Figure 3

We define the *tangent line* to a curve X at time t to be the line passing through $X(t)$ in the direction of $X'(t)$, provided that $X'(t) \neq O$. Otherwise, we don't define a tangent line.

Example 1. Find a parametric equation of the tangent line to the curve $X(t) = (\sin t, \cos t)$ at $t = \pi/3$.

We have

$$X'(\pi/3) = (\tfrac{1}{2}, -\sqrt{3}/2) \quad \text{and} \quad X(\pi/3) = (\sqrt{3}/2, \tfrac{1}{2}).$$

Let $P = X(\pi/3)$ and $A = X'(\pi/3)$. Then a parametric equation of the tangent line at the required point is

$$L(t) = P + tA = \left(\frac{\sqrt{3}}{2}, \frac{1}{2}\right) + \left(\frac{1}{2}, -\frac{\sqrt{3}}{2}\right) t.$$

(We use another letter L because X is already occupied.) In terms of the coordinates $L(t) = \big(x(t), y(t)\big)$, we can write the tangent line as

$$x(t) = \frac{\sqrt{3}}{2} + \frac{1}{2} t,$$

$$y(t) = \frac{1}{2} - \frac{\sqrt{3}}{2} t.$$

We define the *acceleration vector* to be the derivative dX'/dt, provided of course that X' is differentiable. We shall also denote the acceleration vector by X''. We define the *acceleration scalar* to be the length of the acceleration vector.

In the example given by $X(t) = (\cos t, \sin t, t)$ we find that

$$X''(t) = (-\cos t, -\sin t, 0).$$

Therefore $\| X''(t) \| = 1$ and we see that the spiral has a constant acceleration scalar, but not a constant acceleration vector.

We shall list the rules for differentiation. These will concern sums, products, and the chain rule is postponed to the next section. We make a remark concerning products. If X is a curve and f a function, defined on the same interval I, then for each t in this interval we can take the product

$$f(t)X(t)$$

of the *number $f(t)$* by the *vector $X(t)$*. Thus if

$$X(t) = \big(x_1(t), \ldots, x_n(t)\big)$$

then

$$f(t)X(t) = \big(f(t)x_1(t), \ldots, f(t)x_n(t)\big).$$

For instance, if $X(t) = (\cos t, \sin t, t)$ and $f(t) = e^t$, then

$$f(t)X(t) = (e^t \cos t, e^t \sin t, e^t t),$$

and

$$f(\pi)X(\pi) = \big(e^\pi(-1), e^\pi(0), e^\pi \pi\big) = (-e^\pi, 0, e^\pi \pi).$$

The derivative of a curve is defined componentwise. Thus the rules for the derivative will be very similar to the rules for differentiating functions.

Rule 1. *Let $X(t)$ and $Y(t)$ be two differentiable curves (defined for the same values of t). Then the sum $X(t) + Y(t)$ is differentiable, and*

$$\frac{d(X(t) + Y(t))}{dt} = \frac{dX}{dt} + \frac{dY}{dt}.$$

Rule 2. *Let c be a number, and let $X(t)$ be differentiable. Then $cX(t)$ is differentiable, and*

$$\frac{d(cX(t))}{dt} = c\frac{dX}{dt}.$$

Rule 3. *Let $f(t)$ be a differentiable function, and $X(t)$ a differentiable curve (defined for the same values of t). Then $f(t)X(t)$ is differentiable, and*

$$\frac{d(fX)}{dt} = f(t)\frac{dX}{dt} + \frac{df}{dt}X(t).$$

Rule 4. *Let $X(t)$ and $Y(t)$ be two differentiable curves (defined for the same values of t). Then $X(t) \cdot Y(t)$ is a differentiable function whose derivative is*

$$\frac{d}{dt}[X(t) \cdot Y(t)] = X'(t) \cdot Y(t) + X(t) \cdot Y'(t).$$

(This is formally analogous to the derivative of a product of functions, namely the first times the derivative of the second plus the second times the derivative of the first, except that the product is now a scalar product.)

As an example of the proofs we shall give the third one in detail, and leave the others to you as exercises.

Let $X(t) = (x_1(t), \ldots, x_n(t))$, and let $f = f(t)$ be a function. Then by definition

$$f(t)X(t) = (f(t)x_1(t), \ldots, f(t)x_n(t)).$$

We take the derivative of each component and apply the rule for the derivative of a product of functions. We obtain:

$$\frac{d(fX)}{dt} = \left(f(t)\frac{dx_1}{dt} + \frac{df}{dt}x_1(t), \ldots, f(t)\frac{dx_n}{dt} + \frac{df}{dt}x_n(t) \right).$$

Using the rule for the sum of two vectors, we see that the expression on the right is equal to

$$\left(f(t)\frac{dx_1}{dt}, \ldots, f(t)\frac{dx_n}{dt} \right) + \left(\frac{df}{dt}x_1(t), \ldots, \frac{df}{dt}x_n(t) \right).$$

We can take f out of the vector on the left and df/dt out of the vector on the right to obtain

$$f(t)\frac{dX}{dt} + \frac{df}{dt}X(t),$$

as desired.

Example 2. Let A be a fixed vector, and let f be an ordinary differentiable function of one variable. Let $F(t) = f(t)A$. Then $F'(t) = f'(t)A$. For instance, if $F(t) = (\cos t)A$ and $A = (a, b)$ where a, b are fixed numbers, then $F(t) = (a \cos t, b \cos t)$ and thus

$$F'(t) = (-a \sin t, -b \sin t) = (-\sin t)A.$$

Similarly, if A, B are fixed vectors, and

$$G(t) = (\cos t)A + (\sin t)B,$$

then

$$G'(t) = (-\sin t)A + (\cos t)B.$$

One can also give a proof for the derivative of a product which does not use coordinates and is similar to the proof for the derivative of a product of functions. We carry this proof out. We must consider the Newton quotient

$$\frac{X(t + h) \cdot Y(t + h) - X(t) \cdot Y(t)}{h}$$

$$= \frac{X(t + h) \cdot Y(t + h) - X(t) \cdot Y(t + h) + X(t) \cdot Y(t + h) - X(t) \cdot Y(t)}{h}$$

$$= \frac{X(t + h) - X(t)}{h} \cdot Y(t + h) + X(t) \cdot \frac{Y(t + h) - Y(t)}{h}.$$

Taking the limit as $h \to 0$, we find

$$X'(t) \cdot Y(t) + X(t) \cdot Y'(t)$$

as desired.

Note that this type of proof applies without change if we replace the dot product by, say, the cross product. A coordinate proof for the derivative of the cross product can also be given (cf. Exercise 25).

We define the *speed* of the curve $X(t)$ to be the length of the velocity vector. If we denote the speed by $v(t)$, then by definition we have

$$v(t) = \|X'(t)\|,$$

and thus

$$v(t)^2 = X'(t)^2 = X'(t) \cdot X'(t).$$

We can also omit the t from the notation, and write

$$v = X' \cdot X' = X'^2.$$

The length of the acceleration vector is called the *acceleration scalar*, and will be denoted by $a(t)$. *Warning:* $a(t)$ is not necessarily the derivative of $v(t)$. Almost any example shows this. For instance, let

$$X(t) = (\sin t, \cos t).$$

Then $v(t) = \|X(t)\| = 1$ so that $dv/dt = 0$. However, a simple computation shows that $X''(t) = (\cos t, -\sin t)$ and hence $a(t) = 1$.

We define the *length* of a curve X between two values a, b of t ($a \leq b$) in the interval of definition of the curve to be the integral of the speed:

$$\int_a^b v(t)\, dt = \int_a^b \|X'(t)\|\, dt.$$

By definition, we can rewrite this integral in the form

$$\int_a^b \sqrt{\left(\frac{dx_1}{dt}\right)^2 + \cdots + \left(\frac{dx_n}{dt}\right)^2}\, dt.$$

When $n = 2$, this is the same formula for the length which we gave in Volume I of this course. Thus the formula in dimension n is a very natural generalization of the formula in dimension 2. Namely, when

$$X(t) = \big(x(t), y(t)\big)$$

is given by two coordinates, then the length of the curve between a and b is equal to

$$\int_a^b \sqrt{\left(\frac{dx}{dt}\right)^2 + \left(\frac{dy}{dt}\right)^2}\, dt.$$

Example 3. Let the curve be defined by

$$X(t) = (\sin t, \cos t).$$

Then $X'(t) = (\cos t, -\sin t)$ and $v(t) = \sqrt{\cos^2 t + \sin^2 t} = 1$. Hence the length of the curve between $t = 0$ and $t = 1$ is

$$\int_0^1 v(t)\, dt = t \Big|_0^1 = 1.$$

In this case, of course, the integral is easy to evaluate. There is no reason why this should always be the case.

Example 4. Set up the integral for the length of the curve

$$X(t) = (e^t, \sin t, t)$$

between $t = 1$ and $t = \pi$.

We have $X'(t) = (e^t, \cos t, 1)$. Hence the desired integral is

$$\int_1^\pi \sqrt{e^{2t} + \cos^2 t + 1}\, dt.$$

In this case, there is no easy formula for the integral. In the exercises, however, the functions are adjusted in such a way that the integral can be evaluated by elementary techniques of integration. Don't expect this to be the case in real life, though.

EXERCISES

Find the velocity vector of the following curves.

1. $(e^t, \cos t, \sin t)$ 2. $(\sin 2t, \log (1 + t), t)$

3. $(\cos t, \sin t)$ 4. $(\cos 3t, \sin 3t)$

5. In Exercises 3 and 4, show that the velocity vector is perpendicular to the position vector.

6. In Exercises 3 and 4, show that the acceleration vector is in the opposite direction from the position vector.

7. Let A, B be two constant vectors. What is the velocity vector of the curve $X = A + tB$?

8. Let $X(t)$ be a differentiable curve. A plane or line which is perpendicular to the velocity vector $X'(t)$ at the point $X(t)$ is said to be *normal* to the curve at the point t or also at the point $X(t)$. Find the equation of a line normal to the curves of Exercises 3 and 4 at the point $\pi/3$.

9. Find the equation of a plane normal to the curve

$$(e^t, t, t^2)$$

at the point $t = 1$.

10. Same question at the point $t = 0$.

11. Let $X(t)$ be a differentiable curve defined on an open interval. Let Q be a point which is not on the curve.
    (a) Write down the formula for the distance between Q and an arbitrary point on the curve.
    (b) If t_0 is a value of t such that the distance between Q and $X(t_0)$ is at a minimum, show that the vector $Q - X(t_0)$ is normal to the curve, at the point $X(t_0)$. [*Hint:* Investigate the minimum of the square of the distance.]
    (c) If $X(t)$ is the parametric equation of a straight line, show that there exists a unique value t_0 to such that the distance between Q and $X(t_0)$ is a minimum.

12. Find the length of the spiral $(\cos t, \sin t, t)$ between $t = 0$ and $t = 1$.

13. Find the length of the spiral $(\cos 2t, \sin 2t, 3t)$ between $t = 1$ and $t = 3$.

14. Assume that the differentiable curve $X(t)$ lies on the sphere of radius 1. Show that the velocity vector is perpendicular to the position vector. [*Hint:* Start from the condition $X(t)^2 = 1$.]

15. Let A be a non-zero vector, c a number, and Q a point. Let P_0 be the point of intersection of the line passing through Q, in the direction of A, and the plane $X \cdot A = c$. Show that for all points P of the plane, we have

$$\|Q - P_0\| \leq \|Q - P\|.$$

[*Hint:* If $P \neq P_0$, consider the straight line passing through P_0 and P, and use Exercise 11(c).]

16. Write a parametric equation for the tangent line to the given curve at the given point in each of the following cases.

   (a) $(\cos 4t, \sin 4t, t)$ at the point $t = \pi/8$
   (b) $(t, 2t, t^2)$ at the point $(1, 2, 1)$
   (c) $(e^{3t}, e^{-3t}, 3\sqrt{2}t)$ at $t = 1$
   (d) (t, t^3, t^4) at the point $(1, 1, 1)$

17. Find the length of the curves of Exercise 16 for the following intervals.

   (a) $t = 0$ to $t = \pi/8$.   (b) $t = 1$ to $t = 3$.   (c) $t = 0$ to $t = \frac{1}{3}$.

18. Show that the two curves $(e^t, e^{2t}, 1 - e^{-t})$ and $(1 - \theta, \cos \theta, \sin \theta)$ intersect at the point $(1, 1, 0)$. What is the angle between their tangents at that point?

19. At what points does the curve $(2t^2, 1 - t, 3 + t^2)$ intersect the plane $3x - 14y + z - 10 = 0$?

20. Let $X(t)$ be a differentiable curve and suppose that $X'(t) = O$ for all t throughout its interval of definition I. What can you say about the curve? Suppose $X'(t) \neq O$ but $X''(t) = O$ for all t in the interval. What can you say about the curve?

21. Find the length of the curve defined by

$$X(t) = (t - \sin, t, 1 - \cos t)$$

between $t = 0$ and $t = 2\pi$.

22. Find the length of the curve $X(t) = (t, \log t)$ between $t = \frac{1}{2}$ and $t = 2$.

23. Find the length of the curve defined by $X(t) = (t, \log \cos t)$ between $t = 0$ and $t = \pi/4$.

24. Prove that if the acceleration of a curve is always perpendicular to its velocity, then its speed is constant.

25. Using the definition of the cross product by coordinates given in Chapter I, prove that if $X(t)$ and $Y(t)$ are two differentiable curves (defined for the same values of t), then

$$\frac{d[X(t) \times Y(t)]}{dt} = X(t) \times \frac{dY(t)}{dt} + \frac{dX(t)}{dt} \times Y(t).$$

26. Show that

$$\frac{d}{dt}[X(t) \times X'(t)] = X(t) \times X''(t).$$

27. Let $X(t) = (a \cos t, a \sin t, bt)$, where a, b are constant. Let $\theta(t)$ be the angle which the tangent line at a given point of the curve makes with the z-axis. Show that $\cos \theta(t)$ is the constant $b/\sqrt{a^2 + b^2}$.

28. Show that the velocity and acceleration vectors of the curve in Exercise 27 have constant lengths.

29. Let B be a fixed unit vector, and let $X(t)$ be a curve such that $X(t) \cdot B = e^{2t}$ for all t. Assume also that the velocity vector of the curve has a constant angle θ with the vector B, with $0 < \theta < \pi/2$.

   (a) Show that the speed is $2e^{2t}/\cos \theta$.

   (b) Determine the dot product $X'(t) \cdot X''(t)$ in terms of t and θ.

30. Let

$$X(t) = \left(\frac{2t}{1 + t^2}, \frac{1 - t^2}{1 + t^2}, 1 \right).$$

   Show that the cosine of the angle between $X(t)$ and $X'(t)$ is constant.

31. Let A, B be fixed non-zero vectors. Let

$$X(t) = e^{2t}A + e^{-2t}B.$$

   Show that $X''(t)$ has the same direction as $X(t)$.

32. Let $Y(t) = X(t) \times X'(t)$. Show that $Y'(t) = X(t) \times X''(t)$.

33. Let $Y(t) = X(t) \cdot (X'(t) \times X''(t))$. Show that $Y' = X \cdot (X' \times X''')$.

34. Let B be a non-zero vector, and let $X(t)$ be such that $X(t) \cdot B = t$ for all t. Assume also that the angle between $X'(t)$ and B is constant. Show that $X''(t)$ is perpendicular to $X'(t)$.

§2. THE CHAIN RULE AND APPLICATIONS

Let X be a vector and c a number. As a matter of notation it will be convenient to define Xc to be cX, in other words, we allow ourselves to multiply vectors by numbers on the right. If we have a curve $X(t)$ defined for some interval, and a function $g(t)$ defined on the same interval, then we let

$$X(t)g(t) = g(t)X(t).$$

Let $X = X(t)$ be a differentiable curve.

Let f be a function defined on some interval, such that the values of f lie in the domain of definition of the curve $X(t)$. Then we may form the composite curve $X \circ f$. If s is a number at which f is defined, we let the value of $X \circ f$ at s be

$$(X \circ f)(s) = X(f(s)).$$

For example, let $X(t) = (t^2, e^t)$ and let $f(s) = \sin s$. Then

$$X(f(s)) = (\sin^2 s, e^{\sin s}).$$

Each component of $X(f(s))$ becomes a function of s, just as when we studied the chain rule for functions.

The chain rule asserts: *If X is a differentiable curve and f is a differentiable function defined on some interval, whose values are contained in the interval* *of definition of the curve, then the composite curve $X \circ f$ is differentiable, and*

$$(X \circ f)'(s) = X'(f(s))f'(s).$$

The expression on the right can also be written $f'(s)X'(f(s))$. It is the product of the function f' times the vector X'.

In another notation, if we let $t = f(s)$, then we can write the above formula in the form

$$\frac{d(X \circ f)}{ds} = \frac{dX}{dt}\frac{dt}{ds}.$$

The proof of the chain rule is trivial, using the chain rule for functions. Indeed, let $Y(s) = X(f(s))$. Then

$$Y(s) = \left(x_1(f(s)), \ldots, x_n(f(s))\right).$$

Taking the derivative term by term, we find:

$$Y'(s) = \left(x_1'(f(s))f'(s), \ldots, x_n'(f(s))f'(s)\right).$$

We can take $f'(s)$ outside the vector, and get

$$Y'(s) = X'(f(s))f'(s),$$

which is precisely what we want.

The change of variables from t to s is also called a change of parametrization of the curve. Under certain changes of parametrization, certain formulas involving the velocity and acceleration of the curve become simpler and reflect geometric properties more clearly. We shall see examples of this in a moment.

Let us now assume that all the functions with which we dealt above have second derivatives. Using the chain rule, and the rule for the derivative of a product, we obtain the following two formulas:

(1) $\qquad Y'(s) = f'(s)X'(f(s)),$

(2) $\qquad Y''(s) = f''(s)X'(f(s)) + (f'(s))^2 X''(f(s)).$

Since $t = f(s)$, we can also write these in the notation of the physicists:

(1) $\qquad Y'(s) = f'(s)\dot{X}(t),$

(2) $\qquad Y''(s) = f''(s)\dot{X}(t) + (f'(s))^2 \ddot{X}(t).$

We shall consider an important special case of these formulas.

We have defined

$$v(t) = \|\dot{X}(t)\|$$

to be the speed. Let us now assume that each coordinate function of $\dot{X}(t)$ is continuous. In that case, we say that $\dot{X}(t)$ is *continuous*. Then $v(t)$ is a continuous function of t. *We shall assume throughout that* $v(t) \neq 0$

for any value of t in the interval of definition of our curve. Then $v(t) > 0$ for all such values of t. We let

$$s(t) = \int v(t)\, dt$$

be a fixed indefinite integral of $v(t)$ over our interval. (For instance, if a is a point of the interval, we could let

$$s(t) = \int_a^t v(u)\, du.$$

We know that any two indefinite integrals of v over the interval differ by a constant.) Then

$$\frac{ds}{dt} = v(t) > 0$$

for all values of t, and hence s is a strictly increasing function. Consequently, the inverse function exists. Call it

$$t = f(s).$$

We can then write

$$X(t) = X(f(s)) = Y(s).$$

Thus we are in the situation described above.

The velocity vectors of the curve depending on the two different parametrizations are related as in formula (1). From the theory of derivatives of inverse functions, we know that

$$f'(s) = \frac{df}{ds} = \left(\frac{ds}{dt}\right)^{-1}.$$

Hence $f'(s)$ is always positive. This means that in the present case, $Y'(s)$ and $\dot{X}(t)$ have the same direction when $t = f(s)$.

A curve $Y : J \to \mathbf{R}^n$ is said to be *parametrized by arc length* if $\| Y'(s) \| = 1$ for all s in the interval of definition J. The reason for this is contained in the next theorem.

Theorem 1. *Let $X : I \to \mathbf{R}^n$ be a curve whose speed $v(t)$ is > 0 for all t in the interval of definition. Let*

$$s(t) = \int_a^t v(u)\, du$$

and $t = f(s)$ be the inverse function. Then the curve given by

$$s \mapsto Y(s) = X(f(s))$$

is parametrized by arc length, and $Y'(s)$ is perpendicular to $Y''(s)$ for each value of s.

Proof. From formula (1), we get

$$\| Y'(s) \| = |f'(s)| \, \| \dot{X}(t) \| = \frac{df}{ds} \frac{ds}{dt}.$$

By what we just saw above, this last expression is equal to 1. Thus $Y'(s)$ is a vector of length 1, a unit vector, in the same direction as $\dot{X}(t)$. Thus the velocity vector of the curve Y has constant length.

In particular, we have $Y'(s)^2 = 1$. Differentiating with respect to s, we get

$$2 Y' \cdot Y'' = 0.$$

Hence $Y'(s)$ is perpendicular to $Y''(s)$ for each value of s. This proves the theorem.

From (2), we see that the acceleration $Y''(s)$ has two components. First a tangential component

$$f''(s) \dot{X}(t)$$

in the direction of $\dot{X}(t)$, which involves the naive notion of scalar acceleration, namely the second derivative $f''(s)$. Second, another component in the direction of $\ddot{X}(t)$, with a coefficient

$$(f'(s))^2$$

which is positive. [We assume of course that $\dot{X}(t) \neq O$.]

For a given value of t, let us assume that $\dot{X}(t) \neq O$ and $\ddot{X}(t) \neq O$, and also that $\dot{X}(t)$ and $\ddot{X}(t)$ do not lie on the same straight line. Then the plane passing through $X(t)$, parallel to $\dot{X}(t)$ and $\ddot{X}(t)$ is called the *osculating plane* of the curve at time t, or also at the point $X(t)$. [Actually, it is more accurate to say at time t, because there may be two numbers t_1, t_2 in the interval of definition of the curve such that $X(t_1) = X(t_2)$.]

Example 1. Let $X(t) = (\sin t, \cos t, t)$. Find the osculating plane to this curve at $t = \pi/2$.

We have

$$\dot{X}(\pi/2) = (0, -1, 1)$$

and

$$\ddot{X}(\pi/2) = (-1, 0, 0).$$

We find first a vector perpendicular to $\dot{X}(\pi/2)$ and $\ddot{X}(\pi/2)$. For instance, $N = (0, 1, 1)$ is such a vector. Furthermore, let $P = X(\pi/2) = (1, 0, \pi/2)$. Then the osculating plane at $t = \pi/2$ is the plane passing through P, perpendicular to N, and its equation is therefore

$$y + z = \pi/2.$$

In case of parametrization by arc length, or in fact in any other parametrization such that $f'(s) \neq 0$, we see from formulas (1) and (2) that the plane parallel to $\dot{X}(t)$ and $\ddot{X}(t)$ is the same as the plane parallel to $Y'(s)$ and $Y''(s)$ because from these formulas, we can solve back for $\dot{X}(t)$ and $\ddot{X}(t)$ in terms of this other pair of vectors. Thus the osculating plane does not depend on a change of parametrization $t = f(s)$ such that $f'(s) \neq 0$.

Let us assume that a curve is parametrized by arc length. Thus we write the curve as $Y(s)$, and by Theorem 1, we have $\| Y'(s) \| = 1$ and

$$Y'(s) \cdot Y''(s) = 0.$$

Then $Y'(s)$ and $Y''(s)$ look like this:

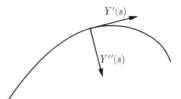

Figure 4

Example 2. Let R be a number > 0. A parametrization for the circle of radius R by arc length is given by

$$Y(s) = \left(R \cos \frac{s}{R}, R \sin \frac{s}{R} \right),$$

as one sees immediately, because $\| Y'(s) \| = 1$.

Differentiating twice shows that

$$Y''(s) = -\frac{1}{R} Y'(s),$$

and hence that

$$\| Y''(s) \| = \frac{1}{R} \quad \text{or} \quad R = \frac{1}{\| Y''(s) \|}.$$

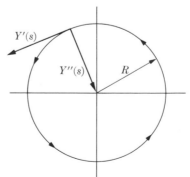

Figure 5

For an arbitrary curve Y parametrized by arc length, it is customary to make a definition which is motivated by the geometry of the special example just discussed, namely we define the *radius of curvature* $R(s)$ to be

$$R(s) = \frac{1}{\|Y''(s)\|}$$

at all points such that $\|Y''(s)\| \neq 0$. (Note that if $Y''(s) = O$ on some interval, then $Y(s) = As + B$ for suitable vectors A, B, and thus Y parametrizes a straight line. Thus intuitively, it is reasonable to view its radius of curvature as infinity.)

The same motivation as above leads us to define the *curvature* itself to be $\|Y''(s)\|$. The curvature is usually denoted by k.

Most curves are not usually given parametrized by arc length, and thus it is useful to have a formula which gives the curvature in terms of the given parameter t. This comes immediately from the chain rule. Indeed, keeping our notation $X(t)$ and $Y(s)$ with $ds/dt = v(t)$, we have the formula

$$Y''(s) = \frac{1}{v(t)} \frac{d}{dt}\left(\frac{1}{v(t)} X'(t)\right)$$

where $v(t) = \|X'(t)\|$ is the length of the velocity vector $X'(t)$.

Proof. From formula (1), we know that

$$Y'(s) = \frac{dt}{ds} X'(t) = \frac{1}{v(t)} X'(t).$$

By the chain rule,

$$Y''(s) = \frac{d(Y'(s(t)))}{dt} \frac{dt}{ds},$$

which yields precisely the formula in the box.

The curvature is then equal to the length of the vector in the box.

Example 3. Find the curvature of the curve given by

$$X(t) = (\cos t, \sin t, t).$$

We have $X'(t) = (-\sin t, \cos t, 1)$ and $v(t) = \sqrt{2}$ is constant. Then $X''(t) = (-\cos t, -\sin t, 0)$, and from the formula for the curvature we find

$$k(t) = \frac{1}{\sqrt{2}}\left\|\frac{1}{\sqrt{2}} X''(t)\right\| = \frac{1}{2}.$$

We see in particular that the curve has constant curvature.

EXERCISES

1. Find the equations of the osculating planes for each of the curves of Exercise 16, §1 at the given point.

2. Prove formula (2) from formula (1) in detail.

3. Let r be a fixed number > 0, let $c > 0$, and let

$$X(t) = (r \cos t, r \sin t, ct).$$

Find the curvature as a function of t.

4. Find the curvature of the curve

$$X(t) = (t, t^2, t^3)$$

at (a) $t = 1$, (b) $t = 0$, (c) $t = -1$.

5. Let the plane curve be defined by $X(t) = (x(t), y(t))$. Show that the curvature is given by

$$k(t) = \frac{|x'(t)y''(t) - x''(t)y'(t)|}{(x'^2(t) + y'^2(t))^{3/2}}.$$

6. If a curve is parametrized by $x = t$, $y = f(t)$ (the natural parametrization arising from a function $y = f(x)$), find a simplification for the curvature given in the preceding exercise.

7. Find the radius of curvature of the curve $X(t) = (t, \log t)$. For which t is the radius of curvature a minimum?

8. Find the curvatures of the curves
   (a) $X(t) = (t, \sin t)$,
   (b) $X(t) = (\sin 3t, \cos 3t)$,
   (c) $X(t) = (\sin 3t, \cos 3t, t)$.

9. Find the radius of curvature of the parabola $y = x^2$.

10. Find the radius of curvature of the ellipse given by

$$X(t) = (a \cos t, b \sin t),$$

where a, b are constants.

11. Find the curvature of the curve defined by

$$x(t) = \int_0^t \cos \frac{\pi u^2}{2} \, du,$$

$$y(t) = \int_0^t \sin \frac{\pi u^2}{2} \, du.$$

12. Find the curvature of the curve defined by

$$x(t) = \int_0^t \frac{\cos u}{\sqrt{u}}\, du,$$

$$y(t) = \int_0^t \frac{\sin u}{\sqrt{u}}\, du$$

in terms of the arc length s.

13. Show that the curvature of the curve defined by

$$X(t) = (e^t, e^{-t}, \sqrt{2}\, t)$$

is equal to $\sqrt{2}/(e^t - e^{-t})^2$.

14. If a curve has constant velocity and acceleration, show that the curvature is constant. Express the curvature in terms of the lengths of the velocity and acceleration vectors.

Chapter III

Functions of Several Variables

We view functions of several variables as functions of points in space. This appeals to our geometric intuition, and also relates such functions more easily with the theory of vectors. The gradient will appear as a natural generalization of the derivative. In this chapter we are mainly concerned with basic definitions and notions. We postpone the important theorems to the next chapter.

§1. GRAPHS AND LEVEL CURVES

In order to conform with usual terminology, and for the sake of brevity, a collection of objects will simply be called a *set*. In this chapter, we are mostly concerned with sets of points in space.

Let S be a set of points in n-space. A *function* (defined on S) is an association which to each element of S associates a number.

In practice, we sometimes omit mentioning explicitly the set S, since the context usually makes it clear for which points the function is defined.

Example 1. In 2-space (the plane) we can define a function f by the rule

$$f(x, y) = x^2 + y^2.$$

It is defined for all points (x, y) and can be interpreted geometrically as the square of the distance between the origin and the point.

Example 2. Again in 2-space, let

$$f(x, y) = \frac{x^2 - y^2}{x^2 + y^2}$$

be defined for all

$$(x, y) \neq (0, 0).$$

We do not define f at $(0, 0)$ (also written O).

Example 3. In 3-space, we can define a function f by the rule

$$f(x, y, z) = x^2 - \sin(xyz) + yz^3.$$

Since a point and a vector are represented by the same thing (namely an n-tuple), we can think of a function such as the above also as a function of vectors. When we do not want to write the coordinates, we write $f(X)$ instead of $f(x_1, \ldots, x_n)$. As with numbers, we call $f(X)$ the *value* of f at the point (or vector) X.

Just as with functions of one variable, one can define the *graph* of a function f of n variables $x_1, \ldots, x_n$ to be the set of points in $(n + 1)$-space of the form

$$\left(x_1, \ldots, x_n, f(x_1, \ldots, x_n)\right),$$

the $(x_1, \ldots, x_n)$ being in the domain of definition of f. Thus when $n = 1$, the graph of a function f is a set of points $(x, f(x))$. When $n = 2$, the graph of a function f is the set of points $(x, y, f(x, y))$. When $n = 2$, it is already difficult to draw the graph since it involves a figure in 3-space. The graph of a function of two variables may look like this:

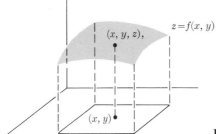

Figure 1

When we get to the graph of a function of three variables, it is of course impossible to draw it, since it exists in 4-space. However, we shall describe another means of visualizing the function.

For each number c, the equation $f(x, y) = c$ is the equation of a curve in the plane. We have considerable experience in drawing the graphs of such curves, and we may therefore assume that we know how to draw this graph in principle. This curve is called the *level curve* of f at c. It gives us the set of points (x, y) where f takes on the value c. By drawing a number of such level curves, we can get a good description of the function.

Example 1 (continued). The level curves are described by equations

$$x^2 + y^2 = c.$$

These have a solution only when $c \geqq 0$. In that case, they are circles (unless $c = 0$ in which case the circle of radius 0 is simply the origin). In Fig. 2, we have drawn the level curves for $c = 1$ and 4.

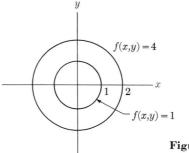

$$f(x,y) = 4$$

$$f(x,y) = 1$$

Figure 2

The graph of the function $z = f(x, y) = x^2 + y^2$ is then a figure in 3-space, which we may represent as follows.

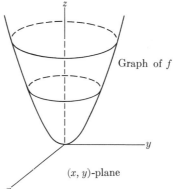

Graph of f

(x, y)-plane

Figure 3

Example 2 (continued). To find the level curves in Example 2, we have to determine the values (x, y) such that

$$x^2 - y^2 = c(x^2 + y^2)$$

for a given number c. This amounts to solving $x^2(1 - c) = y^2(1 + c)$. If $x = 0$, then $f(0, y) = -1$. Thus on the vertical line passing through the origin, our function has the constant value -1. If $x \neq 0$, then we can divide by x in the above equality, and we obtain (for $c \neq -1$)

$$\frac{y^2}{x^2} = \frac{1 - c}{1 + c}.$$

Taking the square root, we obtain two level lines, namely

$$y = ax \quad \text{and} \quad y = -ax, \quad \text{where} \quad a = \sqrt{\frac{1 - c}{1 + c}}.$$

Thus the level curves are straight lines (excluding the origin). We have drawn some of them in Fig. 4. (The numbers indicate the value of the function on the corresponding line.)

It would of course be technically much more disagreeable to draw the level lines in Example 3, and we shall not do so.

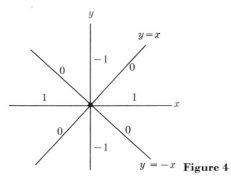

Figure 4

We see that the level lines are based on the same principle as the contour lines of a map. Each line describes, so to speak, the altitude of the function. If the graph is interpreted as a mountainous region, then each level curve gives the set of points of constant altitude. In Example 1, a person wanting to stay at a given altitude need but walk around in circles. In Example 2, such a person should walk on a straight line towards or away from the origin.

If we deal with a function of three variables, say $f(x, y, z)$, then $(x, y, z) = X$ is a point in 3-space. In that case, the set of points satisfying the equation

$$f(x, y, z) = c$$

for some constant c is a surface. The notion analogous to that of level curve is that of level surface.

In physics, a function f might be a potential function, giving the value of the potential energy at each point of space. The level surfaces are then sometimes called surfaces of *equipotential*. The function f might also give a temperature distribution (i.e. its value at a point X is the temperature at X). In that case, the level surfaces are called *isothermal* surfaces.

EXERCISES

Sketch the level curves for the functions $z = f(x, y)$, where $f(x, y)$ is given by the following expressions.

1. $x^2 + 2y^2$ 2. $y - x^2$ 3. $y - 3x^2$

4. $x - y^2$ 5. $3x^2 + 3y^2$ 6. xy

7. $(x - 1)(y - 2)$ 8. $(x + 1)(y + 3)$ 9. $\dfrac{x^2}{4} + \dfrac{y^2}{16}$

10. $2x - 3y$ 11. $\dfrac{xy}{x^2 + y^2}$ 12. $\dfrac{xy^2}{x^2 + y^4}$

13. $\dfrac{4xy(x^2 - y^2)}{x^2 + y^2}$ (try polar coordinates)

14. $\dfrac{x + y}{x - y}$ 15. $\dfrac{x^2 + y^2}{x^2 - y^2}$

(In Exercises 11, 12, and 13, the function is not defined at $(0, 0)$. In Exercise 14, it is not defined for $y = x$, and in Exercise 15 it is not defined for $y = x$ or $y = -x$.)

16. $(x - 1)^2 + (y + 3)^2$ 17. $x^2 - y^2$

§2. PARTIAL DERIVATIVES

In this section and the next, we discuss the notion of differentiability for functions of several variables. When we discussed the derivative of functions of one variable, we assumed that such a function was defined on an interval. We shall have to make a similar assumption in the case of several variables, and for this we need to introduce a new notion.

Let P be a point in n-space, and let a be a number > 0. The set of points X such that

$$\|X - P\| < a$$

will be called the *open ball* of radius a and center P. The set of points X such that

$$\|X - P\| \leq a$$

will be called the *closed ball* of radius a and center P. The set of points X such that

$$\|X - P\| = a$$

will be called the *sphere* of radius a and center P.

Thus when $n = 1$, we are in 1-space, and the open ball of radius a is the open interval centered at P. The sphere of radius a and center P consists only of two points.

When $n = 2$, the open ball of radius a and center P is also called the open *disc*. The sphere is the *circle*.

When $n = 3$, then our terminology coincides with the obvious interpretation we might want to place on the words.

The following are the pictures of the spheres of radius 1 in 2-space and 3-space respectively centered at the origin.

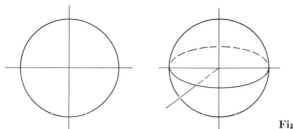

Figure 5

Let S_1 be the sphere of radius 1, centered at the origin. Let a be a number > 0. If X is a point of the sphere S_1, then aX is a point of the sphere of radius a, because

$$\|aX\| = a\|X\| = a.$$

In this manner, we get all points of the sphere of radius a. (Proof?) Thus the sphere of radius a is obtained by stretching the sphere of radius 1, through multiplication by a.

A similar remark applies to the open and closed balls of radius a, they being obtained from the open and closed balls of radius 1 through multiplication by a. (Prove this as an exercise.)

Let U be a set of points in n-space. We shall say that U is an *open set* in n-space if the following condition is satisfied: Given any point P in U, there exists an open ball B of radius $a > 0$ which is centered at P and such that B is contained in U.

Example 1. In the plane, the set consisting of the first quadrant, excluding the x- and y-axes, is an open set.

The x-axis is not open in the plane (i.e. in 2-space). Given a point on the x-axis, we cannot find an open disc centered at the point and contained in the x-axis.

On the other hand, if we view the x-axis as the set of points in 1-space, then it is open in 1-space. Similarly, the interval

$$-1 < x < 1$$

is open in 1-space, but not open in 2-space, or n-space for $n > 1$.

Example 2. Let U be the open ball of radius $a > 0$ centered at the origin. Then U is an open set. To prove this, let P be a point of this ball, so $\|P\| < a$. Say $\|P\| = b$. Let $c = a - b$. If X is a point such that $\|X - P\| < c$, then

$$\|X\| \leq \|X - P\| + \|P\| < a - b + b = a.$$

Hence the open ball of radius c centered at P is contained in U. Hence U is open.

In the next picture we have drawn an open set in the plane, consisting of the region inside the curve, but not containing any point of the boundary. We have also drawn a point P in U, and a sphere (disc) around P contained in U.

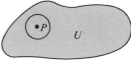

Figure 6

When we defined the derivative as a limit of

$$\frac{f(x + h) - f(x)}{h},$$

we needed the function f to be defined in some open interval around the point x.

Now let f be a function of n variables, defined on an open set U. Then for any point X in U, the function f is also defined at all points which are close to X, namely all points which are contained in an open ball centered at X and contained in U.

For small values of h, the point

$$(x_1 + h, x_2, \ldots, x_n)$$

is contained in such an open ball. Hence the function is defined at that point, and we may form the quotient

$$\frac{f(x_1 + h, x_2, \ldots, x_n) - f(x_1, \ldots, x_n)}{h}.$$

If the limit exists as h tends to 0, then we call it the *first partial derivative* of f and denote it by $D_1 f(x_1, \ldots, x_n)$, or $D_1 f(X)$, or also by

$$\frac{\partial f}{\partial x_1}.$$

Similarly, we let

$$D_i f(X) = \frac{\partial f}{\partial x_i}$$

$$= \lim_{h \to 0} \frac{f(x_1, \ldots, x_i + h, \ldots, x_n) - f(x_1, \ldots, x_n)}{h}$$

if it exists, and call it the *i*-th partial derivative.

When $n = 2$ and we work with variables (x, y), then the first and second partials are also noted

$$\frac{\partial f}{\partial x} \quad \text{and} \quad \frac{\partial f}{\partial y}.$$

By definition, we therefore have

$$\frac{\partial f}{\partial x} = \lim_{h \to 0} \frac{f(x + h, y) - f(x, y)}{h}$$

and

$$\frac{\partial f}{\partial y} = \lim_{k \to 0} \frac{f(x, y + k) - f(x, y)}{k}.$$

A partial derivative is therefore obtained by keeping all but one variable fixed, and taking the ordinary derivative with respect to this one variable.

Example 2. Let $f(x, y) = x^2 y^3$. Then

$$\frac{\partial f}{\partial x} = 2xy^3 \quad \text{and} \quad \frac{\partial f}{\partial y} = 3x^2 y^2.$$

We observe that when the partial derivatives are defined at all points where the function is defined, then they are themselves functions. This is the reason why the notation $D_i f$ is sometimes more useful than the notation $\partial f / \partial x_i$. It allows us to write $D_i f(P)$ for any point P in the set where the partial is defined. There cannot be any ambiguity or confusion with a (meaningless) symbol $D_i(f(P))$, since $f(P)$ is a number. Thus $D_i f(P)$ means $(D_i f)(P)$. It is the value of the function $D_i f$ at P.

Let f be defined in an open set U and assume that the partial derivatives of f exist at each point X of U. The *vector*

$$\left(\frac{\partial f}{\partial x_1}, \ldots, \frac{\partial f}{\partial x_n} \right) = (D_1 f(X), \ldots, D_n f(X)),$$

whose components are the partial derivatives, will be called the *gradient* of f at X and will be denoted by $\operatorname{grad} f(X)$. One must read this

$$(\operatorname{grad} f)(X),$$

but we shall usually omit the parentheses around $\operatorname{grad} f$.

If f is a function of two variables (x, y), then we have

$$\operatorname{grad} f(x, y) = \left(\frac{\partial f}{\partial x}, \frac{\partial f}{\partial y} \right).$$

For example, in Example 2, where $f(x, y) = x^2 y^3$, we have

$$\operatorname{grad} f(x, y) = (2xy^3, 3x^2 y^2),$$

so that in this case,

$$\operatorname{grad} f(1, 2) = (16, 12).$$

Thus the gradient of a function f associates a *vector* to a point X. This is a different kind of thing from a function, which associates a *number* to a point.

If f is a function of three variables (x, y, z), then

$$\text{grad } f(x, y, z) = \left(\frac{\partial f}{\partial x}, \frac{\partial f}{\partial y}, \frac{\partial f}{\partial z} \right).$$

Using the formula for the derivative of a sum of two functions, and the derivative of a constant times a function, we conclude at once that the gradient satisfies the following properties:

Theorem 1. *Let f, g be two functions defined on an open set U, and assume that their partial derivatives exist at every point of U. Let c be a number. Then*

$$\text{grad } (f + g) = \text{grad } f + \text{grad } g$$
$$\text{grad } (cf) = c \text{ grad } f.$$

You should carry out the details of the proof as an exercise.

We shall give later several geometric and physical interpretations for the gradient.

EXERCISES

Find the partial derivatives

$$\frac{\partial f}{\partial x}, \quad \frac{\partial f}{\partial y}, \quad \text{and} \quad \frac{\partial f}{\partial z},$$

for the following functions $f(x, y)$ or $f(x, y, z)$.

1. $xy + z$
2. $x^2 y^5 + 1$
3. $\sin(xy) + \cos z$
4. $\cos(xy)$
5. $\sin(xyz)$
6. e^{xyz}
7. $x^2 \sin(yz)$
8. xyz
9. $xz + yz + xy$
10. $x \cos(y - 3z) + \arcsin(xy)$
11. Find grad $f(P)$ if P is the point $(1, 2, 3)$ in Exercises 1, 2, 6, 8, and 9.
12. Find grad $f(P)$ if P is the point $(1, \pi, \pi)$ in Exercises 4, 5, 7.
13. Find grad $f(P)$ if

$$f(x, y, z) = \log(z + \sin(y^2 - x))$$

and

$$P = (1, -1, 1).$$

14. Find the partial derivatives of x^y.

Find the gradient of the following functions at the given point.

15. $f(x, y, z) = e^{-2x} \cos(yz)$ at $(1, \pi, \pi)$
16. $f(x, y, z) = e^{3x+y} \sin(5z)$ at $(0, 0, \pi/6)$
17. Prove that an open ball of radius $a > 0$ centered at some point Q is in fact an open set.

§3. DIFFERENTIABILITY AND GRADIENT

Let f be a function defined on an open set U. Let X be a point of U. For all vectors H such that $\|H\|$ is small (and $H \neq O$), the point $X + H$ also lies in the open set. However we *cannot* form a quotient

$$\frac{f(X + H) - f(X)}{H}$$

because it is meaningless to divide by a vector. In order to define what we mean for a function f to be differentiable, we must therefore find a way which does not involve dividing by H.

We reconsider the case of functions of one variable. Let us fix a number x. We had defined the derivative to be

$$f'(x) = \lim_{h \to 0} \frac{f(x + h) - f(x)}{h}.$$

Let

$$g(h) = \frac{f(x + h) - f(x)}{h} - f'(x).$$

Then $g(h)$ is not defined when $h = 0$, but

$$\lim_{h \to 0} g(h) = 0.$$

We can write

$$f(x + h) - f(x) = f'(x)h + hg(h).$$

This relation has meaning so far only when $h \neq 0$. However, we observe that if we define $g(0)$ to be 0, then the preceding relation is obviously true when $h = 0$ (because we just get $0 = 0$).

Furthermore, we can replace h by $-h$ if we replace g by $-g$. Thus we have shown that if f is differentiable, there exists a function g such that

(1) $$f(x + h) - f(x) = f'(x)h + |h|g(h),$$

$$\lim_{h \to 0} g(h) = 0.$$

Conversely, suppose that there exists a number a and a function $g(h)$ such that

(1a) $$f(x + h) - f(x) = ah + |h|g(h),$$

$$\lim_{h \to 0} g(h) = 0.$$

We find for $h \neq 0$,

$$\frac{f(x + h) - f(x)}{h} = a + \frac{|h|}{h} g(h).$$

Taking the limit as h approaches 0, we observe that

$$\lim_{h \to 0} \frac{|h|}{h} g(h) = 0.$$

Hence the limit of the Newton quotient exists and is equal to a. Hence f is differentiable, and its derivative $f'(x)$ is equal to a.

Therefore, the existence of a number a and a function g satisfying (1a) above could have been used as the definition of differentiability in the case of functions of one variable. The great advantage of (1) is that no h appears in the denominator. It is this relation which will suggest to us how to define differentiability for functions of several variables, and how to prove the chain rule for them.

We now consider a function of n variables.

Let f be a function defined on an open set U. Let X be a point of U. If $H = (h_1, \ldots, h_n)$ is a vector such that $\|H\|$ is small enough, then $X + H$ will also be a point of U and so $f(X + H)$ is defined. Note that

$$X + H = (x_1 + h_1, \ldots, x_n + h_n).$$

This is the generalization of the $x + h$ with which we dealt previously.

When f is a function of two variables, which we write (x, y), then we use the notation $H = (h, k)$ so that

$$X + H = (x + h, y + k).$$

The point $X + H$ is close to X and we are interested in the difference $f(X + H) - f(X)$, which is the difference of the value of the function at $X + H$ and the value of the function at X.

We say that f is *differentiable* at X if the partial derivatives $D_1 f(X), \ldots,$ $D_n f(X)$ exist, and if there exists a function g (defined for small H) such that

$$\lim_{H \to O} g(H) = 0 \qquad \left(\text{also written } \lim_{\|H\| \to O} g(H) = 0 \right)$$

and

$$f(X + H) - f(X) = D_1 f(X)h_1 + \cdots + D_n f(X)h_n + \|H\|g(H).$$

With the other notation for partial derivatives, this last relation reads:

$$f(X + H) - f(X) = \frac{\partial f}{\partial x_1} h_1 + \cdots + \frac{\partial f}{\partial x_n} h_n + \|H\|g(H).$$

We say that f is *differentiable* in the open set U if it is differentiable at every point of U, so that the above relation holds for every point X in U.

In view of the definition of the gradient in §2, we can rewrite our fundamental relation in the form

$$(2) \qquad f(X + H) - f(X) = \big(\operatorname{grad} f(X)\big) \cdot H + \|H\|g(H).$$

The term $\|H\|g(H)$ has an order of magnitude smaller than the previous term involving the dot product. This is one advantage of the present notation. We know how to handle the formalism of dot products and are accustomed to it, and its geometric interpretation. This will help us later in interpreting the gradient geometrically.

For the moment, we observe that the gradient is the only vector which will make formula (2) valid (cf. Exercise 7).

In two variables, the definition of differentiability reads

$$f(x + h, y + k) - f(x, y) = \frac{\partial f}{\partial x} h + \frac{\partial f}{\partial y} k + \|H\|g(H).$$

We view the term

$$\frac{\partial f}{\partial x} h + \frac{\partial f}{\partial y} k$$

as an approximation to $f(X + H) - f(X)$, depending in a particularly simple way on h and k.

As an abbreviation, one sometimes writes

$$\operatorname{grad} f = \nabla f.$$

Then formula (2) can be written

$$f(X + H) - f(X) = \nabla f(X) \cdot H + \|H\|g(H).$$

As with grad f, one must read $(\nabla f)(X)$ and not the meaningless $\nabla(f(X))$ since $f(X)$ is a number for each value of X, and thus it makes no sense to apply ∇ to a number. The symbol ∇ is applied to the function f, and $(\nabla f)(X)$ is the value of ∇f at X.

Error terms which can be written in the form $\|H\|g(H)$ for some function g such that

$$\lim_{H \to O} g(H) = 0$$

will appear quite frequently in the sequel. Thus we make a definition. A function φ defined for small H is said to be $o(H)$ (read, "little oh of H") for $H \to O$ if

$$\lim_{H \to O} \frac{\varphi(H)}{\|H\|} = 0.$$

If we let $g(H) = \varphi(H)/\|H\|$, then we see that $\varphi(H) = \|H\|g(H)$ is precisely of the type just considered, namely $o(H)$ for $H \to O$.

The following properties of functions which are $o(H)$ will be used constantly, and follow at once from the definition of limits:

(i) *If φ_1, φ_2 are $o(H)$ for $H \to O$, then $\varphi_1 + \varphi_2$ is also $o(H)$ for $H \to O$.*

(ii) *If φ is $o(H)$ for $H \to O$, and ψ is a bounded function defined for all sufficiently small H, then the product function $\varphi\psi$ is also $o(H)$.* [*Note:* The product function is the function such that $(\varphi\psi)(H) = \varphi(H)\psi(H)$.]

(iii) *If φ_1 is $o(H)$ for $H \to O$ and $\|\varphi_2(H)\| \leq \|\varphi_1(H)\|$ for all H sufficiently small, then φ_2 is also $o(H)$.*

As an example we indicate the proof of the first property. We have by the property of limit of a sum:

$$\lim_{H \to O} \frac{\varphi_1(H) + \varphi_2(H)}{\|H\|} = \lim_{H \to O} \frac{\varphi_1(H)}{\|H\|} + \lim_{H \to O} \frac{\varphi_2(H)}{\|H\|}$$
$$= 0.$$

We leave the others to the reader who has read the Appendix on limits.

Example. Consider the situation with $n = 2$, where we write $H = (h, k)$. Then

$$|h| \leq \sqrt{h^2 + k^2} \qquad \text{and} \qquad |k| \leq \sqrt{h^2 + k^2}.$$

If g is a function such that $\lim_{H \to O} g(H) = 0$, then the function φ defined by

$$\varphi(H) = hg(H)$$

is $o(H)$. Indeed,

$$|\varphi(H)| \leq \|H\| \, |g(H)|$$

and we can apply (iii). Estimates such as these will be used in Theorem 2 below.

In the new terminology of functions which are $o(H)$, we can rewrite formula (2) in the form

$$f(X + H) - f(X) = \big(\operatorname{grad} f(X)\big) \cdot H + o(H).$$

The existence of such an expression is then a restatement of the definition of differentiability of f at X.

Formula (2) is the one which is used throughout the applications of differentiability. It is therefore important to know when a function is differentiable. The next theorem will give us a criterion which can be used in practice. In all this course, the functions which will be encountered will be differentiable, and any reader allergic to theory can simply omit the proof of Theorem 2 without impairing his understanding of the rest of the book.

Let g be a function. We shall say that g is *continuous* if for every point X such that $g(X)$ is defined, we have

$$\lim_{Q \to X} g(Q) = g(X).$$

In other words, as Q approaches X, $g(Q)$ must approach $g(X)$.

Theorem 2. *Let f be a function defined on some open set U. Assume that its partial derivatives exist for every point in this open set, and that they are continuous. Then f is differentiable.*

Proof. For simplicity of notation, we shall use two variables. Thus we deal with a function $f(x, y)$. We let $H = (h, k)$. Let (x, y) be a point in U, and take H small, $H \neq (0, 0)$. We have to consider the difference $f(X + H) - f(X)$, which is simply

$$f(x + h, y + k) - f(x, y).$$

This is equal to

$$f(x + h, y + k) - f(x, y + k) + f(x, y + k) - f(x, y).$$

Applying the mean value theorem for functions of *one* variable, and applying the definition of partial derivatives, we see that there is a number s between x and $x + h$ such that

(3) $f(x + h, y + k) - f(x, y + k) = D_1 f(s, y + k)h.$

Similarly, there is a number t between y and $y + k$ such that

(4) $f(x, y + k) - f(x, y) = D_2 f(x, t)k.$

We shall now analyze the expressions on the right-hand side of equations (3) and (4).
  Let

$$g_1(H) = D_1 f(s, y + k) - D_1 f(x, y).$$

As H approaches O, $(s, y + k)$ approaches (x, y) because s is between x and $x + h$. Since $D_1 f$ is continuous, it follows that

$$\lim_{H \to O} g_1(H) = 0.$$

But

$$D_1 f(s, y + k) = D_1 f(x, y) + g_1(H).$$

Hence equation (3) can be rewritten as

(5) $f(x + h, y + k) - f(x, y + k) = D_1 f(x, y)h + h g_1(H).$

By a similar argument, we can rewrite equation (4) in the form

(6) $f(x, y + k) - f(x, y) = D_2 f(x, y)k + k g_2(H)$

with some function $g_2(H)$ such that

$$\lim_{H \to O} g_2(H) = 0.$$

If we add (5) and (6) we obtain

(7) $f(X + H) - f(X) = D_1 f(X)h + D_2 f(X)k + h g_1(H) + k g_2(H).$

The two expressions on the right are $o(H)$, by the Example preceding the theorem, and their sum is also $o(H)$, for $H \to O$. This proves the theorem.

Remark. If we dealt with n variables, then we would consider the expression for $f(X + H) - f(X)$ given by

$$f(x_1 + h_1, \ldots, x_n + h_n) - f(x_1, \dot{x}_2 + h_2, \ldots, x_n + h_n)$$

$$+ f(x_1, x_2 + h_2, \ldots, x_n + h_n) - f(x_1, x_2, \ldots, x_n + h_n)$$

$$\vdots$$

$$+ f(x_1, \ldots, x_{n-1}, x_n + h_n) - f(x_1, \ldots, x_n).$$

We would then apply the mean value theorem at each step, take the sum, and argue in essentially the same way as with two variables.

EXERCISES

1. Show that $|h + k^2| \leq 2\|H\|^2$ if $H = (h, k)$.
2. Show that $|h^2 + 3hk| \leq 4\|H\|^2$.
3. Show that $|h^3 + h^2k + k^3| \leq 3\|H\|^3$.
4. If $\|H\| \leq 1$, show that $|h^2 + k^3 + k^2| \leq 3\|H\|^2$.
5. Show that $|(h + k)^4| \leq 16\|H\|^4$.
6. Let

$$g(h, k) = \frac{h^2 - k^2}{h^2 + k^2}$$

be defined for $(h, k) \neq (0, 0)$. Find

$$\lim_{h \to 0} g(h, k), \qquad \lim_{k \to 0} \left[\lim_{h \to 0} g(h, k) \right]$$

$$\lim_{k \to 0} g(h, k), \qquad \lim_{h \to 0} \left[\lim_{k \to 0} g(h, k) \right].$$

7. Let f be defined on an open set U. Let P be a point of U. Assume that there are two vectors A, B and two functions $g_1(H)$, $g_2(H)$ such that

$$\lim_{H \to O} g_1(H) = 0 \qquad \text{and} \qquad \lim_{H \to O} g_2(H) = 0,$$

and such that

$$f(P + H) - f(P) = A \cdot H + \|H\|g_1(H)$$
$$= B \cdot H + \|H\|g_2(H).$$

Show that $A = B$. [*Hint:* Subtract, and let $H = tK$ for any K, $t \to 0$.]

8. Let the assumptions be as in Exercise 7. Show that all partial derivatives of f exist at P, and that $A = \operatorname{grad} f(P)$. [*Hint:* Take H to be hE_i, with a unit vector E_i.]

9. Let $g(H) = g(h_1, \ldots, h_n)$ be a polynomial, i.e. an expression of the form

$$g(H) = \sum c_{i_1 \ldots i_n} h_1^{i_1} \cdots h_n^{i_n},$$

where $c_{i_1 \ldots i_n}$ are numbers, and the sum is taken over a finite number of n-tuples $(i_1, \ldots, i_n)$ of integers $\geqq 0$. We call $c_{i_1 \ldots i_n}$ the *coefficients* of g, and abbreviate them by $c_{(i)}$. Assume that $g(O) = 0$, and that s is an integer > 0 such that $i_1 + \cdots + i_n \geqq s$ for all (i). Show that for any H with $\|H\| \leqq 1$ we have

$$|g(H)| \leqq NM\|H\|^s,$$

if N is the number of terms in the sum expressing g, and M is a number such that $|c_{(i)}| \leqq M$ for all (i).

Chapter IV

The Chain Rule and the Gradient

In this chapter, we prove the chain rule for functions of several variables and give a number of applications. Among them will be several interpretations for the gradient. These form one of the central points of our theory. They show how powerful the tools we have accumulated turn out to be.

§1. THE CHAIN RULE

Let f be a function defined on some open set U. Let $t \mapsto X(t)$ be a curve such that the values $X(t)$ are contained in U. Then we can form the composite function $f \circ X$, which is a function of t, given by

$$(f \circ X)(t) = f(X(t)).$$

As an example, take $f(x, y) = e^x \sin(xy)$. Let $X(t) = (t^2, t^3)$. Then

$$f(X(t)) = e^{t^2} \sin(t^5).$$

This is a function of t in the old sense of functions of one variable.

The chain rule tells us how to find the derivative of this function, provided we know the gradient of f and the derivative X'. Its statement is as follows.

Let f be a function which is defined and differentiable on an open set U. Let $X: I \to \mathbf{R}^n$ be a differentiable curve (defined for some interval of numbers t) such that the values $X(t)$ lie in the open set U. Then the function

$$t \mapsto f(X(t))$$

is differentiable (as a function of t), and

$$\frac{df(X(t))}{dt} = (\mathrm{grad}\, f\,(X(t))) \cdot X'(t).$$

In the notation dX/dt, this also reads

$$\frac{df(X(t))}{dt} = (\mathrm{grad}\, f)(X(t)) \cdot \frac{dX}{dt}.$$

374

Before proving the chain rule, we restate it in terms of components. If $X = (x_1, \ldots, x_n)$ then

$$\frac{d(f(X(t)))}{dt} = \frac{\partial f}{\partial x_1} \frac{dx_1}{dt} + \cdots + \frac{\partial f}{\partial x_n} \frac{dx_n}{dt}.$$

If f is a function of two variables (x, y) then

$$\frac{df(X(t))}{dt} = \frac{\partial f}{\partial x} \frac{dx}{dt} + \frac{\partial f}{\partial y} \frac{dy}{dt}.$$

This can be applied to the seemingly more general situation when x, y are functions of more than one variable t. Suppose for instance that

$$x = \varphi(t, u) \qquad \text{and} \qquad y = \psi(t, u)$$

are differentiable functions of two variables. Let

$$g(t, u) = f(\varphi(t, u), \psi(t, u)).$$

If we keep u fixed and take the partial derivative of g with respect to t, then we can apply our chain rule, and obtain

$$\frac{\partial g}{\partial t} = \frac{\partial f}{\partial x} \frac{\partial x}{\partial t} + \frac{\partial f}{\partial y} \frac{\partial y}{\partial t}.$$

The components are of course useful in computations, to determine partial derivatives explicitly, but they will not be used in the proof.

Proof of the chain rule. By definition, we must investigate the quotient

$$\frac{f(X(t + h)) - f(X(t))}{h}.$$

Let

$$K = K(t, h) = X(t + h) - X(t).$$

Then our quotient can be rewritten in the form

$$\frac{f(X(t) + K) - f(X(t))}{h}.$$

Using the definition of differentiability for f, we have

$$f(X + K) - f(X) = (\text{grad} f)(X) \cdot K + \|K\| g(K)$$

and

$$\lim_{\|K\| \to 0} g(K) = 0.$$

Replacing K by what it stands for, namely $X(t + h) - X(t)$, and dividing by h, we obtain:

$$\frac{f(X(t + h)) - f(X(t))}{h} = (\text{grad } f)(X(t)) \cdot \frac{X(t + h) - X(t)}{h}$$

$$\pm \left\| \frac{X(t + h) - X(t)}{h} \right\| g(K).$$

As h approaches 0, the first term of the sum approaches what we want, namely

$$(\text{grad } f)(X(t)) \cdot X'(t).$$

The second term approaches

$$\pm \| X'(t) \| \lim_{h \to 0} g(K),$$

and when h approaches 0, so does $K = X(t + h) - X(t)$. Hence the second term of the sum approaches 0. This proves our chain rule

Example 1. Let $f(x, y) = x^2 + 2xy$. Let $x = r \cos \theta$ and $y = r \sin \theta$. Let $g(r, \theta) = f(r \cos \theta, r \sin \theta)$ be the composite function. Find $\partial g / \partial \theta$.

We have

$$\frac{\partial x}{\partial \theta} = -r \sin \theta \qquad \text{and} \qquad \frac{\partial y}{\partial \theta} = r \cos \theta.$$

Hence

$$\frac{\partial g}{\partial \theta} = (2x + 2y)(-r \sin \theta) + 2x(r \cos \theta).$$

If you want the answer completely in terms of r, θ, you can substitute $r \cos \theta$ and $r \sin \theta$ for x and y respectively in this expression.

Example 2. Let $w = f(x, y, z) = e^{xy} \cos z$ and let

$$x = tu, \qquad y = \sin(tu), \qquad z = u^2.$$

Then

$$\frac{\partial w}{\partial u} = \frac{\partial f}{\partial x} \frac{\partial x}{\partial u} + \frac{\partial f}{\partial y} \frac{\partial y}{\partial u} + \frac{\partial f}{\partial z} \frac{\partial z}{\partial u}$$

$$= ye^{xy}(\cos z)t + xe^{xy}(\cos z)(\cos tu)t - e^{xy}(\sin z)2u$$

$$= \sin(tu)e^{tu \sin(tu)}(\cos u^2)t + tue^{tu \sin(tu)}(\cos u^2)(\cos tu)t$$

$$- e^{tu \sin(tu)}(\sin u^2)2u.$$

In this last expression, we have substituted the values for x, y, z in terms of t and u, thus giving the partial derivative completely in terms of these variables.

EXERCISES

(All functions are assumed to be differentiable as needed.)

1. If $x = u(r, s, t)$ and $y = v(r, s, t)$ and $z = f(x, y)$, write out the formula for

$$\frac{\partial z}{\partial r} \quad \text{and} \quad \frac{\partial z}{\partial t} .$$

2. Find the partial derivatives with respect to x, y, s, and t for the following functions.

(a) $f(x, y, z) = x^3 + 3xyz - y^2z$, $x = 2t + s$, $y = -t - s$, $z = t^2 + s^2$

(b) $f(x, y) = (x + y)/(1 - xy)$, $x = \sin 2t$, $y = \cos(3t - s)$

3. Let $f(x, y, z) = (x^2 + y^2 + z^2)^{1/2}$. Find $\partial f/\partial x$ and $\partial f/\partial y$.

4. Let $r = (x_1^2 + \cdots + x_n^2)^{1/2}$. What is $\partial r/\partial x_i$?

5. If $u = f(x - y, y - x)$, show that

$$\frac{\partial u}{\partial x} + \frac{\partial u}{\partial y} = 0.$$

6. If $u = x^3 f(y/x, z/x)$, show that

$$x\frac{\partial u}{\partial x} + y\frac{\partial u}{\partial y} + z\frac{\partial u}{\partial z} = 3u.$$

7. (a) Let $x = r \cos \theta$ and $y = r \sin \theta$. Let $z = f(x, y)$. Show that

$$\frac{\partial z}{\partial r} = \frac{\partial f}{\partial x} \cos \theta + \frac{\partial f}{\partial y} \sin \theta, \qquad \frac{1}{r}\frac{\partial z}{\partial \theta} = -\frac{\partial f}{\partial x} \sin \theta + \frac{\partial f}{\partial y} \cos \theta.$$

(b) If we let $z = g(r, \theta) = f(r \cos \theta, r \sin \theta)$, show that

$$\left(\frac{\partial g}{\partial r}\right)^2 + \frac{1}{r^2}\left(\frac{\partial g}{\partial \theta}\right)^2 = \left(\frac{\partial f}{\partial x}\right)^2 + \left(\frac{\partial f}{\partial y}\right)^2 .$$

8. (a) Let g be a function of r, let $r = \|X\|$, and $X = (x, y, z)$. Let $f(X) = g(r)$. Show that

$$\left(\frac{dg}{dr}\right)^2 = \left(\frac{\partial f}{\partial x}\right)^2 + \left(\frac{\partial f}{\partial y}\right)^2 + \left(\frac{\partial f}{\partial z}\right)^2 .$$

(b) Let $g(x, y) = f(x + y, x - y)$, where f is a differentiable function of two variables, say $f = f(u, v)$. Show that

$$\frac{\partial g}{\partial x}\frac{\partial g}{\partial y} = \left(\frac{\partial f}{\partial u}\right)^2 - \left(\frac{\partial f}{\partial v}\right)^2 .$$

(c) Let $g(x, y) = f(2x + 7y)$, where f is a differentiable function of one variable. Show that

$$2\frac{\partial g}{\partial y} = 7\frac{\partial g}{\partial x} .$$

9. Let g be a function of r, and $r = \|X\|$. Let $f(X) = g(r)$. Find $\operatorname{grad} f(X)$ for the following functions.

(a) $g(r) = 1/r$ (b) $g(r) = r^2$

(c) $g(r) = 1/r^3$ (d) $g(r) = e^{-r^2}$

(e) $g(r) = \log \dfrac{1}{r}$ (f) $g(r) = 4/r^m$ (m integer $\neq 1$)

10. Let $x = u \cos \theta - v \sin \theta$, and $y = u \sin \theta + v \cos \theta$, with θ equal to a constant. Let $f(x, y) = g(u, v)$. Show that

$$\left(\frac{\partial g}{\partial u}\right)^2 + \left(\frac{\partial g}{\partial v}\right)^2 = \left(\frac{\partial f}{\partial x}\right)^2 + \left(\frac{\partial f}{\partial y}\right)^2.$$

11. Let f be a differentiable function (in two variables) such that $\operatorname{grad} f(X) = cX$ for some constant c and all X in 2-space. Show that f is constant on any circle of radius $a > 0$, centered at the origin. [*Hint:* Put $x = a \cos t$ and $y = a \sin t$ and find df/dt.]

12. (a) Generalize the preceding exercise to the case of n variables. You may assume that any two points on the sphere of radius a centered at the origin are connected by a differentiable curve.

(b) Let f be a differentiable function in n variables, and assume that there exists a function g such that $\operatorname{grad} f(X) = g(X)X$. Show that f is constant on the sphere of radius $a > 0$ centered at the origin. (In other words, in Exercise 11, the hypothesis about the constant c can be weakened to an arbitrary function.)

13. Let $r = \|X\|$. Let g be a differentiable function of one variable whose derivative is never equal to 0. Let $f(X) = g(r)$. Show that $\operatorname{grad} f(X)$ is parallel to X for $X \neq O$.

14. Let f be a differentiable function of two variables and assume that there is an integer $m \geq 1$ such that

$$f(tx, ty) = t^m f(x, y)$$

for all numbers t and all x, y. Prove *Euler's relation*

$$x \frac{\partial f}{\partial x} + y \frac{\partial f}{\partial y} = m f(x, y).$$

15. Generalize Exercise 14 to n variables, namely let f be a differentiable function of n variables and assume that there exists an integer $m \geq 1$ such that $f(tX) = t^m f(X)$ for all numbers t and all points X in $\mathbf{R}^n$. Show that

$$x_1 \frac{\partial f}{\partial x_1} + \cdots + x_n \frac{\partial f}{\partial x_n} = m f(X),$$

which can also be written $X \cdot \operatorname{grad} f(X) = m f(X)$. How does this exercise apply to Exercise 6?

16. Let f be a differentiable function defined on all of $\mathbf{R}^n$. Assume that $f(tP) = tf(P)$ for all numbers t and all points P in $\mathbf{R}^n$. Show that for all P we have

$$f(P) = \operatorname{grad} f(O) \cdot P.$$

17. Let A, B be two unit vectors such that $A \cdot B = 0$. Let

$$F(t) = (\cos t)A + (\sin t)B.$$

Show that $F(t)$ lies on the sphere of radius 1 centered at the origin, for each value of t.

18. Let P, Q be two points on the sphere of radius 1, centered at the origin. Let $L(t) = P + t(Q - P)$, with $0 \leq t \leq 1$. If there exists a value of t in $[0, 1]$ such that $L(t) = O$, show that $t = \frac{1}{2}$, and that $P = -Q$.

19. Let P, Q be two points on the sphere of radius 1. Assume that $P \neq -Q$. Show that there exists a differentiable curve joining P and Q on the sphere of radius 1, centered at the origin. [*Hint:* Divide $L(t)$ in Exercise 17 by its length.]

20. If P, Q are two unit vectors such that $P = -Q$, show that there exists a differentiable curve joining P and Q on the sphere of radius 1, centered at the origin. You may assume that there exists a unit vector A which is perpendicular to P. Then use Exercise 17.

21. Parametrize the ellipse

$$\frac{x^2}{a^2} + \frac{y^2}{b^2} = 1$$

by a differentiable curve.

§2. TANGENT PLANE

Let f be a differentiable function and c a number. The set of points X such that $f(X) = c$ and $\operatorname{grad} f(X) \neq O$ is called a *surface*.

Let $X(t)$ be a differentiable curve. We shall say that the curve *lies on* the surface if, for all t, we have

$$f\big(X(t)\big) = c.$$

This simply means that all the points of the curve satisfy the equation of the surface. If we differentiate this relation, we get from the chain rule:

$$\operatorname{grad} f\big(X(t)\big) \cdot X'(t) = 0.$$

Let P be a point of the surface, and let $X(t)$ be a curve on the surface passing through P. This means that there is a number t_0 such that $X(t_0) = P$. For this value t_0, we obtain

$$\operatorname{grad} f(P) \cdot X'(t_0) = 0.$$

Thus the gradient of f at P is perpendicular to the tangent vector of the curve at P. [We assume that $X'(t_0) \neq O$.] This is true for *any* differentiable curve passing through P. It is therefore very reasonable to *define* the *plane* (or hyperplane) *tangent* to the surface at P to be the plane passing through P and perpendicular to the vector $\operatorname{grad} f(P)$. (We know from Chapter I how to find such planes.) This definition applies only when $\operatorname{grad} f(P) \neq O$. If $\operatorname{grad} f(P) = O$, then we do not define the notion of tangent plane.

The fact that $\operatorname{grad} f(P)$ is perpendicular to every curve passing through P on the surface also gives us an interpretation of the gradient as being perpendicular to the surface

$$f(X) = c,$$

which is one of the level surfaces for the function f (Fig. 1).

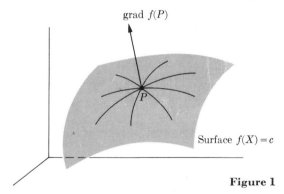

Figure 1

Example 1. Find the tangent plane to the surface

$$x^2 + y^2 + z^2 = 3$$

at the point $(1, 1, 1)$.

Let $f(X) = x^2 + y^2 + z^2$. Then at the point $P = (1, 1, 1)$,

$$\operatorname{grad} f(P) = (2, 2, 2).$$

The equation of a plane passing through P and perpendicular to a vector N is

$$X \cdot N = P \cdot N.$$

In the present case, this yields

$$2x + 2y + 2z = 2 + 2 + 2 = 6.$$

Observe that our arguments also give us a means of finding a vector perpendicular to a curve in 2-space at a given point, simply by applying the preceding discussion to the plane instead of 3-space.

Example 2. Find the tangent line to the curve

$$x^2y + y^3 = 10$$

at the point (1, 2), and find a vector perpendicular to the curve at that point.

Let $f(x, y) = x^2y + y^3$. The gradient at the given point P is easily computed, and we find

$$\operatorname{grad} f(P) = (4, 13).$$

This is a vector N perpendicular to the curve at the given point. The tangent line is also given by $X \cdot N = P \cdot N$, and thus is

$$4x + 13y = 4 + 26 - 30.$$

Example 3. A surface may also be given in the form $z = g(x, y)$ where g is some function of two variables. In this case, the tangent plane is determined by viewing the surface as expressed by the equation

$$g(x, y) - z = 0.$$

For instance, suppose the surface is given by $z = x^2 + y^2$. We wish to determine the tangent plane at (1, 2, 5). Let $f(x, y, z) = x^2 + y^2 - z$. Then $\operatorname{grad} f(x, y, z) = (2x, 2y, -1)$ and

$$\operatorname{grad} f(1, 2, 5) = (1, 4, -1).$$

The equation of the tangent plane at $P = (1, 2, 5)$ perpendicular to $N = (1, 4, -1)$ is

$$x + 4y - z = P \cdot N = 4.$$

This is the desired equation.

EXERCISES

1. Find the equation of the tangent plane and normal line to each of the following surfaces at the specific point.
   (a) $x^2 + y^2 + z^2 = 49$ at (6, 2, 3)
   (b) $xy + yz + zx - 1 = 0$ at (1, 1, 0)
   (c) $x^2 + xy^2 + y^3 + z + 1 = 0$ at $(2, -3, 4)$
   (d) $2y - z^3 - 3xz = 0$ at (1, 7, 2)
   (e) $x^2y^2 + xz - 2y^3 = 10$ at (2, 1, 4)
   (f) $\sin xy + \sin yz + \sin xz = 1$ at $(1, \pi/2, 0)$

2. Let $f(x, y, z) = z - e^x \sin y$, and $P = (\log 3, 3\pi/2, -3)$. Find:
   (a) $\operatorname{grad} f(P)$,
   (b) the normal line at P to the level surface for f which passes through P,
   (c) the tangent plane to this surface at P.

3. Find the parametric equation of the tangent line to the curve of intersection of the following surfaces at the indicated point.

   (a) $x^2 + y^2 + z^2 = 49$ and $x^2 + y^2 = 13$ at $(3, 2, -6)$
   (b) $xy + z = 0$ and $x^2 + y^2 + z^2 = 9$ at $(2, 1, -2)$
   (c) $x^2 - y^2 - z^2 = 1$ and $x^2 - y^2 + z^2 = 9$ at $(3, 2, 2)$

   [*Note.* The tangent line above may be defined to be the line of intersection of the tangent planes of the given point.]

4. Let $f(X) = 0$ be a differentiable surface. Let Q be a point which does not lie on the surface. Given a differentiable curve $X(t)$ on the surface, defined on an open interval, give the formula for the distance between Q and a point $X(t)$. Assume that this distance reaches a minimum for $t = t_0$. Let $P = X(t_0)$. Show that the line joining Q to P is perpendicular to the curve at P.

5. Find the equation of the tangent plane to the surface $z = f(x, y)$ at the given point P when f is the following function:

   (a) $f(x, y) = x^2 + y^2$, $P = (3, 4, 25)$
   (b) $f(x, y) = x/(x^2 + y^2)^{1/2}$, $P = (3, -4, \frac{3}{5})$
   (c) $f(x, y) = \sin(xy)$ at $P = (1, \pi, 0)$

6. Find the equation of the tangent plane to the surface $x = e^{2y-z}$ at $(1, 1, 2)$.

§3. DIRECTIONAL DERIVATIVE

Let f be defined on an open set and assume that f is differentiable. Let P be a point of the open set, and let A be a unit vector (i.e. $\|A\| = 1$). Then $P + tA$ is the parametric equation of a straight line in the direction of A and passing through P. We observe that

$$\frac{d(P + tA)}{dt} = A.$$

For instance, if $n = 2$ and $P = (p, q)$, $A = (a, b)$, then

$$P + tA = (p + ta, q + tb),$$

or in terms of coordinates,

$$x = p + ta, \qquad y = q + tb.$$

Hence

$$\frac{dx}{dt} = a \quad \text{and} \quad \frac{dy}{dt} = b$$

so that

$$\frac{d(P + tA)}{dt} = (a, b) = A.$$

The same argument works in higher dimensions.

Hence by the chain rule, if we take the derivative of the function $t \mapsto f(P + tA)$, which is defined for small values of t, we obtain

$$\frac{df(P + tA)}{dt} = \text{grad } f(P + tA) \cdot A.$$

When t is equal to 0, this derivative is equal to

$$\text{grad } f(P) \cdot A.$$

For obvious geometrical reasons, we call it the *directional derivative* of f in the direction of A. We interpret it as the rate of change of f along the straight line in the direction of A, at the point P. Thus if we agree on the notation $D_A f(P)$ for the directional derivative of f at P in the direction of the unit vector A, then we have

$$D_A f(P) = \left. \frac{df(P + tA)}{dt} \right|_{t=0} = \text{grad } f(P) \cdot A.$$

In using this formula, the reader should remember that A is taken to be a *unit vector*. When a direction is given in terms of a vector whose length is not 1, then one must first divide this vector by its length before applying the formula.

   Example. Let $f(x, y) = x^2 + y^3$ and let $B = (1, 2)$. Find the directional derivative of f in the direction of B, at the point $(-1, 3)$.
   We note that B is not a unit vector. Its length is $\sqrt{5}$. Let

$$A = \frac{1}{\sqrt{5}} B.$$

Then A is a unit vector having the same direction as B. Let $P = (-1, 3)$. Then $\text{grad } f(P) = (-2, 27)$. Hence by our formula, the directional derivative is equal to:

$$\text{grad } f(P) \cdot A = \frac{1}{\sqrt{5}}(-2 + 54) = \frac{52}{\sqrt{5}}.$$

Consider again a differentiable function f on an open set U.
   Let P be a point of U. *Let us assume that* $\text{grad } f(P) \neq O$, and let A be a unit vector. We know that

$$\text{grad } f(P) \cdot A = \|\text{grad } f(P)\| \, \|A\| \cos \theta,$$

where θ is the angle between $\text{grad } f(P)$ and A. Since $\|A\| = 1$, we see that the directional derivative is equal to $\|\text{grad } f(P)\| \cos \theta$. The value of $\cos \theta$ varies between -1 and $+1$ when we select all possible unit vectors A.

The maximal value of $\cos \theta$ is obtained when we select A such that $\theta = 0$, i.e. when we select A to have the same direction as $\operatorname{grad} f(P)$. In that case, the directional derivative is equal to the length of the gradient [cf. Exercise 10 of Chapter I, §4].

Thus we have obtained another interpretation for the gradient: *Its direction is that of maximal increase of the function, and its length is the rate of increase of the function in that direction.*

The directional derivative in the direction of A is at a minimum when $\cos \theta = -1$. This is the case when we select A to have opposite direction to $\operatorname{grad} f(P)$. That direction is therefore the direction of maximal decrease of the function.

For example, f might represent a temperature distribution in space. At any point P, a particle which feels cold and wants to become warmer fastest should move in the direction of $\operatorname{grad} f(P)$. Another particle which is warm and wants to cool down fastest should move in the direction of $-\operatorname{grad} f(P)$.

EXERCISES

1. In Exercise 2 of the preceding section, find:
   (a) the directional derivative of f at P in the direction of $(1, 2, 2)$,
   (b) the maximum and minimum values for the directional derivatives of f at P.

2. Find the directional derivatives of the following functions at the specified points in the specified directions.
   (a) $\log (x^2 + y^2)^{1/2}$ at $(1, 1)$, direction $(2, 1)$
   (b) $xy + yz + zx$ at $(-1, 1, 7)$, direction $(3, 4, -12)$
   (c) $4x^2 + 9y^2$ at $(2, 1)$ in the direction of maximum directional derivative

3. A temperature distribution in space is given by the function
   $$f(x, y) = 10 + 6 \cos x \cos y + 3 \cos 2x + 4 \cos 3y.$$
   At the point $(\pi/3, \pi/3)$, find the direction of greatest increase of temperature, and the direction of greatest decrease of temperature.

4. In what direction are the following functions of X increasing most rapidly at the given point?
   (a) $x/\|X\|^{3/2}$ at $(1, -1, 2)$ $(X = (x, y, z))$
   (b) $\|X\|^5$ at $(1, 2, -1, 1)$ $(X = (x, y, z, w))$

5. Find the tangent plane to the surface $x^2 + y^2 - z^2 = 18$ at the point $(3, 5, -4)$.

6. Let $f(x, y, z) = (x + y)^2 + (y + z)^2 + (z + x)^2$. What is the direction of greatest increase of the function at the point $(2, -1, 2)$. What is the directional derivative of f in this direction at that point?

7. Let $f(x, y) = x^2 + xy + y^2$. What is the direction in which f is increasing most rapidly at the point $(-1, 1)$? Find the directional derivative of f in this direction.

§4. CONSERVATION LAW

As a final application of the chain rule, we derive the conservation law of physics.

Let U be an open set. By a *vector field* on U we mean an association which to every point of U associates a vector of the same dimension.

If f is a differentiable function on U, then we observe that grad f is a vector field, which associates the vector grad $f(P)$ to the point P of U.

A vector field in physics is often interpreted as a field of forces.

If F is a vector field on U, and X a point of U, then we denote by $F(X)$ the vector associated to X by F and call it the value of F at X, as usual.

If F is a vector field, and if there exists a differentiable function f such that $F = \text{grad} f$, then the vector field is called *conservative*. Since $-\text{grad} f = \text{grad} (-f)$, it does not matter whether we use f or $-f$ in the definition of conservative.

Let us assume that F is a conservative field on U, and let Φ be a differentiable function such that for all points X in U we have

$$F(X) = -\text{grad } \Phi.$$

In physics, one interprets Φ as a potential function. Suppose that a particle of mass m moves along a differentiable curve $X(t)$ in U, and let us assume that this particle obeys Newton's law:

$$F(X) = m\ddot{X}, \quad \text{i.e.} \quad F\big(X(t)\big) = m\ddot{X}(t)$$

for all t where $X(t)$ is defined. Then according to our hypotheses,

$$m\ddot{X} + \text{grad } \Phi (X) = O.$$

Take the dot product of both sides with $\dot{X}$. We obtain

$$m\ddot{X} \cdot \dot{X} + \text{grad } \Phi (X) \cdot \dot{X} = 0.$$

But the derivative (with respect to t) of $\dot{X}^2$ is $2\ddot{X} \cdot \dot{X}$. The derivative with respect to t of $\Phi\big(X(t)\big)$ is equal to

$$\text{grad } \Phi (X) \cdot \dot{X}$$

by the chain rule. Hence the expression on the left of our last equation is the derivative of the *function*

$$\tfrac{1}{2}m\dot{X}^2 + \Phi(X),$$

and that derivative is 0. Hence this function is equal to a constant. This is what one means by the conservation law.

The function $\frac{1}{2}m\dot{X}^2$ is called the *kinetic energy*, and the conservation law states that the sum of the kinetic and potential energies is constant.

It is not true that all vector fields are conservative. We shall discuss the problem of determining which ones are conservative in the next chapter.

The fields of classical physics are for the most part conservative. For instance, consider a force which is inversely proportional to the square of the distance from the point to the origin, and in the direction of the position vector. Then there is a constant C such that for $X \neq O$ we have

$$F(X) = C \frac{1}{\|X\|^2} \frac{X}{\|X\|},$$

because $\dfrac{X}{\|X\|}$ is a unit vector in the direction of X. Thus

$$F(X) = C \frac{1}{r^3} X,$$

where $r = \|X\|$. A potential function for F is given by

$$-\frac{C}{r}.$$

This is immediately verified by taking the partial derivatives of this function.

EXERCISES

1. Find a potential function for a force field which is inversely proportional to the distance from the point to the origin, and is in the direction of the position vector.

2. Same question, replacing "distance" with "cube of the distance".

3. Let k be an integer ≥ 1. Find a potentital function for the vector field F given by

$$F(X) = \frac{1}{r^k} X, \qquad \text{where } r = \|X\|.$$

[*Hint:* Cf. Exercise 9(f) of §1.]

Chapter V

Potential Functions and Curve Integrals

We are going to deal systematically with the possibility of finding a potential function for a vector field. The discussion of the existence of such a function will be limited to the case of two variables. Actually, there is no essential difficulty in extending the results to arbitrary n-space, but we leave this to the reader.

The problem is one of integration, and the line integrals are a natural continuation of the integrals at the end of §1 (taken on vertical and horizontal lines).

§1. POTENTIAL FUNCTIONS

Let F be a vector field on an open set U. If φ is a differentiable function on U such that $F = \operatorname{grad} \varphi$, then we say that φ is a *potential function* for F.

One can raise two questions about potential functions. Are they unique, and do they exist?

We consider the first question, and we shall be able to give a satisfactory answer to it. The problem is analogous to determining an integral for a function of one variable, up to a constant, and we shall formulate and prove the analogous statement in the present situation.

We recall that even in the case of functions of one variable, it is *not* true that whenever two functions f, g are such that

$$\frac{df}{dx} = \frac{dg}{dx},$$

then f and g differ by a constant, unless we assume that f, g are defined on some interval. As we emphasized in the *First Course*, we could for instance take

$$f(x) = \begin{cases} \dfrac{1}{x} + 5 & \text{if } x < 0, \\[2mm] \dfrac{1}{x} - \pi & \text{if } x > 0, \end{cases}$$

$$g(x) = \frac{1}{x} \quad \text{if } x \neq 0.$$

Then f, g have the same derivative, but there is no constant C such that for all $x \neq 0$ we have $f(x) = g(x) + C$.

In the case of functions of several variables, we shall have to make a similar restriction on the domain of definition of the functions.

Let U be an open set and let P, Q be two points of U. We shall say that P, Q can be joined by a *differentiable curve* if there exists a differentiable curve $X(t)$ (with t ranging over some interval of numbers) which is contained in U, and two values of t, say t_1 and t_2 in that interval, such that

$$X(t_1) = P \qquad \text{and} \qquad X(t_2) = Q.$$

For example, if U is the entire plane, then any two points can be joined by a straight line. In fact, if P, Q are two points, then we take

$$X(t) = P + t(Q - P).$$

When $t = 0$, then $X(0) = P$. When $t = 1$, then $X(1) = Q$.

It is not always the case that two points of an open set can be joined by a straight line. We have drawn a picture of two points P, Q in an open set U which cannot be so joined.

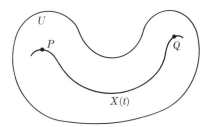

Figure 1

We are now in position to state the theorem we had in mind.

Theorem 1. *Let U be an open set, and assume that any two points in U can be joined by a differentiable curve. Let f, g be two differentiable functions on U. If $\operatorname{grad} f(X) = \operatorname{grad} g(X)$ for every point X of U, then there exists a constant C such that*

$$f(X) = g(X) + C$$

for all points X of U.

Proof. We note that $\operatorname{grad}(f - g) = \operatorname{grad} f - \operatorname{grad} g = O$, and we must prove that $f - g$ is constant. Letting $\varphi = f - g$, we see that it suffices to prove: If $\operatorname{grad} \varphi(X) = O$ for every point X of U, then φ is constant.

Let P be a fixed point of U and let Q be any other point. Let $X(t)$ be a differentiable curve joining P to Q, which is contained in U, and defined over an interval. The derivative of the function $\varphi(X(t))$ is, by the chain rule,

$$\text{grad } \varphi\ (X(t)) \cdot X'(t).$$

But $X(t)$ is a point of U for all values of t in the interval. Hence by our assumption, the derivative of $\varphi(X(t))$ is 0 for all t in the interval. Hence there is a constant C such that

$$\varphi(X(t)) = C$$

for all t in the interval. In other words, the function φ is constant on the curve. Hence $\varphi(P) = \varphi(Q)$.

This result is true for any point Q of U. Hence φ is constant on U, as was to be shown.

Our theorem proves the uniqueness of potential functions (within the restrictions placed by our extra hypothesis on the open set U).

We still have the problem of determining when a vector field F admits a potential function.

We first make some remarks in the case of functions of two variables. Let F be a vector field (in 2-space), so that we can write

$$F(x, y) = (f(x, y), g(x, y))$$

with functions f and g, defined over a suitable open set. We want to know when there exists a function $\varphi(x, y)$ such that

$$\frac{\partial \varphi}{\partial x} = f \quad \text{and} \quad \frac{\partial \varphi}{\partial y} = g.$$

Such a function would be a potential function for F, by definition. (We assume throughout that all hypotheses of differentiability are satisfied as needed.)

Suppose that such a function φ exists. Then

$$\frac{\partial f}{\partial y} = \frac{\partial}{\partial y}\left(\frac{\partial \varphi}{\partial x}\right) \quad \text{and} \quad \frac{\partial g}{\partial x} = \frac{\partial}{\partial x}\left(\frac{\partial \varphi}{\partial y}\right).$$

We shall show in the next chapter that under suitable hypotheses, the two partial derivatives on the right are equal. This means that if there exists a potential function for F, then

$$\frac{\partial f}{\partial y} = \frac{\partial g}{\partial x}.$$

This gives us a simple test in practice to tell whether a potential function may exist.

Theorem 2. *Let f, g be differentiable functions having continuous partial derivatives on an open set U in 2-space. If*

$$\frac{\partial f}{\partial y} \neq \frac{\partial g}{\partial x}$$

then the vector field given by $F(x, y) = (f(x, y), g(x, y))$ does not have a potential function.

Example. Consider the vector field given by

$$F(x, y) = (x^2 y, \sin xy).$$

Then we let $f(x, y) = x^2 y$ and $g(x, y) = \sin xy$. We have:

$$\frac{\partial f}{\partial y} = x^2 \quad \text{and} \quad \frac{\partial g}{\partial x} = y \cos xy.$$

Since $\partial f/\partial y \neq \partial g/\partial x$, it follows that the vector field does not have a potential function.

We shall prove in §3 that the converse of Theorem 2 is true in some very important cases. Before stating and proving the pertinent theorem, we first discuss an auxiliary situation.

EXERCISES

Determine which of the following vector fields have potential functions. The vector fields are described by the functions $(f(x, y), g(x, y))$.

1. $(1/x, xe^{xy})$

2. $(\sin(xy), \cos(xy))$

3. (e^{xy}, e^{x+y})

4. $(3x^4 y^2, x^3 y)$

5. $(5x^4 y, x \cos(xy))$

6. $\left(\dfrac{x}{\sqrt{x^2 + y^2}}, 3xy^2 \right)$

§2. DIFFERENTIATING UNDER THE INTEGRAL

Let f be a continuous function on a rectangle $a \leq x \leq b$ and $c \leq y \leq d$. We can then form a function of y by taking

$$\psi(y) = \int_a^b f(x, y) \, dx.$$

Example 1. We can determine explicitly the function ψ if we let $f(x, y) = \sin(xy)$, namely:

$$\psi(y) = \int_0^\pi \sin(xy) \, dx = -\frac{\cos(xy)}{y} \bigg|_{x=0}^{x=\pi} = -\frac{\cos(\pi y) - 1}{y}.$$

We are interested in finding the derivative of ψ. The next theorem allows us to do this in certain cases, by differentiating with respect to y under the integral sign.

Theorem 3. *Assume that f is continuous on the preceding rectangle, and that $D_2 f$ exists and is continuous. Let*

$$\psi(y) = \int_a^b f(x, y)\, dx.$$

Then ψ is differentiable, and

$$\frac{d\psi}{dy} = D\psi(y) = \int_a^b D_2 f(x, y)\, dx = \int_a^b \frac{\partial f(x, y)}{\partial y}\, dx.$$

Proof. By definition, we have to investigate the Newton quotient for ψ. We have

$$\frac{\psi(y + h) - \psi(y)}{h} = \int_a^b \left[\frac{f(x, y + h) - f(x, y)}{h}\right] dx.$$

We then have to find

$$\lim_{h \to 0} \int_a^b \frac{f(x, y + h) - f(x, y)}{h}\, dx.$$

If we knew that we can put the limit sign inside the integral, we would then conclude that the preceding limit is equal to

$$\int_a^b \lim_{h \to 0} \frac{f(x, y + h) - f(x, y)}{h}\, dx = \int_a^b D_2 f(x, y)\, dx,$$

thus proving our theorem. We shall not give the argument which justifies moving the limit sign inside the integral, because it depends on (ϵ, δ) considerations which are mostly omitted in this book.

Example 2. Letting $f(x, y) = \sin(xy)$ as before, we find that

$$D_2 f(x, y) = x \cos(xy).$$

If we let

$$\psi(y) = \int_0^\pi f(x, y)\, dx,$$

then

$$D\psi(y) = \int_0^\pi D_2 f(x, y)\, dx = \int_0^\pi x \cos(xy)\, dx.$$

By evaluating this last integral, or by differentiating the expression found for ψ at the beginning of the section, the reader will find the same value, namely

$$D\psi(y) = -\left[\frac{\pi y \sin(\pi y) - \cos(\pi y)}{y^2} + \frac{1}{y^2}\right].$$

We can apply the previous theorem using any x as upper limit of the integration. Thus we may let

$$\psi(x, y) = \int_a^x f(t, y)\, dt,$$

in which case the theorem reads

$$\frac{\partial \psi}{\partial y} = D_2\psi(x, y) = \int_a^x D_2 f(t, y)\, dt = \int_a^x \frac{\partial f(t, y)}{\partial y}\, dt.$$

We use t as a variable of integration to distinguish it from the x which is now used as an end point of the interval $[a, x]$ instead of $[a, b]$.

The preceding way of determining the derivative of ψ with respect to y is called *differentiating under the integral sign*. Note that it is completely different from the differentiation in the fundamental theorem of calculus. In this case, we have an integral

$$g(x) = \int_a^x f(t)\, dt,$$

and

$$\frac{dg}{dx} = Dg(x) = f(x).$$

Thus when f is a function of two variables, and ψ is defined as above, the fundamental theorem of calculus states that

$$\frac{\partial \psi}{\partial x} = D_1\psi(x, y) = f(x, y).$$

For example, if we let

$$\psi(x, y) = \int_0^x \sin(ty)\, dt,$$

then

$$D_1\psi(x, y) = \sin(xy),$$

but by Theorem 3,

$$D_2\psi(x, y) = \int_0^x \cos(ty)t\, dt.$$

EXERCISES

In each of the following cases, find $D_1\psi(x, y)$ and $D_2\psi(x, y)$, by evaluating the integrals.

1. $\psi(x, y) = \displaystyle\int_1^x e^{ty}\, dt$

2. $\psi(x, y) = \displaystyle\int_0^x \cos(ty)\, dt$

3. $\psi(x, y) = \displaystyle\int_1^x (y + t)^2\, dt$

4. $\psi(x, y) = \displaystyle\int_1^x e^{y+t}\, dt$

5. $\psi(x, y) = \displaystyle\int_1^x e^{y-t}\, dt$
6. $\psi(x, y) = \displaystyle\int_0^x t^2 y^3\, dt$

7. $\psi(x, y) = \displaystyle\int_1^x \frac{\log(ty)}{t}\, dt$
8. $\psi(x, y) = \displaystyle\int_1^x \sin(3ty)\, dt$

§3. LOCAL EXISTENCE OF POTENTIAL FUNCTIONS

We shall state a theorem which will give us conditions under which the converse of Theorem 2 is true.

Theorem 4. *Let f, g be differentiable functions on an open set of the plane. If this open set is the entire plane, or if it is an open disc, or the inside of a rectangle, if the partial derivatives of f, g exist and are continuous, and if*

$$\frac{\partial f}{\partial y} = \frac{\partial g}{\partial x},$$

then the vector field $F(x, y) = \bigl(f(x, y), g(x, y)\bigr)$ has a potential function.

We shall indicate how a proof of Theorem 4 might go for a rectangle after we have discussed some examples.

Example 1. Determine whether the vector field F given by

$$F(x, y) = (e^{xy}, e^{x+y})$$

has a potential function.

Here, $f(x, y) = e^{xy}$ and $g(x, y) = e^{x+y}$. We have:

$$\frac{\partial f}{\partial y} = xe^{xy} \qquad \text{and} \qquad \frac{\partial g}{\partial x} = e^{x+y}.$$

Since these are not equal, we know that there cannot be a potential function.

If the partial derivatives $\partial f/\partial y$ and $\partial g/\partial x$ turn out to be equal, then one can try to find a potential function by integrating with respect to one of the variables. Thus we try to find

$$\int f(x, y)\, dx,$$

keeping y constant, and taking the ordinary integral of functions of one variable. If we can find such an integral, it will be a function $\psi(x, y)$, whose partial with respect to x will be equal to $f(x, y)$ (by definition). Adding a function of y, we can then adjust it so that its partial with respect to y is equal to $g(x, y)$.

Example 2. Let $F(x, y) = (2xy, x^2 + 3y^2)$. Determine whether this vector field has a potential function, and if it does, find it.

Applying the test which we mentioned above, we find that a potential function may exist. To find it, we consider first the integral

$$\int 2xy \, dx,$$

viewing y as constant. We obtain x^2y for the indefinite integral. We must now find a function $u(y)$ such that

$$\frac{\partial}{\partial y}(x^2y + u(y)) = x^2 + 3y^2.$$

This means that we must find a function $u(y)$ such that

$$x^2 + \frac{du}{dy} = x^2 + 3y^2,$$

or in other words,

$$\frac{du}{dy} = 3y^2.$$

This is a simple integration problem in one variable, and we find $u(y) = y^3$. Thus finally, if we let

$$\varphi(x, y) = x^2y + y^3,$$

we see that φ is a potential function for F.

Proof of Theorem 4. We let the rectangle be defined by

$$a \leqq x \leqq b \qquad \text{and} \qquad c \leqq y \leqq d.$$

We let

$$\varphi(x, y) = \int_a^x f(t, y) \, dt + \int_c^y g(a, u) \, du.$$

Then the second integral on the right does not depend on x, and by the fundamental theorem of calculus,

$$D_1\varphi(x, y) = f(x, y)$$

as wanted. On the other hand, using Theorem 3, and differentiating with respect to y, we get:

$$D_2\varphi(x, y) = \int_a^x D_2f(t, y) \, dt + g(a, y)$$

$$= \int_a^x D_1g(t, y) \, dt + g(a, y)$$

$$= g(t, y)\Big|_{t=a}^{t=x} + g(a, y)$$

$$= g(x, y) - g(a, y) + g(a, y)$$

$$= g(x, y)$$

thus yielding the desired expression for the second partial of φ. This proves Theorem 4.

Note that the proof is entirely similar to that of the example preceding it. The first integral with respect to x solves the requirements or the first partial of φ, and we correct it by an integral involving only y in order to adjust the answer to give the desired partial with respect to y.

EXERCISES

Determine which of the following vector fields admit potential functions.

1. $(e^z, \sin xy)$ 2. $(2x^2y, y^3)$
3. $(2xy, y^2)$ 4. $(y^2x^2, x + y^4)$

Find potential functions for the following vector fields.

5. (a) $F(X) = \dfrac{1}{r} X$ (b) $F(X) = \dfrac{1}{r^2} X$
   (c) $F(X) = r^n X$ (if n is an integer $\neq -2$). In this Exercise,

$$r = \|X\|, \quad \text{and} \quad X \neq O.$$

6. $(4xy, 2x^2)$ 7. $(xy \cos xy + \sin xy, x^2 \cos xy)$
8. $(3x^2y^2, 2x^3y)$ 9. $(2x, 4y^3)$
10. (ye^{xy}, xe^{xy})

11. Let $r = \|X\|$. Let g be a differentiable function of one variable. Show that the vector field defined by

$$F(X) = \frac{g'(r)}{r} X$$

in the domain $X \neq O$ always admits a potential function. What is this potential function?

12. Generalize Theorem 4 to functions of three variables, indicating how a proof might go along the same lines as the proof we gave for two variables.

13. Find a potential function f for the following vector fields F given as $F(x, y, z)$.
   (a) $(2x, 3y, 4z)$ (b) $(y + z, x + z, x + y)$
   (c) $(e^{y+2z}, xe^{y+2z}, 2xe^{y+2z})$ (d) $(y \sin z, x \sin z, xy \cos z)$

§4. CURVE INTEGRALS

Let U be an open set (of n-space), and let F be a vector field on U. We can represent F by components:

$$F(X) = (f_1(X), \ldots, f_n(X)),$$

each f_i being a function. When $n = 2$,

$$F(X) = (f(x, y), g(x, y)).$$

If each function $f_1(X), \ldots, f_n(X)$ is continuous, then we shall say that F is a *continuous* vector field. If each function $f_1(X), \ldots, f_n(X)$ is differentiable, then we shall say that F is a *differentiable* vector field.

We shall also deal with curves. Rather than use the letter X to denote a curve, we shall use another letter, for instance C, to avoid certain confusions which might arise in the present context. Furthermore, it is now convenient to assume that our curve C is defined on a *closed* interval $I = [a, b]$, with $a < b$. For each number t in I, the value $C(t)$ is a point in n-space. We shall say that the curve C lies in U if $C(t)$ is a point of U for all t in I. We say that C is *continuously differentiable* if its derivative $C'(t) = dC/dt$ exists and is continuous. We abbreviate the expression "continuously differentiable" by saying that the curve is a C^1-curve, or of class C^1.

Let F be a continuous vector field on U, and let C be a continuously differentiable curve in U. The dot product

$$F(C(t)) \cdot \frac{dC}{dt}$$

is a *function* of t, and it can be shown easily that this function is continuous (by ϵ and δ techniques which we always omit).

Example 1. Let $F(x, y) = (e^{xy}, y^2)$, and $C(t) = (t, \sin t)$. Then

$$C'(t) = (1, \cos t)$$

and

$$F(C(t)) = (e^{t \sin t}, \sin^2 t).$$

Hence

$$F(C(t)) \cdot C'(t) = e^{t \sin t} + (\cos t)(\sin^2 t).$$

Suppose that C is defined on the interval $[a, b]$. We define the *integral of F along C* to be

$$\int_C F = \int_a^b F(C(t)) \cdot \frac{dC}{dt} \, dt.$$

This integral is a direct generalization of the familiar notion of the integral of functions of one variable. If we are given a function $f(u)$, and u is a function of t, then

$$\int_{u(a)}^{u(b)} f(u) \, du = \int_a^b f(u(t)) \frac{du}{dt} \, dt.$$

(This is the formula describing the substitution method for evaluating integrals.)

In n-space, $C(a)$ and $C(b)$ are points, and our curve passes through these two points. Thus the integral we have written down can be interpreted as an integral of the vector field, along the curve, between the two points. It will also be convenient to write the integral in the form

$$\int_{P,C}^{Q} F = \int_{C(a)}^{C(b)} F(C) \cdot dC$$

to denote the integral along the curve C, from P to Q.

Example 2. Let $F(x, y) = (x^2 y, y^3)$. Find the integral of F along the straight line from the origin to the point $(1, 1)$.

We can parametrize the line in the form

$$C(t) = (t, t).$$

Thus

$$F(C(t)) = (t^3, t^3).$$

Furthermore,

$$\frac{dC}{dt} = (1, 1).$$

Hence

$$F(C(t)) \cdot \frac{dC}{dt} = 2t^3.$$

The integral we must find is therefore equal to:

$$\int_C F = \int_0^1 2t^3 \, dt = \frac{2t^4}{4}\bigg|_0^1 = \frac{1}{2}.$$

Remark 1. Our integral of a vector field along a curve is defined for *parametrized curves*. In practice, a curve is sometimes given in a non-parametrized way. For instance, we may want to integrate over the curve defined by $y = x^2$. Then we select some parametrization which is usually the most natural, in this case

$$x = t, \qquad y = t^2.$$

In general, if a curve is defined by a function $y = g(x)$, we select the parametrization

$$x = t, \qquad y = g(t).$$

For a circle of radius R centered at the origin, we select the parametrization

$$x = R \cos t, \qquad y = R \sin t, \qquad\qquad 0 \leqq t \leqq 2\pi.$$

whenever we wish to integrate counterclockwise.

For a straight line segment between two points P and Q, we take the parametrization C given by

$$C(t) = P + t(Q - P), \qquad\qquad 0 \leqq t \leqq 1.$$

The context should always make it clear which parametrization is intended.

Remark 2. If we are given a finite number of C^1-curves forming a path as indicated in the following figure:

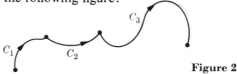

$$C_3$$

$$C_1 \qquad C_2$$

Figure 2

then the integral over the path is simply defined to be the sum of the integrals over each segment. Thus formally, we define a *path* C to be a finite sequence $\{C_1, \ldots, C_m\}$, where each C_i is a C^1-curve, defined on an interval $[a_i, b_i]$, such that the end point of C_i is the beginning point of C_{i+1}. Thus if $P_i = C_i(a_i)$ and $Q_i = C_i(b_i)$, then

$$Q_i = P_{i+1}.$$

We define the integral of F along such a path C to be the sum

$$\int_C F = \int_{C_1} F + \int_{C_2} F + \cdots + \int_{C_m} F.$$

We say that the path C is a *closed path* if the end point of C_m is the beginning point of C_1.

In the following picture, we have drawn a closed path such that the beginning point of C_1, namely P_1, is the end point of the path C_4, which joins P_4 to P_1.

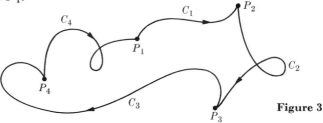

Figure 3

Example 3. Let $F(x, y) = (x^2, xy)$ and let the path consist of the segment of the parabola $y = x^2$ between $(0, 0)$ and $(1, 1)$, and the line segment from $(1, 1)$ and $(0, 0)$. (Cf. Fig. 4.)

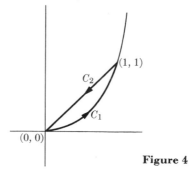

Figure 4

Then we let $C_1(t) = (t, t^2)$ and $C_2(t) = (1 - t, 1 - t)$. We let $C = \{C_1, C_2\}$. To find the integral of F along C we find the integral along C_1 and C_2, and add these integrals. We get:

$$\int_{C_1} F = \int_0^1 F(C_1(t)) \cdot (1, 2t) \, dt = \int_0^1 (t^2 + 2t^4) \, dt = \tfrac{1}{3} + \tfrac{2}{5}.$$

$$\int_{C_2} F = \int_0^1 F(C_2(t)) \cdot (-1, -1) \, dt = \int_0^1 -2(1 - 2t + t^2) \, dt = -\tfrac{2}{3}.$$

Hence

$$\int_C F = -\tfrac{1}{3} + \tfrac{2}{5}.$$

When the vector field F admits a potential function φ, then the integral of F along a curve has a simple expression in terms of φ.

Theorem 5. *Let F be a continuous vector field on the open set U and assume that $F = \text{grad } \varphi$ for some differentiable function φ on U. Let C be a C^1-curve in U, joining the points P and Q. Then*

$$\int_{P,C}^Q F = \varphi(Q) - \varphi(P).$$

In particular, the integral of F is independent of the curve C joining P and Q.

Proof. Let C be defined on the interval $[a, b]$, so that $C(a) = P$ and $C(b) = Q$. By definition, we have

$$\int_{P,C}^Q F = \int_a^b F(C(t)) \cdot C'(t) \, dt = \int_a^b \text{grad } \varphi \, (C(t)) \cdot C'(t) \, dt.$$

But the expression inside the integral is nothing but the derivative with respect to t of the function g given by $g(t) = \varphi(C(t))$, because of the chain rule. Thus our integral is equal to

$$\int_a^b g'(t) \, dt = g(b) - g(a) = \varphi(C(b)) - \varphi(C(a)).$$

This proves our theorem.

This theorem is easily extended to paths. We leave this to the reader.

We observe that in physics, one may interpret a vector field F as describing a force. Then the integral of this vector field along a path C describes the *work* done by the force along this path. In particular, when the vector field is conservative, as in Theorem 5, the work is expressed in terms of the potential function for F, and the end points of the path.

Example 4. Let $F(X) = kX/r^3$, where $r = \|X\|$, and k is a constant. This is the vector field inversely proportional to the square of the distance from the origin, used so often in physics. Then F has a potential function, namely the function φ such that $\varphi(X) = -k/r$. Thus the integral of F from $P = (1, 1, 1)$ to $Q = (1, 2, -1)$ is simply equal to

$$\varphi(Q) - \varphi(P) = -k\left(\frac{1}{\|Q\|} - \frac{1}{\|P\|}\right) = -k\left(\frac{1}{\sqrt{6}} - \frac{1}{\sqrt{3}}\right).$$

On the other hand, if P_1, Q_1 are two points at the same distance from the origin (i.e. lying on the same circle, centered at the origin), then the integral of F from P_1 to Q_1 along any curve is equal to 0.

EXERCISES

Compute the curve integrals of the vector field over the indicated curves.

1. $F(x, y) = (x^2 - 2xy, y^2 - 2xy)$ along the parabola $y = x^2$ from $(-2, 4)$ to $(1, 1)$.

2. $(x, y, xz - y)$ over the line segment from $(0, 0, 0)$ to $(1, 2, 4)$.

3. Let $r = (x^2 + y^2)^{1/2}$. Let $F(X) = r^{-1}X$. Find the integral of F over the circle of radius 2, taken in counterclockwise direction.

4. Let C be a circle of radius 20 with center at the origin. Let F be a vector field such that $F(X)$ has the same direction as X. What is the integral of F around C?

5. What is the work done by the force $F(x, y) = (x^2 - y^2, 2xy)$ moving a particle of mass m along the square bounded by the coordinate axes and the lines $x = 3$, $y = 3$ in counterclockwise direction?

6. Let $F(x, y) = (cxy, x^6y^2)$, where c is a positive constant. Let a, b be numbers > 0. Find a value of a in terms of c such that the line integral of F along the curve $y = ax^b$ from $(0, 0)$ to the line $x = 1$ is independent of b.

Find the values of the indicated integrals of vector fields along the given curves in Exercises 7 through 13.

7. $(y^2, -x)$ along the parabola $x = y^2/4$ from $(0, 0)$ to $(1, 2)$.

8. $(x^2 - y^2, x)$ along the arc in the first quadrant of the circle $x^2 + y^2 = 4$ from $(0, 2)$ to $(2, 0)$.

9. (x^2y^2, xy^2) along the closed path formed by parts of the line $x = 1$ and the parabola $y^2 = x$, counterclockwise.

10. $(x^2 - y^2, x)$ counterclockwise around the circle $x^2 + y^2 = 4$.

11. The vector field

$$\left(\frac{-y}{x^2 + y^2}, \frac{x}{x^2 + y^2}\right)$$

counterclockwise along the circle $x^2 + y^2 = 2$ from $(1, 1)$ to $(-\sqrt{2}, 0)$.

12. The same vector field along the line $x + y = 1$ from $(0, 1)$ to $(1, 0)$.

13. $(2xy, -3xy)$ clockwise around the square bounded by the lines $x = 3$, $x = 5$, $y = 1$, $y = 3$.

14. Let $C = (C_1, \ldots, C_m)$ be a piecewise C^1-path in an open set U. Let F be a continuous vector field on U, admitting a differentiable potential function φ. Let P be the beginning point of the path and Q its end point. Show that

$$\int_{P,C}^{Q} F = \varphi(Q) - \varphi(P).$$

[*Hint:* Apply Theorem 5 to the beginning point P_i and end point Q_i for each curve C_i.]

15. Find the integral of the vector field $F(x, y, z) = (2x, 3y, 4z)$ along the straight line $C(t) = (t, t, t)$ between the points $(0, 0, 0)$ and $(1, 1, 1)$.

16. Find the integral of the vector field $F(x, y, z) = (y + z, x + z, x + y)$ along the straight line $C(t) = (t, t, t)$ between $(0, 0, 0)$ and $(1, 1, 1)$.

17. Find the integral of the vector field given in Exercises 15 and 16 between the given points along the curve $C(t) = (t, t^2, t^4)$. Compare your answers with those previously found.

18. Let $F(x, y, z) = (y, x, 0)$. Find the integral of F along the straight line from $(1, 1, 1)$ to $(3, 3, 3)$.

19. Let P, Q be points of 3-space. Show that the integral of the vector field given by

$$F(x, y, z) = (z^2, 2y, 2xz)$$

from P to Q is independent of the curve selected between P and Q.

20. Let $F(x, y) = (x/r^3, y/r^3)$ where $r = (x^2 + y^2)^{1/2}$. Find the integral of F along the curve $C(t) = (e^t \cos t, e^t \sin t)$ from the point $(1, 0)$ to the point $(e^{2\pi}, 0)$.

21. Let $F(x, y, z) = (z^2, 2y, 2xz)$. Show that the integral of F between two points is independent of the curve between the points.

§5. DEPENDENCE OF THE INTEGRAL ON THE PATH

By a path from now on, we mean a piecewise C^1-path, and all vector fields are assumed continuous.

Given two points P, Q in some open set U, and a vector field F on U, it may be that the integral of F along two paths from P to Q depends on the path. The main theorem of this section gives three equivalent conditions that this integral should be independent of the path. Before discussing this theorem, we describe what we mean by integrating along a curve in opposite direction.

Let $C: [a, b] \to \mathbf{R}^n$ be a curve. We define the *opposite curve* C^- (or the *negative curve*) by letting

$$C^-(t) = C(a + b - t).$$

Thus when $t = b$ we find that $C^-(b) = C(a)$, and when $t = a$ we find that $C^-(a) = C(b)$. As t increases from a to b, we see that $a + b - t$

decreases from b to a and thus we visualize C^- as going from $C(b)$ to $C(a)$ in reverse direction from C (Fig. 5).

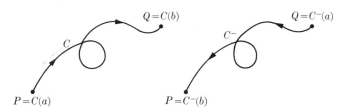

Figure 5

Lemma. *Let F be a vector field on the open set U, and let C be a curve in U, of class C^1, defined on the interval $[a, b]$. Then*

$$\int_{C^-} F = -\int_C F.$$

Proof. This is a simple application of the change of variables formula. Let $u = a + b - t$. Then $du/dt = -1$. By definition and the chain rule, we get:

$$\int_{C^-} F = \int_a^b F(C^-(t)) \cdot \frac{dC^-}{dt} \, dt$$

$$= \int_a^b F(C(a + b - t)) \cdot C'(a + b - t)(-1) \, dt.$$

We now change variables, with $du = -dt$. When $t = a$ then $u = b$, and when $t = b$ then $u = a$. Thus our integral is equal to

$$\int_b^a F(C(u)) \cdot C'(u) \, du = -\int_a^b F(C(u)) \cdot C'(u) \, du,$$

thereby proving the lemma.

The lemma expresses the expected result, that if we integrate the vector field along the opposite direction, then the value of the integral is the negative of the value obtained by integrating F along the curve itself.

Theorem 6. *Let U be an open set in $\mathbf{R}^n$ and let F be a vector field on U. Assume that any two points of U can be connected by a path in U. Then the following conditions are equivalent:*

  (i) *The vector field F has a potential function.*
  (ii) *The integral of F along any closed path in U is equal to 0.*
  (iii) *If P, Q are two points in U then the integral of F from P to Q is independent of the path.*

Proof. Assume condition (i).   Let $C = (C_1, \ldots, C_m)$ be a path in U where each C_i is a C^1-curve. Let P_i be the beginning point of C_i and let Q_i be its end point, so that $Q_i = P_{i+1}$. By Theorem 5, we find that

$$\int_C F = \varphi(Q_m) - \varphi(P_m) + \varphi(Q_{m-1}) - \varphi(P_{m-1}) + \cdots + \varphi(Q_1) - \varphi(P_1).$$

All intermediate terms cancel, leaving the first and the last terms, and our integral is equal to

$$\varphi(Q_m) - \varphi(P_1).$$

If the path is a closed path, then $Q_m = P_1$ and thus the integral is equal to 0. If $P_1 = P$ and $Q_m = Q$, then we see that the value of the integral is independent of the path; it depends only on P, Q and the potential function, namely $\varphi(Q) - \varphi(P)$. *Thus both conditions* (ii) *and* (iii) *follow from* (i).

Furthermore, condition (ii) *implies* (iii).   Indeed, let C and D be paths from P to Q in U. Let $D = (D_1, \ldots, D_k)$ where each D_j is a C^1-curve. Then we may form the opposite path

$$D^- = (D_k^-, \ldots, D_1^-),$$

and by the lemma,

$$\int_{D^-} F = -\int_D F.$$

If $C = (C_1, \ldots, C_m)$, then the path $(C_1, \ldots, C_m, D_k^-, \ldots, D_1^-)$ is a closed path from P to P (Fig. 6), and assuming (ii), we conclude that the integral of F along this closed path is equal to 0. Thus

$$\int_C F + \int_{D^-} F = 0.$$

From this it follows that

$$\int_C F = \int_D F,$$

whence condition (iii) holds.

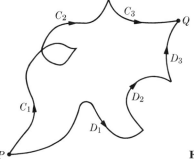

Figure 6

We shall now prove that condition (iii) implies (i). Let P_0 be a fixed point of U and define a function φ on U by the rule

$$\varphi(P) = \int_{P_0}^{P} F,$$

where the integral is taken along any path from P_0 to P. By assumption, this integral does not depend on the path, so we don't need to specify the path in the notation. We must show that the partial derivatives $D_i\varphi(P)$ exist for all P in U, and if the vector field F has coordinate functions

$$F = (f_1, \ldots, f_n),$$

then $D_i\varphi(P) = f_i(P)$.

To do this, let E_i be the unit vector with 1 in the i-th component and 0 in the other components. Then for any vector $X = (x_1, \ldots, x_n)$ we have $X \cdot E_i = x_i$. To determine $D_i\varphi(P)$ we must consider the Newton quotient

$$\frac{\varphi(P + hE_i) - \varphi(P)}{h} = \frac{1}{h}\left[\int_{P_0}^{P+hE_i} F - \int_{P_0}^{P} F\right]$$

and show that its limit as $h \to 0$ is $f_i(P)$. The integral from P_0 to $P + hE_i$ can be taken along a path going first from P_0 to P and then from P to $P + hE_i$.

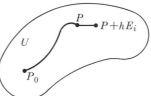

Figure 7

We can then cancel the integrals from P_0 to P and obtain

$$\frac{\varphi(P + hE_i) - \varphi(P)}{h} = \frac{\int_{P}^{P+hE_i} F(C) \cdot dC}{h},$$

taking the integral along any curve C between P and $P + hE_i$. In fact, we take C to be the parametrized straight line segment given by

$$C(t) = P + tE_i$$

with $0 \leq t \leq h$ in case h is positive. (The case of h negative is handled similarly. Cf. Exercise 1.) Then $C'(t) = E_i$ and

$$F\big(C(t)\big) \cdot C'(t) = f_i\big(C(t)\big).$$

The Newton quotient is therefore equal to

$$\frac{\int_0^h f_i(C(t))\, dt}{h}.$$

By the fundamental theorem of calculus, for any continuous function g we have (cf. Remark after the proof):

$$\lim_{h \to 0} \frac{1}{h} \int_0^h g(t)\, dt = g(0).$$

We apply this to the function given by $g(t) = f_i(C(t))$. Then

$$g(0) = f_i(C(0)) = f_i(P + 0E_i) = f_i(P).$$

Therefore we obtain the limit

$$\lim_{h \to 0} \frac{\varphi(P + hE_i) - \varphi(P)}{h} = f_i(P).$$

This proves what we wanted.

Remark. The use of the fundamental theorem of calculus in the preceding proof should be recognized as absolutely straightforward. If G is an indefinite integral for g, then

$$\int_0^h g(t)\, dt = G(h) - G(0),$$

and hence

$$\frac{1}{h} \int_0^h g(t)\, dt = \frac{G(h) - G(0)}{h}$$

is the ordinary Newton quotient for G. The fundamental theorem of calculus asserts precisely that the limit as $h \to 0$ is equal to $G'(0) = g(0)$.

EXERCISE

1. To take care of the case when h is negative in the proof of Theorem 6, use the parametrization $C(t) = P + thE_i$ with $0 \leq t \leq 1$. Making a change of variables, $u = th$, $du = h\, dt$, show that the proof follows exactly the same pattern as that given in the text.

Chapter VI

Higher Derivatives

In this chapter, we discuss two things which are of independent interest. First, we define partial differential operators (with constant coefficients). It is very useful to have facility in working with these formally.

Secondly, we apply them to the derivation of Taylor's formula for functions of several variables, which will be very similar to the formula for one variable. The formula, as before, tells us how to approximate a function by means of polynomials. In the present theory, these polynomials involve several variables, of course. We shall see that they are hardly more difficult to handle than polynomials in one variable in the matters under consideration.

The proof that the partial derivatives commute is tricky. It can be omitted without harm in a class allergic to theory, because the technique involved never reappears in the rest of this book.

§1. REPEATED PARTIAL DERIVATIVES

Let f be a function of two variables, defined on an open set U in 2-space. Assume that its first partial derivative exists. Then $D_1 f$ (which we also write $\partial f/\partial x$ if x is the first variable) is a function defined on U. We may then ask for its first or second partial derivatives, i.e. we may form $D_2 D_1 f$ or $D_1 D_1 f$ if these exist. Similarly, if $D_2 f$ exists, and if the first partial derivative of $D_2 f$ exists, we may form $D_1 D_2 f$.

Suppose that we write f in terms of the two variables (x, y). Then we can write

$$D_1 D_2 f(x, y) = \frac{\partial}{\partial x}\left(\frac{\partial f}{\partial y}\right) = (D_1(D_2 f))(x, y),$$

and

$$D_2 D_1 f(x, y) = \frac{\partial}{\partial y}\left(\frac{\partial f}{\partial x}\right) = (D_2(D_1 f))(x, y).$$

For example, let $f(x, y) = \sin(xy)$. Then

$$\frac{\partial f}{\partial x} = y\cos(xy) \qquad \text{and} \qquad \frac{\partial f}{\partial y} = x\cos(xy).$$

Hence

$$D_2 D_1 f(x, y) = -xy\sin(xy) + \cos(xy).$$

406

But differentiating $\partial f/\partial y$ with respect to x, we see that

$$D_1 D_2 f(x, y) = -xy \sin(xy) + \cos(xy).$$

These two repeated partial derivatives are equal!
   The next theorem tells us that in practice, this will always happen.

   Theorem 1. *Let f be a function of two variables, defined on an open set U of 2-space. Assume that the partial derivatives $D_1 f$, $D_2 f$, $D_1 D_2 f$, and $D_2 D_1 f$ exist and are continuous. Then*

$$D_1 D_2 f = D_2 D_1 f.$$

Proof. A direct use of the definition of these partial and repeated partial derivatives would lead to a blind alley. Hence we shall have to use a special trick to pull through.
   Let (x, y) be a point in U, and let $H = (h, k)$ be small, $h \neq 0$, $k \neq 0$. We consider the expression

$$g(x) = f(x, y + k) - f(x, y).$$

If we apply the mean value theorem to g, then we conclude that there exists a number s_1 between x and $x + h$ such that

$$g(x + h) - g(x) = g'(s_1)h,$$

or in other words, using the definitions of partial derivative:

(1) $g(x + h) - g(x) = [D_1 f(s_1, y + k) - D_1 f(s_1, y)]h.$

But the difference on the left of this equation is

(2) $f(x + h, y + k) - f(x + h, y) - f(x, y + k) + f(x, y).$

On the other hand, we can now apply the mean value theorem to the expression in brackets in (1) *with respect to the second variable*. If we do this, we see that the long expression in (2) is equal to

(3) $D_2 D_1 f(s_1, s_2)kh$

for some number s_2 lying between y and $y + k$.
   We now start all over again, and consider the expression

$$g_2(y) = f(x + h, y) - f(x, y).$$

We apply the mean value theorem to g_2, and conclude that there is a number t_2 between y and $y + k$ such that

$$g_2(y + k) - g_2(y) = g_2'(t_2)k,$$

or in other words, is equal to

(4) $[D_2 f(x + h, t_2) - D_2 f(x, t_2)]k.$

If you work out $g_2(y + k) - g_2(y)$, you will see that it is equal to the long expression of (2). Furthermore, proceeding as before, and applying the mean value theorem to the first variable in (4), we see that (4) becomes

(5) $$D_1 D_2 f(t_1, t_2) hk$$

for some number t_1 between x and $x + h$. Since (5) and (3) are both equal to the long expression in (2), they are equal to each other. Thus finally we obtain

$$D_2 D_1 f(s_1, s_2) kh = D_1 D_2 f(t_1, t_2) hk.$$

Since we assume from the beginning that $h \neq 0$ and $k \neq 0$, we can cancel hk, and get

$$D_2 D_1 f(s_1, s_2) = D_1 D_2 f(t_1, t_2).$$

Now as h, k approach 0, the left side of this equation approaches $D_2 D_1 f(x, y)$ because $D_2 D_1 f$ is assumed to be continuous. Similarly, the right-hand side approaches $D_1 D_2 f(x, y)$. We can therefore conclude that

$$D_1 D_2 f(x, y) = D_2 D_1 f(x, y),$$

as desired.

Consider now a function of three variables $f(x, y, z)$. We can then take three kinds of partial derivatives: D_1, D_2, or D_3 (in other notation, $\partial/\partial x$, $\partial/\partial y$, and $\partial/\partial z$). Let us assume throughout that all the partial derivatives which we shall consider exist and are continuous, so that we may form as many repeated partial derivatives as we please. Then using Theorem 1, we can show that it does not matter in which order we take these partials.

For instance, we see that

$$D_3 D_1 f = D_1 D_3 f.$$

This is simply an application of Theorem 1, keeping the second variable fixed. We may take a further partial derivative, for instance

$$D_1 D_3 D_1 f.$$

Here D_1 occurs twice and D_3 once. Then this expression will be equal to any other repeated partial derivative of f in which D_1 occurs twice and D_3 once. For example, we apply the theorem to the function $(D_1 f)$. Then the theorem allows us to interchange D_1 and D_3 in front of $(D_1 f)$ (always assuming that all partials we want to take exist and are continuous). We obtain

$$D_1 D_3 (D_1 f) = D_3 D_1 (D_1 f).$$

As another example, consider

(6) $$D_2 D_1 D_3 D_2 f.$$

We wish to show that it is equal to $D_1 D_2 D_2 D_3 f$. By Theorem 1, we have $D_3 D_2 f = D_2 D_3 f$. Hence:

(7) $$D_2 D_1 (D_3 D_2 f) = D_2 D_1 (D_2 D_3 f).$$

We then apply Theorem 1 again, and interchange D_2 and D_1 to obtain the desired expression.

In general, suppose that we are given three positive integers m_1, m_2, and m_3. We wish to take the repeated partial derivatives of f by using m_1 times the first partial D_1, using m_2 times the second partial D_2, and using m_3 times the third partial D_3. Then it does not matter in which order we take these partial derivatives, we shall always get the same answer.

To see this, note that by repeated application of Theorem 1, we can always interchange any occurrence of D_3 with D_2 or D_1 so as to push D_3 towards the right. We can perform such interchanges until all occurrences of D_3 occur furthest to the right, in the same way as we pushed D_3 towards the right going from expression (6) to expression (7). Once this is done, we start interchanging D_2 with D_1 until all occurrences of D_2 pile up just behind D_3. Once this is done, we are left with D_1 repeated a certain number of times on the left.

No matter with what arrangement of D_1, D_2, D_3 we started, we end up with the *same* arrangement, namely

$$\underbrace{D_1 \cdots D_1}_{m_1} \underbrace{D_2 \cdots D_2}_{m_2} \underbrace{D_3 \cdots D_3}_{m_3} f,$$

with D_1 occurring m_1 times, D_2 occurring m_2 times, and D_3 occurring m_3 times.

Exactly the same argument works for functions of more variables.

EXERCISES

In all problems, functions are assumed to be differentiable as needed.

Find the partial derivatives of order 2 for the following functions and verify explicitly in each case that $D_1 D_2 f = D_2 D_1 f$.

1. e^{xy} 2. $\sin(xy)$

3. $x^2 y^3 + 3xy$ 4. $2xy + y^2$

5. $e^{x^2 + y^2}$ 6. $\sin(x^2 + y)$

7. $\cos(x^3 + xy)$ 8. $\arctan(x^2 - 2xy)$

9. e^{x+y} 10. $\sin(x + y)$.

Find $D_1 D_2 D_3 f$ and $D_3 D_2 D_1 f$ in the following cases.

11. xyz 12. $x^2 yz$

13. e^{xyz} 14. $\sin(xyz)$

15. $\cos(x + y + z)$ 16. $\sin(x + y + z)$

17. $(x^2 + y^2 + z^2)^{-1}$ 18. $x^3y^2z + 2(x + y + z)$.

19. Let $x = r \cos \theta$ and $y = r \sin \theta$. Let $f(x, y) = g(r, \theta)$. Show that

$$\frac{\partial f}{\partial x} = \cos \theta \frac{\partial g}{\partial r} - \frac{\sin \theta}{r} \frac{\partial g}{\partial \theta}$$

$$\frac{\partial f}{\partial y} = \sin \theta \frac{\partial g}{\partial r} + \frac{\cos \theta}{r} \frac{\partial g}{\partial \theta}.$$

[*Hint:* Using the chain rule, find first $\dfrac{\partial g}{\partial r}$ and $\dfrac{\partial g}{\partial \theta}$ in terms of $\dfrac{\partial f}{\partial x}$ and $\dfrac{\partial f}{\partial y}$. Then solve back a system of two equations in two unknowns.]

20. Let $x = r \cos \theta$ and $y = r \sin \theta$. Let $f(x, y) = g(r, \theta)$. Show that

$$\frac{\partial^2 g}{\partial r^2} + \frac{1}{r} \frac{\partial g}{\partial r} + \frac{1}{r^2} \frac{\partial^2 g}{\partial \theta^2} = \frac{\partial^2 f}{\partial x^2} + \frac{\partial^2 f}{\partial y^2}.$$

21. Let $f(X) = g(r)$ (with $r = \|X\|$), and assume $X = (x, y, z)$. Show that

$$\frac{d^2 g}{dr^2} + \frac{2}{r} \frac{dg}{dr} = \frac{\partial^2 f}{\partial x^2} + \frac{\partial^2 f}{\partial y^2} + \frac{\partial^2 f}{\partial z^2}.$$

22. Let $f(x, y)$ satisfy $f(tx, ty) = t^n f(x, y)$ for all t (n being some integer ≥ 1). Show that

$$x \frac{\partial f}{\partial x} + y \frac{\partial f}{\partial y} = n f(x, y).$$

23. Let f be as in Exercise 22. Show that

$$x^2 \frac{\partial^2 f}{\partial x^2} + 2xy \frac{\partial^2 f}{\partial x \partial y} + y^2 \frac{\partial^2 f}{\partial y^2} = n(n - 1) f(x, y).$$

(It is understood throughout that all functions are as many times differentiable as is necessary.)

24. A function of three variables $f(x, y, z)$ is said to satisfy *Laplace's equation* if

$$\frac{\partial^2 f}{\partial x^2} + \frac{\partial^2 f}{\partial y^2} + \frac{\partial^2 f}{\partial z^2} = 0.$$

Verify that the following functions satisfy Laplace's equation.

(a) $x^2 + y^2 - 2z^2$ (b) $\log \sqrt{x^2 + y^2 + z^2}$

(c) $\dfrac{1}{\sqrt{x^2 + y^2 + z^2}}$ (d) $e^{3x+4y} \cos(5z)$

25. Let $z = f(u, v)$ and $u = x + y$, $v = x - y$. Show that

$$\frac{\partial^2 z}{\partial x \partial y} = \frac{\partial^2 z}{\partial u^2} - \frac{\partial^2 z}{\partial v^2}.$$

26. Let $z = f(x + y) - g(x - y)$, where f, g are functions of one variable. Let $u = x + y$ and $v = x - y$. Show that

$$\frac{\partial^2 z}{\partial x^2} = \frac{\partial^2 z}{\partial y^2} = f''(u) + g''(v).$$

27. Let c be a constant, and let $z = \sin(x + ct) + \cos(2x + 2ct)$. Show that

$$\frac{\partial^2 z}{\partial t^2} = c^2 \frac{\partial^2 z}{\partial x^2}.$$

28. Let $z = f\left(\dfrac{x - y}{y}\right)$. Show that $x(\partial z/\partial x) + y(\partial z/\partial y) = 0$.

29. Let c be a constant, and let $z = f(x + ct) + g(x - ct)$. Let $u = x + ct$ and $v = x - ct$. Show that

$$\frac{\partial^2 z}{\partial t^2} = c^2 \frac{\partial^2 z}{\partial x^2} = c^2(f''(u) + g''(v)).$$

30. Let F be a vector field on an open set in 3-space, so that F is given by three coordinate functions, say $F = (f_1, f_2, f_3)$. Define the *curl* of F to be the vector field given by

$$(\text{curl } F)(x_1, x_2, x_3) = \left(\frac{\partial f_3}{\partial x_2} - \frac{\partial f_2}{\partial x_3}, \ \frac{\partial f_1}{\partial x_3} - \frac{\partial f_3}{\partial x_1}, \ \frac{\partial f_2}{\partial x_1} - \frac{\partial f_1}{\partial x_2}\right).$$

Define the *divergence* of F to be the function $g = \text{div } F$ given by

$$g(x, y, z) = \frac{\partial f_1}{\partial x} + \frac{\partial f_2}{\partial y} + \frac{\partial f_3}{\partial z}.$$

(a) Prove that if $F = \text{grad } \varphi$ for some function φ, then

$$\text{div grad } \varphi = 0.$$

(b) Prove that curl grad $\varphi = O$.

§2. PARTIAL DIFFERENTIAL OPERATORS

We shall continue the discussion at the end of the last section, but we shall build up a convenient system to talk about iterated partial derivatives.

For simplicity, let us begin with functions of one variable x. We can then take only one type of derivative,

$$D = \frac{d}{dx}.$$

Let f be a function of one variable, and let us assume that all the iterated derivatives of f exist. Let m be a positive integer. Then we can take the

m-th derivative of f, which we once denoted by $f^{(m)}$. We now write it

$$DD \cdots Df \quad \text{or} \quad \frac{d}{dx}\left(\frac{d}{dx} \cdots \left(\frac{df}{dx}\right) \cdots\right),$$

the derivative D (or d/dx) being iterated m times. What matters here is the number of times D occurs. We shall use the notation D^m or $(d/dx)^m$ to mean the iteration of D, m times. Thus we write

$$D^m f \quad \text{or} \quad \left(\frac{d}{dx}\right)^m f$$

instead of the above expressions. This is shorter. But even better, we have the rule

$$D^m D^n f = D^{m+n} f$$

for any positive integers m, n. So this iteration of derivatives begins to look like a multiplication. Furthermore, if we define $D^0 f$ to be simply f, then the rule above also holds if m, n are ≥ 0.

The expression D^m will be called a *simple differential operator of order m* (in one variable, so far).

Let us now look at the case of two variables, say (x, y). We can then take two partials D_1 and D_2 (or $\partial/\partial x$ and $\partial/\partial y$). Let m_1, m_2 be two integers ≥ 0. Instead of writing

$$\underbrace{D_1 \cdots D_1}_{m_1}\underbrace{D_2 \cdots D_2 f}_{m_2} \quad \text{or} \quad \underbrace{\frac{\partial}{\partial x} \cdots \left(\frac{\partial}{\partial x}}_{m_1}\underbrace{\left(\frac{\partial}{\partial y} \cdots \left(\frac{\partial f}{\partial y}\right) \cdots\right)}_{m_2}\right),$$

we shall write

$$D_1^{m_1} D_2^{m_2} f \quad \text{or} \quad \left(\frac{\partial}{\partial x}\right)^{m_1}\left(\frac{\partial}{\partial y}\right)^{m_2} f.$$

For instance, taking $m_1 = 2$ and $m_2 = 5$ we would write

$$D_1^2 D_2^5 f.$$

This means: take the first partial twice and the second partial five times (in any order). (We assume throughout that all repeated partials exist and are continuous.)

An expression of type

$$D_1^{m_1} D_2^{m_2}$$

will be called a simple differential operator, and we shall say that its *order* is $m_1 + m_2$. In the example we just gave, the order is $5 + 2 = 7$.

It is now clear how to proceed with three or more variables, and it is no harder to express our thoughts in terms of n variables than in terms of three. Consequently, if we deal with functions of n variables, all of whose repeated partial derivatives exist and are continuous in some open set U, and if $D_1, \ldots, D_n$ denote the partial derivatives with respect to these variables, then we call an expression

$$D_1^{m_1} \cdots D_n^{m_n} \quad \text{or} \quad \left(\frac{\partial}{\partial x_1}\right)^{m_1} \cdots \left(\frac{\partial}{\partial x_n}\right)^{m_n}$$

a *simple differential operator*, $m_1, \ldots, m_n$ being integers ≥ 0. We say that its *order* is $m_1 + \cdots + m_n$.

Given a function f (satisfying the above stated conditions), and a simple differential operator D, we write Df to mean the function obtained from f by applying repeatedly the partial derivatives $D_1, \ldots, D_n$, the number of times being the number of times each D_i occurs in D.

Example 1. Consider functions of three variables (x, y, z). Then

$$D = \left(\frac{\partial}{\partial x}\right)^3 \left(\frac{\partial}{\partial y}\right)^5 \left(\frac{\partial}{\partial z}\right)^2$$

is a simple differential operator of order $3 + 5 + 2 = 10$. Let f be a function of three variables satisfying the usual hypotheses. To take Df means that we take the partial derivative with respect to z twice, the partial with respect to y five times, and the partial with respect to x three times.

We observe that a simple differential operator gives us a rule which to each function f associates another function Df.

As a matter of notation, referring to Example 1, one would also write the differential operator D in the form

$$D = \frac{\partial^{10}}{\partial x^3 \partial y^5 \partial z^2}.$$

In this notation, one would thus have

$$\left(\frac{\partial}{\partial x}\right)^2 f = \frac{\partial^2 f}{\partial x^2}$$

and

$$\frac{\partial}{\partial x}\left(\frac{\partial f}{\partial y}\right) = \frac{\partial^2 f}{\partial x \, \partial y}.$$

All the above notations are used in the scientific literature, and this is the reason for including them here.

Warning. Do not confuse the two expressions

$$\left(\frac{\partial}{\partial x}\right)^2 f = \frac{\partial^2 f}{\partial x^2} \quad \text{and} \quad \left(\frac{\partial f}{\partial x}\right)^2,$$

which are usually **not** equal. For instance, if $f(x, y) = x^2y$, then

$$\frac{\partial^2 f}{\partial x^2} = 2y \qquad \text{and} \qquad \left(\frac{\partial f}{\partial x}\right)^2 = 4x^2y^2.$$

We shall now show how one can add simple differential operators and multiply them by constants.

Let D, D' be two simple differential operators. For any function f we define $(D + D')f$ to be $Df + D'f$. If c is a number, then we define $(cD)f$ to be $c(Df)$. In this manner, taking iterated sums, and products with constants, we obtain what we shall call *differential operators*. Thus a *differential operator* D is a sum of terms of type

$$cD_1^{m_1} \cdots D_n^{m_n},$$

where c is a number and $m_1, \ldots, m_n$ are integers ≥ 0.

Example 2. Dealing with two variables, we see that

$$D = 3\frac{\partial}{\partial x} + 5\left(\frac{\partial}{\partial x}\right)^2 - \pi\frac{\partial}{\partial x}\frac{\partial}{\partial y}$$

is a differential operator. Let $f(x, y) = \sin(xy)$. We wish to find Df. By definition,

$$Df(x, y) = 3\frac{\partial f}{\partial x} + 5\left(\frac{\partial}{\partial x}\right)^2 f - \pi\frac{\partial}{\partial x}\frac{\partial f}{\partial y}$$

$$= 3y\cos(xy) + 5(-y^2\sin(xy))$$

$$- \pi[y(-\sin(xy))x + \cos(xy)].$$

We see that a differential operator associates with each function f (satisfying the usual conditions) another function Df.

Let c be a number and f a function. Let D_i be any partial derivative. Then

$$D_i(cf) = cD_if.$$

This is simply the old property that the derivative of a constant times a function is equal to the constant times the derivative of the function. Iterating partial derivatives, we see that this same property applies to differential operators. For any differential operator D, and any number c, we have

$$D(cf) = cDf.$$

Furthermore, if f, g are two functions (defined on the same open set, and having continuous partial derivatives of all orders), then for any partial derivative D_i, we have

$$D_i(f + g) = D_if + D_ig.$$

Iterating the partial derivatives, we find that for any differential operator D, we have

$$D(f + g) = Df + Dg.$$

Having learned how to add differential operators, we now learn how to multiply them.

Let D, D' be two differential operators. Then we define the differential operator DD' to be the one obtained by taking first D' and then D. In other words, if f is a function, then

$$(DD')f = D(D'f).$$

Example 3. Let

$$D = 3\frac{\partial}{\partial x} + 2\frac{\partial}{\partial y} \quad \text{and} \quad D' = \frac{\partial}{\partial x} + 4\frac{\partial}{\partial y}.$$

Then

$$DD' = \left(3\frac{\partial}{\partial x} + 2\frac{\partial}{\partial y}\right)\left(\frac{\partial}{\partial x} + 4\frac{\partial}{\partial y}\right)$$

$$= 3\left(\frac{\partial}{\partial x}\right)^2 + 14\frac{\partial}{\partial x}\frac{\partial}{\partial y} + 8\left(\frac{\partial}{\partial y}\right)^2.$$

Differential operators multiply just like polynomials and numbers, and their addition and multiplication satisfy all the rules of addition and multiplication of polynomials. For instance:

If D, D' are two differential operators, then

$$DD' = D'D.$$

If D, D', D'' are three differential operators, then

$$D(D' + D'') = DD' + DD''.$$

It would be tedious to list all the properties here and to give in detail all the proofs (even though they are quite simple). We shall therefore omit these proofs. The main purpose of this section is to insure that you develop as great a facility in adding and multiplying differential operators as you have in adding and multiplying numbers or polynomials.

When a differential operator is written as a sum of terms of type

$$cD_1^{m_1} \cdots D_n^{m_n},$$

then we shall say that it is in *standard form*.

For example,

$$3\left(\frac{\partial}{\partial x}\right)^2 + 14\frac{\partial}{\partial x}\frac{\partial}{\partial y} + 8\left(\frac{\partial}{\partial y}\right)^2$$

is in standard form, but

$$\left(3\frac{\partial}{\partial x} + 2\frac{\partial}{\partial y}\right)\left(\frac{\partial}{\partial x} + 4\frac{\partial}{\partial y}\right)$$

is not.

Each term

$$cD_1^{m_1} \cdots D_n^{m_n}$$

is said to have degree $m_1 + \cdots + m_n$. If a differential operator is expressed as a sum of simple differential operators which all have the same degree, say m, then we say that it is *homogeneous* of degree m.

The differential operator of Example 2 is not homogeneous. The differential operator DD' of Example 3 is homogeneous of degree 2.

EXERCISES

Put the following differential operators in standard form.

1. $(3D_1 + 2D_2)^2$ 2. $(D_1 + D_2 + D_3)^2$

3. $(D_1 - D_2)(D_1 + D_2)$ 4. $(D_1 + D_2)^2$

5. $(D_1 + D_2)^3$ 6. $(D_1 + D_2)^4$

7. $(2D_1 - 3D_2)(D_1 + D_2)$ 8. $(D_1 - D_3)(D_2 + 5D_3)$

9. $\left(\dfrac{\partial}{\partial x} + 4\dfrac{\partial}{\partial y}\right)^3$ 10. $\left(2\dfrac{\partial}{\partial x} + \dfrac{\partial}{\partial y}\right)^2$

11. $\left(h\dfrac{\partial}{\partial x} + k\dfrac{\partial}{\partial y}\right)^2$ 12. $\left(h\dfrac{\partial}{\partial x} + k\dfrac{\partial}{\partial y}\right)^3$

Find the values of the differential operator of Exercise 10 applied to the following functions at the given point.

13. x^2y at $(0, 1)$ 14. xy at $(1, 1)$

15. $\sin(xy)$ at $(0, \pi)$ 16. e^{xy} at $(0, 0)$

17. Let f, g be two functions (of two variables) with continuous partial derivatives of order ≤ 2 in an open set U. Assume that

$$\frac{\partial f}{\partial x} = -\frac{\partial g}{\partial y} \quad \text{and} \quad \frac{\partial f}{\partial y} = \frac{\partial g}{\partial x}.$$

Show that

$$\frac{\partial^2 f}{\partial x^2} + \frac{\partial^2 f}{\partial y^2} = 0.$$

18. Let f be a function of three variables, defined for $X \neq O$ by $f(X) = 1/\|X\|$. Show that

$$\frac{\partial^2 f}{\partial x^2} + \frac{\partial^2 f}{\partial y^2} + \frac{\partial^2 f}{\partial z^2} = 0.$$

19. In Exercise 20 of the preceding section, compute

$$\left(\frac{\partial}{\partial x}\right)^2 + \left(\frac{\partial}{\partial y}\right)^2$$

in terms of $\partial/\partial r$ and $\partial/\partial\theta$. Watch out! The coefficients are not constant.

§3. TAYLOR'S FORMULA

In the theory of functions of one variable, we derived an expression for the values of a function f near a point a by means of the derivatives, namely

$$f(a + h) = f(a) + f'(a)h + \frac{f^{(2)}(a)}{2!}h^2 + \cdots + \frac{f^{(r-1)}(a)}{(r-1)!}h^{r-1} + R_r,$$

where

$$R_r = \frac{f^{(r)}(c)}{r!}h^r,$$

for some point c between a and $a + h$. We shall now derive a similar formula for functions of several variables. We begin with the case of two variables.

We let $P = (a, b)$ and $H = (h, k)$. We assume that P is in an open set U and that f is a function on U all of whose partial derivatives up to order n exist and are continuous. We are interested in finding an expression

$$f(P + H) = f(P) + ?\ ?\ ?$$

The idea is to reduce the problem to the one variable case. Thus we define the function

$$g(t) = f(P + tH) = f(a + th, b + tk)$$

for $0 \leqq t \leqq 1$. We assume that U contains all points $P + tH$ for $0 \leqq t \leqq 1$. Then

$$g(1) = f(P + H) \qquad \text{and} \qquad g(0) = f(P).$$

We can use Taylor's formula in one variable applied to the function g and we know that

$$g(1) = g(0) + \frac{g'(0)}{1!} + \cdots + \frac{g^{(r-1)}(0)}{(r-1)!} + \frac{g^{(r)}(\tau)}{r!}$$

for some number τ between 0 and 1, provided that g has r continuous derivatives. We shall now prove that the derivatives of g can be expressed in terms of the partial derivatives of f, and thus obtain the desired Taylor formula for f. We shall first do it for $n = 2$.

We let $x = a + th$ and $y = b + tk$. By the chain rule:

(1) $$g'(t) = \frac{\partial f}{\partial x}\frac{\partial x}{\partial t} + \frac{\partial f}{\partial y}\frac{\partial y}{\partial t} = \frac{\partial f}{\partial x}h + \frac{\partial f}{\partial y}k.$$

For the second derivative, we must find the derivative with respect to t of each one of the functions $\partial f/\partial x$ and $\partial f/\partial y$. By the chain rule applied to each such function, we have:

(2)
$$\frac{d}{dt}\left(\frac{\partial f}{\partial x}\right) = \frac{\partial^2 f}{\partial x^2}\frac{dx}{dt} + \frac{\partial^2 f}{\partial y\,\partial x}\frac{dy}{dt} = \frac{\partial^2 f}{\partial x^2}h + \frac{\partial^2 f}{\partial y\,\partial x}k,$$

$$\frac{d}{dt}\left(\frac{\partial f}{\partial y}\right) = \frac{\partial^2 f}{\partial x\,\partial y}h + \frac{\partial^2 f}{\partial y^2}k.$$

Hence using (2) to take the derivative of (1), we find:

$$g''(t) = h\left[\frac{\partial^2 f}{\partial x^2}h + \frac{\partial^2 f}{\partial y\,\partial x}k\right] + k\left[\frac{\partial^2 f}{\partial x\,\partial y}h + \frac{\partial^2 f}{\partial y^2}k\right]$$

$$= h^2\frac{\partial^2 f}{\partial x^2} + 2hk\frac{\partial^2 f}{\partial x\,\partial y} + k^2\frac{\partial^2 f}{\partial y^2}.$$

This expression can be rewritten more easily in terms of differential operators, namely we see that the expression for $g''(t)$ is equal to

$$\left(h\frac{\partial}{\partial x} + k\frac{\partial}{\partial y}\right)^2 f.$$

If we wish to free the notation from the x and y, then we can use the notation

$$g''(t) = (hD_1 + kD_2)^2 f(P + tH)$$
$$= (hD_1 + kD_2)^2 f(a + th, b + tk).$$

As usual, this means that we apply $(hD_1 + kD_2)^2$ to f, and then evaluate this function at the point $(a + th, b + tk)$.

The expression $hD_1 + kD_2$ looks like a dot product, and thus it is useful to abbreviate the notation and write

$$hD_1 + kD_2 = H \cdot \nabla.$$

With this abbreviation, our first derivative for g can then be written [from (1)]:

$$g'(t) = (H \cdot \nabla)f(P + tH),$$

and the second derivative can be written

$$g''(t) = (H \cdot \nabla)^2 f(P + tH).$$

Here again, we emphasize that $(H \cdot \nabla)$ and $(H \cdot \nabla)^2$ are first applied to f, so that strictly speaking we should write an extra set of parentheses, e.g.

$$g'(t) = \big((H \cdot \nabla)f\big)(a + th, b + tk)$$

and similarly for $g''(t)$.

The higher derivatives of g are determined similarly by induction.

Theorem 2. *Let r be a positive integer. Let f be a function defined on an open set U, and having continuous partial derivatives of orders $\leqq r$. Let P be a point of U, and H a vector. Let $g(t) = f(P + tH)$. Then*

$$g^{(r)}(t) = ((H \cdot \nabla)^r f)(P + tH)$$

for all values of t such that $P + tH$ lies in U.

Proof. The case $r = 1$ (even $r = 2$) has already been verified. Suppose our formula proved for some integer r. Let $\psi = (H \cdot \nabla)^r f$. Then

$$g^{(r)}(t) = \psi(P + tH).$$

Hence by the case for $r = 1$ we get

$$g^{(r+1)}(t) = ((H \cdot \nabla)\psi)(P + tH).$$

Substituting the value for ψ yields

$$g^{(r+1)}(t) = ((H \cdot \nabla)^{r+1} f)(P + tH),$$

thus proving our theorem by induction.

In terms of the $\partial/\partial x$ and $\partial/\partial y$ notation, we see that

$$\boxed{g^{(r)}(t) = \left(h\frac{\partial}{\partial x} + k\frac{\partial}{\partial y} \right)^r f\,(P + tH).}$$

Taylor's Formula. *Let f be a function defined on an open set U, and having continuous partial derivatives up to order r. Let P be a point of U, and H a vector. Assume that the line segment*

$$P + tH, \qquad 0 \leqq t \leqq 1,$$

is contained in U. Then there exists a number τ between 0 and 1 such that

$$f(P + H) = f(P) + \frac{(H \cdot \nabla)f(P)}{1!} + \cdots + \frac{(H \cdot \nabla)^{r-1} f(P)}{(r-1)!}$$

$$+ \frac{(H \cdot \nabla)^r f(P + \tau H)}{r!}.$$

Proof. This is obtained by plugging the expression for the derivatives of the function $g(t) = f(P + tH)$ into the Taylor formula for one variable. We see that

$$g^{(s)}(0) = (H \cdot \nabla)^s f(P)$$

and

$$g^{(r)}(\tau) = (H \cdot \nabla)^r f(P + \tau H).$$

This proves Taylor's formula as stated.

Rewritten in terms of the $\partial/\partial x$ and $\partial/\partial y$ notation, we have

$$f(a + h, b + k) = f(a, b) + \left(h \frac{\partial}{\partial x} + k \frac{\partial}{\partial y}\right) f(a, b) + \cdots$$

$$+ \left(h \frac{\partial}{\partial x} + k \frac{\partial}{\partial y}\right)^{r-1} f(a, b)$$

$$+ \left(h \frac{\partial}{\partial x} + k \frac{\partial}{\partial y}\right)^{r} f(a + \tau h, b + \tau k).$$

The powers of the differential operators

$$\left(h \frac{\partial}{\partial x} + k \frac{\partial}{\partial y}\right)^{s}$$

are found by the usual binomial expansion. For instance:

$$\left(h \frac{\partial}{\partial x} + k \frac{\partial}{\partial y}\right)^{2} = h^2 \frac{\partial^2}{\partial x^2} + 2hk \frac{\partial^2}{\partial x\, \partial y} + k^2 \frac{\partial^2}{\partial y^2},$$

$$\left(h \frac{\partial}{\partial x} + k \frac{\partial}{\partial y}\right)^{3} = h^3 \left(\frac{\partial}{\partial x}\right)^3 + 3h^2 k \left(\frac{\partial}{\partial x}\right)^2 \left(\frac{\partial}{\partial y}\right)$$

$$+ 3hk^2 \left(\frac{\partial}{\partial x}\right)\left(\frac{\partial}{\partial y}\right)^2 + k^3 \left(\frac{\partial}{\partial y}\right)^3.$$

Example 1. Find the terms of degree ≤ 2 in the Taylor formula for the function $f(x, y) = \log (1 + x + 2y)$ at the point $(2, 1)$.

We compute the partial derivatives. They are:

$$f(2, 1) = \log 5,$$

$$D_1 f(x, y) = \frac{1}{1 + x + 2y}, \qquad D_1 f(2, 1) = \frac{1}{5} = \frac{\partial f}{\partial x}(2, 1),$$

$$D_2 f(x, y) = \frac{2}{1 + x + 2y}, \qquad D_2 f(2, 1) = \frac{2}{5} = \frac{\partial f}{\partial y}(2, 1),$$

$$D_1^2 f(x, y) = -\frac{1}{(1 + x + 2y)^2}, \qquad D_1^2 f(2, 1) = -\frac{1}{25} = \frac{\partial^2 f}{\partial x^2}(2, 1),$$

$$D_2^2 f(x, y) = -\frac{4}{(1 + x + 2y)^2}, \qquad D_2^2 f(2, 1) = -\frac{4}{25} = \frac{\partial^2 f}{\partial y^2}(2, 1),$$

$$D_1 D_2 f(x, y) = -\frac{2}{(1 + x + 2y)^2}, \qquad D_1 D_2 f(2, 1) = -\frac{2}{25} = \frac{\partial^2 f}{\partial x\, \partial y}(2, 1).$$

Hence

$$f(2 + h, 1 + k) = \log 5 + \left(\frac{1}{5} h + \frac{2}{5} k\right)$$

$$+ \frac{1}{2!}\left[-\frac{1}{25} h^2 - \frac{4}{25} hk - \frac{4}{25} k^2\right] + \cdots.$$

In many cases, we take $P = O$ and we wish to approximate $f(x, y)$ by a polynomial in x, y. Thus we let $H = (x, y)$. In that case, the notation $\partial/\partial x$ and $\partial/\partial y$ becomes even worse than usual since it is not entirely clear in taking the square

$$\left(x\frac{\partial}{\partial x} + y\frac{\partial}{\partial y}\right)^2$$

what is to be treated as a constant and what is not. Thus it is better to write

$$(xD_1 + yD_2)^2,$$

and similarly for higher powers. We then obtain a polynomial expression for f, with a remainder term. The terms of degree ≤ 3 are as follows:

$$f(x, y)$$
$$= f(0, 0) + D_1f(0, 0)x + D_2f(0, 0)y$$
$$+ \frac{1}{2!}[D_1^2f(0, 0)x^2 + 2D_1D_2f(0, 0)xy + D_2^2f(0, 0)y^2]$$
$$+ \frac{1}{3!}[D_1^3f(0, 0)x^3 + 3D_1^2D_2f(0, 0)x^2y + 3D_1D_2^2f(0, 0)xy^2 + D_2^3f(0, 0)y^3]$$
$$+ R_4.$$

In general, the Taylor formula gives us an expression

$$f(x, y) - f(0, 0) + G_1(x, y) + \cdots + G_{r-1}(x, y) + R_r,$$

where $G_d(x, y)$ is a homogeneous polynomial in x, y of degree d, and R_r is the remainder term. We call

$$f(0, 0) + G_1(x, y) + \cdots + G_s(x, y)$$

the *polynomial approximation of f*, of degree $\leq s$.

Example 2. Find the polynomial approximation of the function

$$f(x, y) = \log (1 + x + 2y)$$

up to degree 2.

We computed the partial derivatives in Example 1. For the present application, we have

$$f(0, 0) = 0,$$

$$D_1f(0, 0) = 1, \qquad D_2f(0, 0) = 2,$$

$$D_1^2f(0, 0) = -1, \qquad D_2^2f(0, 0) = -4,$$

$$D_1D_2f(0, 0) = -2.$$

Hence the polynomial approximation of f up to degree 2 is

$$G(x, y) = x + 2y - \tfrac{1}{2}(x^2 + 4xy + 4y^2).$$

Example 3. In some special cases, there is a way of getting the polynomial approximation to the function more simply by using more directly the Taylor formula for one variable. Consider for instance the function $f(x, y) = \sin(xy)$. For any number u we know that

$$\sin u = u + R_3(u)$$

where $R_3(u)$ is the remainder of the Taylor formula for the sine function of one variable. From the *First Course in Calculus,* you should know that this remainder term satisfies the estimate

$$|R_3(u)| \leq \frac{|u|^3}{3!}.$$

Thus if we let $u = xy$, then we find that

$$\sin(xy) = xy + R_3(xy),$$

and hence

$$|\sin(xy) - xy| \leq \frac{|xy|^3}{3!}.$$

Also we see that, for example, for $y \neq 0$, we have

$$\frac{\sin(xy) - xy}{y} = \frac{R_3(xy)}{y}.$$

In particular, we get the estimate

$$\left| \frac{\sin(xy) - xy}{y} \right| \leq \frac{|x|^3 |y|^2}{3!}.$$

From this we see that the limit of

$$\frac{\sin(xy) - xy}{y}$$

as (x, y) approaches $(0, 0)$ is equal to 0.

Finally, we observe that the treatment of functions of several variables follows exactly the same pattern. In this case, we let

$$H = (h_1, \ldots, h_n)$$

and

$$H \cdot \nabla = h_1 D_1 + \cdots + h_n D_n = h_1 \frac{\partial}{\partial x_1} + \cdots + h_n \frac{\partial}{\partial x_n}.$$

Not a single word need be changed in Theorems 2 and 3 to get Taylor's formula for several variables.

EXERCISES

Find the terms up to order 2 in the Taylor formula of the following functions (taking $P = O$).

1. $\sin(xy)$ 2. $\cos(xy)$ 3. $\log(1 + xy)$

4. $\sin(x^2 + y^2)$ 5. e^{x+y} 6. $\cos(x^2 + y)$

7. $(\sin x)(\cos y)$ 8. $e^x \sin y$ 9. $x + xy + 2y^2$

10. Does $\dfrac{\sin(xy)}{x}$ approach a limit as (x, y) approaches $(0, 0)$? If so, what limit?

11. Same questions for

$$\frac{e^{xy} - 1}{x} \quad \text{and} \quad \frac{\log(1 + x^2 + y^2)}{x^2 + y^2}.$$

12. Same questions for

$$\frac{\cos(xy) - 1}{x}.$$

13. Same questions for

$$\frac{\sin(xy) - xy}{x^2 y}.$$

14. Find the terms up to order 3 in Taylor's formula for the function $e^x \cos y$.

15. What is the term of degree 7 in Taylor's formula for the function

$$x^3 - 2xy^4 + (x - 1)^2 y^{10}?$$

16. Show that if $f(x, y, z)$ is a polynomial in x, y, z, then it is equal to its own Taylor series, i.e. there exists an integer n such that $R_n = 0$.

17. Find the polynomial approximation of the function

$$f(x, y) = \log(1 + x + 2y)$$

up to degree 3.

18. In each one of Exercises 1 through 9, find the terms of degree ≤ 2 in the Taylor expansion of the function at the indicated point.

1. $P = (1, \pi)$ 2. $P = (\pi/2, \pi)$ 3. $P = (2, 3)$

4. $P = (\pi, \pi)$ 5. $P = (1, 2)$ 6. $P = (0, \pi)$

7. $P = (\pi/2, \pi)$ 8. $P = (2, \pi/4)$ 9. $P = (1, 1)$

19. Let f be a function of two variables with continuous partial derivatives of order ≤ 2. Assume that $f(0) = 0$ and also that $f(ta, tb) = t^2 f(a, b)$ for all numbers t and all vectors (a, b). Show that for all points $P = (a, b)$ we have

$$f(P) = \frac{(P \cdot \nabla)^2 f(0)}{2!}.$$

20. Let U be an open set having the following property. Given two points X, Y in U, the line segment joining X and Y is contained in the open set.

(a) What is the parametric equation for this line segment?

(b) Let f have continuous partial derivatives in U. Assume that

$$\|\operatorname{grad} f(P)\| \leq M$$

for some number M, and all points P in U. Show that for any two points X, Y in U we have

$$|f(X) - f(Y)| \leq M\|X - Y\|.$$

§4. INTEGRAL EXPRESSIONS

Quite often, instead of the mean value type of remainder obtained previously in Taylor's formula, it is useful to deal with an integral form of the remainder. For instance, we have

$$(1) \qquad f(x, y) = f(0, 0) + \int_0^1 \frac{d}{dt}\left(f(tx, ty)\right) dt.$$

This is a direct application of the definition of the integral, since we can put $\psi(t) = f(tx, ty)$, and since

$$\int_0^1 \frac{d\psi}{dt}\, dt = \psi(1) - \psi(0).$$

If we now evaluate the derivative with respect to t under the integral, using the chain rule, we obtain

$$f(x, y) = f(0, 0) + \int_0^1 [D_1 f(tx, ty)x + D_2 f(tx, ty)y]\, dt$$

or

$$\boxed{f(x, y) = f(0, 0) + xg_1(x, y) + yg_2(x, y),}$$

where

$$g_1(x, y) = \int_0^1 D_1 f(tx, ty)\, dt \qquad \text{and} \qquad g_2(x, y) = \int_0^2 D_2 f(tx, ty)\, dt.$$

The advantage of such an expression is that the dependence of g_1 and g_2 on (x, y) is quite smooth—just as smooth as that of $D_1 f$ and $D_2 f$. From Chapter V, §2 we know that we can differentiate under the integral sign with respect to x and y. Thus this type of expression is often better than the remainder of Taylor's formula, with an undetermined τ which usually cannot be given explicitly, and depends on the specific choice of (x, y).

EXERCISE

1. Let f be a function of two variables, with continuous partials of order ≤ 2. Assume that $f(0, 0) = 0$ and $D_i f(0, 0) = 0$ for $i = 1, 2$. Show that there exist continuous functions h_i such that

$$f(x, y) = h_1(x, y)x^2 + h_2(x, y)xy + h_3(x, y)y^2.$$

[*Hint:* Apply the arguments of the text to the functions

$$D_1 f(tx, ty) \quad \text{and} \quad D_2 f(tx, ty)$$

using an integral with respect to some new variable, say s.]

Chapter VII

Maximum and Minimum

When we studied functions of one variable, we found maxima and minima by first finding critical points, i.e. points where the derivative is equal to 0, and then determining by inspection which of these are maxima or minima. We can carry out a similar investigation for functions of several variables. The condition that the derivative is equal to 0 must be replaced by the vanishing of all partial derivatives.

§1. CRITICAL POINTS

Let f be a differentiable function defined on an open set U. Let P be a point of U. If all partial derivatives of f are equal to 0 at P, then we say that P is a *critical point* of the function. In other words, for P to be a critical point, we must have

$$D_1 f(P) = 0, \quad \ldots, \quad D_n f(P) = 0.$$

Example. Find the critical points of the function $f(x, y) = e^{-(x^2+y^2)}$. Taking the partials, we see that

$$\frac{\partial f}{\partial x} = -2xe^{-(x^2+y^2)} \quad \text{and} \quad \frac{\partial f}{\partial y} = -2ye^{-(x^2+y^2)}.$$

The only value of (x, y) for which both these quantities are equal to 0 is $x = 0$ and $y = 0$. Hence the only critical point is $(0, 0)$.

A critical point of a function of one variable is a point where the derivative is equal to 0. We have seen examples where such a point need not be a local maximum or a local minimum, for instance as in the following picture:

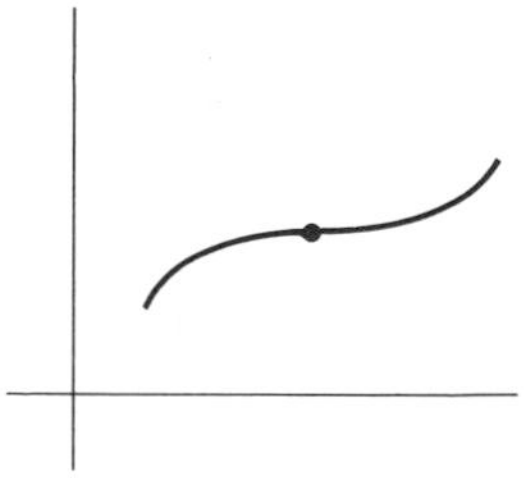

Figure 1

A fortiori, a similar thing may occur for functions of several variables. However, once we have found critical points, it is usually not too difficult to tell by inspection whether they are of this type or not.

426

Let f be any function (differentiable or not), defined on an open set U. We shall say that a point P of U is a *local maximum* for the function if there exists an open ball (of positive radius) B, centered at P, such that for all points X of B, we have

$$f(X) \leq f(P).$$

As an exercise, define *local minimum* in an analogous manner.

In the case of functions of one variable, we took an open interval instead of an open ball around the point P. Thus our notion of local maximum in n-space is the natural generalization of the notion in 1-space.

Theorem 1. *Let f be a function which is defined and differentiable on an open set U. Let P be a local maximum for f in U. Then P is a critical point of f.*

Proof. The proof is exactly the same as for functions of one variable. In fact, we shall prove that the directional derivative of f at P in any direction is 0. Let H be a non-zero vector. For small values of t, $P + tH$ lies in the open set U, and $f(P + tH)$ is defined. Furthermore, for small values of t, tH is small, and hence $P + tH$ lies in our open ball such that

$$f(P + tH) \leq f(P).$$

Hence the function of one variable $g(t) = f(P + tH)$ has a local maximum at $t = 0$. Hence its derivative $g'(0)$ is equal to 0. By the chain rule, we obtain as usual:

$$\operatorname{grad} f(P) \cdot H = 0.$$

This equation is true for every non-zero vector H, and hence

$$\operatorname{grad} f(P) = O.$$

This proves what we wanted.

EXERCISES

Find the critical points of the following functions.

1. $x^2 + 4xy - y^2 - 8x - 6y$ 2. $x + y \sin x$
3. $x^2 + y^2 + z^2$ 4. $(x + y)e^{-xy}$
5. $xy + xz$ 6. $\cos(x^2 + y^2 + z^2)$
7. $x^2 y^2$ 8. $x^4 + y^2$
9. $(x - y)^4$ 10. $x \sin y$
11. $x^2 + 2y^2 - x$ 12. $e^{-(x^2 + y^2 + z^2)}$
13. $e^{(x^2 + y^2 + z^2)}$

14. In each of the preceding exercises, find the minimum value of the given function, and give all points where the value of the function is equal to this minimum. [*Do this exercise after you have read* §3.]

§2. THE QUADRATIC FORM

Let f be a differentiable function on an open set U, and assume that all partial derivatives up to order 3 exist and are continuous. Let P be a point of U, and assume that P is a critical point of f. We assume that we work in 2-space, so that we can express f near the point $P = (a, b)$ in the form

$$f(a + h, b + k) = f(a, b)$$
$$+ \frac{1}{2}\left[h^2 \frac{\partial^2 f}{\partial x^2}(a, b) + 2hk \frac{\partial^2 f}{\partial x\, \partial y}(a, b) + k^2 \frac{\partial^2 f}{\partial y^2}(a, b) \right]$$
$$+ R_3,$$

where R_3 is a remainder term. Actually, we prefer to write in the other notation:

$$f(a + h, b + k) = f(a, b)$$
$$+ \tfrac{1}{2}[h^2 D_1^2 f(a, b) + 2hk D_1 D_2 f(a, b) + k^2 D_2^2 f(a, b)]$$
$$+ R_3$$

because we want to use x, y for other purposes.

The *function* $q(x, y)$ of x, y given by

$$q(x, y) = \tfrac{1}{2}[x^2 D_1^2 f(P) + 2xy D_1 D_2 f(P) + y^2 D_2^2 f(P)]$$

is called the *quadratic form* associated with f àt P, whenever P is a critical point of f. This quadratic form approximates the values of f so that one gets some general idea of the behavior of f near P when the terms of degree 1 vanish.

Example 1. Let $f(x, y) = e^{-(x^2+y^2)}$. Then it is a simple matter to verify that

$$\operatorname{grad} f(0, 0) = 0.$$

We let $P = (0, 0)$ be the origin. Standard computations show that

$$D_1^2 f(O) = -2, \qquad D_1 D_2 f(O) = 0, \qquad D_2^2 f(O) = -2.$$

Substituting these values in the general formula gives the expression for the quadratic form, namely

$$q(x, y) = -(x^2 + y^2).$$

We see that the quadratic form is nothing but the term of degree 2 in the Taylor expansion of the function at the given point.

We shall now describe the level curves for some quadratic forms to get an idea of their behavior near the origin.

Example 2. $q(x, y) = x^2 + y^2$. Then a graph of the function q and the level curves look like those in Figs. 2 and 3.

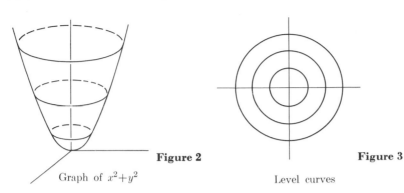

Figure 2

Graph of $x^2 + y^2$

Figure 3

Level curves

In this example, we see that the origin $(0, 0)$ is a local minimum point for the form.

Example 3. $q(x, y) = -(x^2 + y^2)$. The graph and level curves look like these:

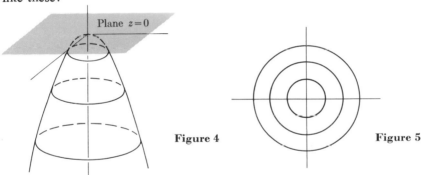

Plane $z = 0$

Figure 4

Figure 5

The origin is a local maximum for the form.

Example 4. $q(x, y) = x^2 - y^2$. The level curves are then hyperbolas, determined for each number c by the equation $x^2 - y^2 = c$:

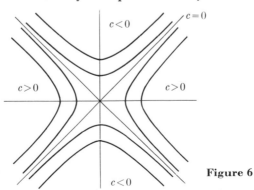

$c < 0$

$c = 0$

$c > 0$ $c > 0$

Figure 6

$c < 0$

Of course, when $c = 0$, we get the two straight lines as shown.

Example 5. $q(x, y) = xy$. The level curves look like the following (similar to the preceding example, but turned around):

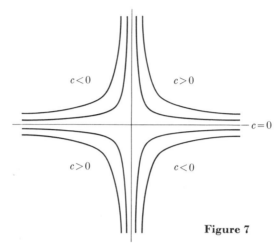

$c < 0$ $c > 0$

$c = 0$

$c > 0$ $c < 0$

Figure 7

In Examples 4 and 5, we see that the origin, which is a critical point, is neither a local maximum nor local minimum.

EXERCISES

1. Let $f(x, y) = 3x^2 - 4xy + y^2$. Show that the origin is a critical point of f.

2. More generally, let a, b, c be numbers. Show that the function f given by $f(x, y) = ax^2 + bxy + cy^2$ has the origin as a critical point.

3. Find the quadratic form associated to the function f at the critical points P in the Exercises of §1.

4. Sketch the level curves for the following quadratic forms. Determine whether the origin is a local maximum, minimum, or neither.

  (a) $q(x, y) = 2x^2 - y^2$ (b) $q(x, y) = 3x^2 + 4y^2$
  (c) $q(x, y) = -(4x^2 + 5y^2)$ (d) $q(x, y) = y^2 - x^2$
  (e) $q(x, y) = 2y^2 - x^2$ (f) $q(x, y) = y^2 - 4x^2$
  (g) $q(x, y) = -(3x^2 + 2y^2)$ (h) $q(x, y) = 2xy$

§3. BOUNDARY POINTS

In considering intervals, we had to distinguish between closed and open intervals. We must make an analogous distinction when considering sets of points in space.

Let S be a set of points, in some n-space. Let P be a point of S. We shall say that P is an *interior point* of S if there exists an open ball B of positive radius, centered at P, and such that B is contained in S. The next picture illustrates an interior point (for the set consisting of the region enclosed by the curve).

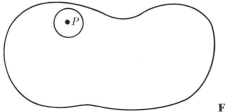

Figure 8

We have also drawn an open ball around P.

From the very definition, we conclude that the set consisting of all interior points of S is an open set.

A point P (not necessarily in S) is called a *boundary point* of S if every open ball B centered at P includes a point of S, and also a point which is not in S. We illustrate a boundary point in the following picture:

Figure 9

For example, the set of boundary points of the closed ball of radius $a > 0$ is the sphere of radius a. In 2-space, the plane, the region consisting of all points with $y > 0$ is open. Its boundary points are the points lying on the x-axis.

If a set contains all of its boundary points, then we shall say that the set is *closed*.

Finally, a set is said to be *bounded* if there exists a number $b > 0$ such that, for every point X of the set, we have

$$\|X\| \leqq b.$$

We are now in a position to state the existence of maxima and minima for continuous functions.

Theorem 2. *Let S be a closed and bounded set. Let f be a continuous function defined on S. Then f has a maximum and a minimum in S. In other words, there exists a point P in S such that*

$$f(P) \geqq f(X)$$

for all X in S, and there exists a point Q in S such that

$$f(Q) \leqq f(X)$$

for all X in S.

We shall not prove this theorem. It depends on an analysis which is beyond the level of this course.

When trying to find a maximum (say) for a function f, one should first determine the critical points of f in the interior of the region under consideration. If a maximum lies in the interior, it must be among these critical points.

Next, one should investigate the function on the boundary of the region. By parametrizing the boundary, one frequently reduces the problem of finding a maximum on the boundary to a lower-dimensional problem, to which the technique of critical points can also be applied.

Finally, one has to compare the possible maximum of f on the boundary and in the interior to determine which points are maximum points.

Example. In the Example in §1, we observe that the function

$$f(x, y) = e^{-(x^2+y^2)}$$

becomes very small as x or y becomes large. Consider some big closed disc centered at the origin. We know by Theorem 2 that the function has a maximum in this disc. Since the value of the function is small on the boundary, it follows that this maximum must be an interior point, and hence that the maximum is a critical point. But we found in the Example in §1 that the only critical point is at the origin. Hence we conclude that the origin is *the* only maximum of the function $f(x, y)$. The value of f at the origin is $f(0, 0) = 1$. Furthermore, the function has no minimum, because $f(x, y)$ is always positive and approaches 0 as x and y become large.

EXERCISES

Find the maximum and minimum points of the following functions in the indicated region.

1. $x + y$ in the square with corners at $(\pm 1, \pm 1)$

2. (a) $x + y + z$ in the region $x^2 + y^2 + z^2 < 1$
   (b) $x + y$ in the region $x^2 + y^2 < 1$

3. $xy - (1 - x^2 - y^2)^{1/2}$ in the region $x^2 + y^2 \leq 1$

4. $144x^3y^2(1 - x - y)$ in the region $x \geq 0$ and $y \geq 0$ (the first quadrant together with its boundary)

5. $(x^2 + 2y^2)e^{-(x^2+y^2)}$ in the plane

6. (a) $(x^2 + y^2)^{-1}$ in the region $(x - 2)^2 + y^2 \leq 1$
   (b) $(x^2 + y^2)^{-1}$ in the region $x^2 + (y - 2)^2 \leq 1$

7. Which of the following functions have a maximum and which have a minimum in the whole plane?

(a) $(x + 2y)e^{-x^2-y^4}$ (b) e^{x-y}

(c) $e^{x^2-y^2}$ (d) $e^{x^2+y^{10}}$

(e) $(3x^2 + 2y^2)e^{-(4x^2+y^2)}$ (f) $-x^2 e^{x^4+y^{10}}$

(g) $\begin{cases} \dfrac{x^2 + y^2}{|x| + |y|} & \text{if} \quad (x, y) \neq (0, 0) \\ \quad 0 & \text{if} \quad (x, y) = (0, 0) \end{cases}$

8. Which is the point on the curve $\left(\cos t, \sin t, \sin(t/2)\right)$ farthest from the origin?

§4. LAGRANGE MULTIPLIERS

In this section, we shall investigate another method for finding the maximum or minimum of a function on some set of points. This method is particularly well adapted to the case when the set of points is described by means of an equation.

We shall work in 3-space. Let g be a differentiable function of three variables x, y, z. We consider the surface

$$g(X) = 0.$$

Let U be an open set containing this surface, and let f be a differentiable function defined for all points of U. We wish to find those points P on the surface $g(X) = 0$ such that $f(P)$ is a maximum or a minimum on the surface. In other words, we wish to find all points P such that $g(P) = 0$, and either

$$f(P) \geq f(X) \quad \text{for all } X \text{ such that } g(X) = 0,$$

or

$$f(P) \leq f(X) \quad \text{for all } X \text{ such that } g(X) = 0.$$

Any such point will be called an *extremum for f subject to the constraint g.*

In what follows, we consider only points P such that $g(P) = 0$ but grad $g\ (P) \neq 0$.

Theorem 3. *Let g be a continuously differentiable function on an open set U. Let S be the set of points X in U such that $g(X) = 0$ but*

$$\text{grad } g\ (X) \neq O.$$

Let f be a continuously differentiable function on U and assume that P is a point of S such that P is an extremum for f. (In other words, P is an extremum for f, subject to the constraint g.) Then there exists a number λ such that

$$\text{grad} f\ (P) = \lambda \text{ grad } g\ (P).$$

Proof. Let $X: J \to S$ be a differentiable curve on the surface S passing through P, say $X(t_0) = P$. Then the function $t \mapsto f(X(t))$ has a maximum or a minimum at t_0. Its derivative

$$\frac{d}{dt} f(X(t))$$

is therefore equal to 0 at t_0. But this derivative is equal to

$$\operatorname{grad} f(P) \cdot X'(t_0) = 0.$$

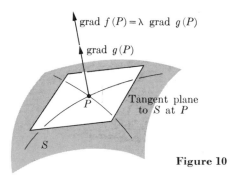

Figure 10

Hence $\operatorname{grad} f(P)$ is perpendicular to every curve on the surface passing through P (Fig. 10). It can be shown that under these circumstances, and the hypothesis that $\operatorname{grad} g(P) \neq O$, there exists a number λ such that

(1) $\operatorname{grad} f(P) = \lambda \operatorname{grad} g(P),$

or in other words, $\operatorname{grad} f(P)$ has the same, or opposite direction, as $\operatorname{grad} g(P)$, provided it is not O. Intuitively, this is rather clear, since the direction of $\operatorname{grad} g(P)$ is the direction perpendicular to the surface, and we have seen that $\operatorname{grad} f(P)$ is also perpendicular to the surface. To give a complete proof would require technical arguments in linear algebra, which we shall omit here. One can use the result proved in Chapter XVI, Theorem 7, §2, that for a subspace W of $\mathbf{R}^3$ we have

$$\dim W + \dim W^\perp = 3.$$

Conversely, when we want to find an extremum point for f subject to the constraint g, we find all points P such that $g(P) = 0$, and such that relation (1) is satisfied. We can then find our extremum points among these by inspection.

(Note that this procedure is analogous to the procedure used to find maxima or minima for functions of one variable. We first determined all points at which the derivative is equal to 0, and then determined maxima or minima by inspection.)

Example 1. Find the maximum of the function $f(x, y) = x + y$ subject to the constraint $x^2 + y^2 = 1$.

We let $g(x, y) = x^2 + y^2 - 1$, so that S consists of all points (x, y) such that $g(x, y) = 0$. We have

$$\operatorname{grad} f(x, y) = (1, 1),$$
$$\operatorname{grad} g(x, y) = (2x, 2y).$$

Let (x_0, y_0) be a point for which there exists a number λ satisfying

$$\operatorname{grad} f(x_0, y_0) = \lambda \operatorname{grad} g(x_0, y_0),$$

or in other words

$$1 = 2x_0\lambda \quad \text{and} \quad 1 = 2y_0\lambda.$$

Then $x_0 \neq 0$ and $y_0 \neq 0$. Hence $\lambda = 1/2x_0 = 1/2y_0$, and consequently $x_0 = y_0$. Since the point (x_0, y_0) must satisfy the equation $g(x_0, y_0) = 1$, we get the possibilities:

$$x_0 = \pm \frac{1}{\sqrt{2}} \quad \text{and} \quad y_0 = \pm \frac{1}{\sqrt{2}}.$$

It is then clear that $(1/\sqrt{2}, 1/\sqrt{2})$ is a maximum for f since the only other possibility $(-1/\sqrt{2}, -1/\sqrt{2})$ is a point at which f takes on a negative value, and $f(1/\sqrt{2}, 1/\sqrt{2}) = 2/\sqrt{2} > 0$.

Example 2. Find the extrema for the function $x^2 + y^2 + z^2$ subject to the constraint $x^2 + 2y^2 - z^2 - 1 = 0$.

Computing the partial derivatives of the functions f and g, we find that we must solve the system of equations

(a) $2x = \lambda \cdot 2x$,   (b) $2y = \lambda \cdot 4y$,
(c) $2z = \lambda \cdot (-2z)$,   (d) $g(X) = x^2 + 2y^2 - z^2 - 1 = 0$.

Let (x_0, y_0, z_0) be a solution. If $z_0 \neq 0$, then from (c) we conclude that $\lambda = -1$. The only way to solve (a) and (b) with $\lambda = -1$ is that $x = y = 0$. In that case, from (d), we would get

$$z_0^2 = -1,$$

which is impossible. Hence any solution must have $z_0 = 0$.

If $x_0 \neq 0$, then from (a) we conclude that $\lambda = 1$. From (b) and (c) we then conclude that $y_0 = z_0 = 0$. From (d), we must have $x_0 = \pm 1$. In this manner, we have obtained two solutions satisfying our conditions, namely

$$(1, 0, 0) \quad \text{and} \quad (-1, 0, 0).$$

Similarly, if $y_0 \neq 0$, we find two more solutions, namely

$$(0, \sqrt{\tfrac{1}{2}}, 0) \quad \text{and} \quad (0, -\sqrt{\tfrac{1}{2}}, 0).$$

These four points are therefore the extrema of the function f subject to the constraint g.

If we ask for the minimum of f, then a direct computation shows that the last two points

$$(0, \pm\sqrt{\tfrac{1}{2}}, 0)$$

are the only possible solutions (because $1 > \tfrac{1}{2}$).

EXERCISES

1. Find the minimum of the function $x + y^2$ subject to the constraint $2x^2 + y^2 = 1$.

2. Find the maximum value of $x^2 + xy + y^2 + yz + z^2$ on the sphere of radius 1.

3. Let $A = (1, 1, -1)$, $B = (2, 1, 3)$, $C = (2, 0, -1)$. Find the point at which the function

$$f(X) = (X - A)^2 + (X - B)^2 + (X - C)^2$$

reaches its minimum, and find the minimum value.

4. Do Exercise 3 in general, for any three distinct vectors

$$A = (a_1, a_2, a_3), \qquad B = (b_1, b_2, b_3), \qquad C = (c_1, c_2, c_3).$$

5. Find the maximum of the function $3x^2 + 2\sqrt{2}\, xy + 4y^2$ on the circle of radius 3 in the plane.

6. Find the maximum of the functions xyz subject to the constraints $x \geq 0$, $y \geq 0$, $z \geq 0$, and $xy + yz + xz = 2$.

7. Find the maximum and minimum distance from points on the curve

$$5x^2 + 6xy + 5y^2 = 0$$

and the origin in the plane.

8. Find the extreme values of the function $\cos^2 x + \cos^2 y$ subject to the constraint $x - y = \pi/4$ and $0 \leq x \leq \pi$.

9. Find the points on the surface $z^2 - xy = 1$ nearest to the origin.

10. Find the extreme values of the function xy subject to the condition $x + y = 1$.

11. Find the shortest distance between the point $(1, 0)$ and the curve $y^2 = 4x$.

12. Find the maximum and minimum points of the function

$$f(x, y, z) = x + y + z$$

in the region $x^2 + y^2 + z^2 \leq 1$.

13. Find the extremum values of the function $f(x, y, z) = x - 2y + 2z$ on the sphere $x^2 + y^2 + z^2 = 1$.

14. Find the maximum of the function $f(x, y, z) = x + y + z$ on the sphere $x^2 + y^2 + z^2 = 4$.

15. Find the extreme values of the function f given by $f(x, y, z) = xyz$ subject to the condition $x + y + z = 1$.

16. Find the extreme values of the function given by $f(x, y, z) = (x + y + z)^2$ subject to the condition $x^2 + 2y^2 + 3z^2 = 1$.

17. Find the maximum of the function $f(x, y, z) = x^2 + y^2 + z^2$ subject to the condition $3x + 2y - 7z = 5$.

18. In general, if a, b, c, d are numbers with not all of a, b, c equal to 0, find the maximum of the function $x^2 + y^2 + z^2$ subject to the condition

$$ax + by + cz = d.$$

19. Find the points on the curve $x^2 + y^4 + 3xy = 2$ which are closest to the origin. Find the points which are farthest from the origin.

Chapter VIII

Vector Spaces

As usual, a collection of objects will be called a *set*. A member of the collection is also called an *element* of the set. It is useful in practice to use short symbols to denote certain sets. For instance we denote by **R** the set of all numbers. To say that "x is a number" or that "x is an element of **R**" amounts to the same thing. The set of n-tuples of numbers will be denoted by $\mathbf{R}^n$. Thus "X is an element of $\mathbf{R}^n$" and "X is an n-tuple" mean the same thing. Instead of saying that u is an element of a set S, we shall also frequently say that u *lies in S*. If S and S' are two sets, and if every element of S' is an element of S, then we say that S' is a *subset* of S. Thus the set of rational numbers is a subset of the set of (real) numbers. To say that S is a subset of S' is to say that S is part of S'. To denote the fact that S is a subset of S', we write $S \subset S'$.

If S_1, S_2 are sets, then the *intersection* of S_1 and S_2, denoted by $S_1 \cap S_2$, is the set of elements which lie in both S_1 and S_2. The *union* of S_1 and S_2, denoted by $S_1 \cup S_2$, is the set of elements which lie in S_1 or S_2.

§1. DEFINITIONS

We have met already several types of objects which can be added and multiplied by numbers. Among these are vectors (of the same dimension) and functions. It is now convenient to define in general a notion which includes these as a special case.

A *vector space V* is a set of objects which can be added and multiplied by numbers, in such a way that the sum of two elements of V is again an element of V, the product of an element of V by a number is an element of V, and the following properties are satisfied:

VS 1. *Given elements u, v, w of V, we have*

$$(u + v) + w = u + (v + w).$$

VS 2. *There is an element of V, denoted by O, such that*

$$O + u = u + O = u$$

for all elements u of V.

VS 3. *Given an element u of V, the element $(-1)u$ is such that*

$$u + (-1)u = O.$$

VS 4. *For all elements u, v of V, we have*

$$u + v = v + u.$$

VS 5. *If c is a number, then $c(u + v) = cu + cv$.*

VS 6. *If a, b are two numbers, then $(a + b)v = av + bv$.*

VS 7. *If a, b are two numbers, then $(ab)v = a(bv)$.*

VS 8. *For all elements u of V, we have $1 \cdot u = u$ (1 here is the number one).*

We have used all these rules when dealing with vectors, or with functions but we wish to be more systematic from now on, and hence have made a list of them. Further properties which can be easily deduced from these are given in the exercises and will be assumed from now on.

The sum $u + (-1)v$ is usually written $u - v$. We also write $-v$ instead of $(-1)v$.

We shall use 0 to denote the number zero, and O to denote the element of any vector space V satisfying property VS 2. We also call it zero, but there is never any possibility of confusion. We observe that this zero element O is uniquely determined by condition VS 2 (cf. Exercise 5).

It is possible to add several elements of a vector space. Suppose we wish to add four elements, say u, v, w, z. We first add any two of them, then a third, and finally a fourth. Using the rules VS 1 and VS 4, we see that it does not matter in which order we perform the additions. This is exactly the same situation as we had with vectors. For example, we have

$$\begin{aligned}
((u + v) + w) + z &= (u + (v + w)) + z \\
&= ((v + w) + u) + z \\
&= (v + w) + (u + z) \quad \text{etc.}
\end{aligned}$$

Thus it is customary to leave out the parentheses, and write simply

$$u + v + w + z.$$

The same remark applies to the sum of any number n of elements of V, and a formal proof could easily be given by induction.

Let V be a vector space, and let W be a subset of V. Assume that W satisfies the following conditions.

(i) If v, w are elements of W, their sum $v + w$ is also an element of W.
(ii) If v is an element of W and c a number, then cv is an element of W.
(iii) The element O of V is also an element of W.

Then W itself is a vector space. Indeed, properties VS 1 through VS 8, being satisfied for all elements of V, are satisfied a fortiori for the elements of W. We shall call W a *subspace* of V.

Example 1. Let $V = \mathbf{R}^n$ and let W be the set of vectors in V whose last coordinate is equal to 0. Then W is a subspace of V, which we could identify with $\mathbf{R}^{n-1}$.

Example 2. Let V be an arbitrary vector space, and let $v_1, \ldots, v_n$ be elements of V. Let $x_1, \ldots, x_n$ be numbers. An expression of type

$$x_1 v_1 + \cdots + x_n v_n$$

is called a *linear combination* of $v_1, \ldots, v_n$. The set of all linear combinations of $v_1, \ldots, v_n$ is a subspace of V.

Proof. Let $y_1, \ldots, y_n$ be numbers. Then

$$(x_1 v_1 + \cdots + x_n v_n) + (y_1 v_1 + \cdots + y_n v_n)$$
$$= (x_1 + y_1) v_1 + \cdots + (x_n + y_n) v_n.$$

Thus the sum of two elements of W is again an element of W, i.e. a linear combination of $v_1, \ldots, v_n$. Furthermore, if c is a number, then

$$c(x_1 v_1 + \cdots + x_n v_n) = c x_1 v_1 + \cdots + c x_n v_n$$

is a linear combination of $v_1, \ldots, v_n$, and hence is an element of W. Finally,

$$O = 0 v_1 + \cdots + 0 v_n$$

is an element of W. This proves that W is a subspace of V.

In Example 2, the subspace W is called the subspace *generated* by $v_1, \ldots, v_n$. If $W = V$, i.e. if every element of V is a linear combination of $v_1, \ldots, v_n$, then we say that $v_1, \ldots, v_n$ *generate* V.

Example 3. Let V be the set of all functions defined for all numbers. If f, g are two functions, then we know how to form their sum $f + g$. It is the function whose value at a number t is $f(t) + g(t)$. We also know how to multiply f by a number c. It is the function cf whose value at a number t is $cf(t)$. In dealing with functions, we have used properties VS 1 through VS 8 many times. We now realize that the set of functions is a vector space.

If f, g are two continuous functions, then $f + g$ is continuous. If c is a number, then cf is continuous. The zero function is continuous. Hence the continuous functions form a subspace of the vector space of all functions.

If f, g are two differentiable functions, then their sum $f + g$ is differentiable. If c is a number, then cf is differentiable. The zero function is differentiable. Hence the differentiable functions form a subspace of the vector space of all functions. Furthermore, every differentiable function is continuous. Hence the differentiable functions form a subspace of the vector space of continuous functions.

Consider the two functions e^t, e^{2t}. These generate a subspace of the space of all differentiable functions. The function $3e^t + 2e^{2t}$ is an element of this subspace. So is the function $\sqrt{2}\, e^t + \pi e^{2t}$.

EXERCISES

1. Let V be a vector space. Using the properties VS 1 through VS 8, show that if v is an element of V and 0 is the number zero, then $0v = O$.

2. Let c be a number $\neq 0$, and v an element of V. Prove that if $cv = O$, then $v = O$.

3. In the vector space of functions, what is the function satisfying the condition VS 2?

4. Let V be a vector space and v, w two elements of V. If $v + w = O$, show that $w = -v$.

5. Let V be a vector space, and v, w two elements of V such that $v + w = v$. Show that $w = O$.

§2. BASES

Let V be a vector space, and let $v_1, \ldots, v_n$ be elements of V. We shall say that $v_1, \ldots, v_n$ are *linearly dependent* if there exist numbers $a_1, \ldots, a_n$ not all equal to 0 such that

$$a_1 v_1 + \cdots + a_n v_n = O.$$

If there do not exist such numbers, then we say that $v_1, \ldots, v_n$ are *linearly independent*. In other words, vectors $v_1, \ldots, v_n$ are linearly independent if and only if the following condition is satisfied:

Whenever $a_1, \ldots, a_n$ are numbers such that

$$a_1 v_1 + \cdots + a_n v_n = 0,$$

then $a_i = 0$ for all $i = 1, \ldots, n$.

Example 1. Let $V = \mathbf{R}^n$ and consider the vectors

$$E_1 = (1, 0, \ldots, 0)$$
$$\vdots$$
$$E_n = (0, 0, \ldots, 1).$$

Then $E_1, \ldots, E_n$ are linearly independent. Indeed, let $a_1, \ldots, a_n$ be numbers such that $a_1 E_1 + \cdots + a_n E_n = O$. Since

$$a_1 E_1 + \cdots + a_n E_n = (a_1, \ldots, a_n),$$

it follows that all $a_i = 0$.

Example 2. Let V be the vector space of all functions of a variable t. Let $f_1, \ldots, f_n$ be n functions. To say that they are linearly dependent is to say that there exist n numbers $a_1, \ldots, a_n$ not all equal to 0 such that

$$a_1 f_1(t) + \cdots + a_n f_n(t) = 0$$

for *all* values of t.

The two functions e^t, e^{2t} are linearly independent. To prove this, suppose that there are numbers a, b such that

$$a e^t + b e^{2t} = 0$$

(for all values of t). Differentiate this relation. We obtain

$$a e^t + 2 b e^{2t} = 0.$$

Subtract the first from the second relation. We obtain $be^t = 0$, and hence $b = 0$. From the first relation, it follows that $ae^t = 0$, and hence $a = 0$. Hence e^t, e^{2t} are linearly independent.

Consider again an arbitrary vector space V. Let $v_1, \ldots, v_n$ be linearly independent elements of V. Let $x_1, \ldots, x_n$ and $y_1, \ldots, y_n$ be numbers. Suppose that we have

$$x_1 v_1 + \cdots + x_n v_n = y_1 v_1 + \cdots + y_n v_n.$$

In other words, two linear combinations of $v_1, \ldots, v_n$ are equal. Then we must have $x_i = y_i$ for each $i = 1, \ldots, n$. Indeed, subtracting the right-hand side from the left-hand side, we get

$$x_1 v_1 - y_1 v_1 + \cdots + x_n v_n - y_n v_n = O.$$

We can write this relation also in the form

$$(x_1 - y_1)v_1 + \cdots + (x_n - y_n)v_n = O.$$

By definition, we must have $x_i - y_i = 0$ for all $i = 1, \ldots, n$, thereby proving our assertion.

If elements $v_1, \ldots, v_n$ of V generate V and in addition are linearly independent, then the set consisting of these elements is called a *basis* of V. We shall also say that the elements $v_1, \ldots, v_n$ *constitute* or *form* a basis of V.

As a matter of notation, if $s_1, \ldots, s_n$ are objects, then the set consisting of these objects is denoted by $\{s_1, \ldots, s_n\}$. If elements $v_1, \ldots, v_n$ of V generate V and are linearly independent, then we shall say that $\{v_1, \ldots, v_n\}$ is a basis.

The vectors $E_1, \ldots, E_n$ of Example 1 form a basis of $\mathbf{R}^n$.

Let W be the vector space of functions generated by the two functions e^t, e^{2t}. Then $\{e^t, e^{2t}\}$ is a basis of W.

Let V be a vector space, and let $\{v_1, \ldots, v_n\}$ be a basis of V. The elements of V can be represented by n-tuples relative to this basis, as follows. If an element v of V is written as a linear combination

$$v = x_1 v_1 + \cdots + x_n v_n$$

of the basis elements, then we call $(x_1, \ldots, x_n)$ the *coordinates* of v with respect to our basis, and we call x_i the i-th coordinate.

For example, let V be the vector space of functions generated by the two functions e^t, e^{2t}. Then the coordinates of the function

$$3e^t + 5e^{2t}$$

with respect to the basis e^t, e^{2t} are $(3, 5)$.

Example 3. Show that the vectors $(1, 1)$ and $(-3, 2)$ are linearly independent.

Let a, b be two numbers such that

$$a(1, 1) + b(-3, 2) = O.$$

Writing this equation in terms of components, we find

$$a - 3b = 0,$$
$$a + 2b = 0.$$

This is a system of two equations which we solve for a and b. Subtracting the second from the first, we get $-5b = 0$, whence $b = 0$. Substituting in either equation, we find $a = 0$. Hence a, b are both 0, and our vectors are linearly independent.

Example 4. Find the coordinates of $(1, 0)$ with respect to the two vectors $(1, 1)$ and $(-1, 2)$.

We must find numbers a, b such that

$$a(1, 1) + b(-1, 2) = (1, 0).$$

Writing this equation in terms of coordinates, we find

$$a - b = 1,$$
$$a + 2b = 0.$$

Solving for a and b in the usual manner yields $b = -\frac{1}{3}$ and $a = \frac{2}{3}$. Hence the coordinates of $(1, 0)$ with respect to $(1, 1)$ and $(-1, 2)$ are $(\frac{2}{3}, -\frac{1}{3})$.

Let $\{v_1, \ldots, v_n\}$ be a set of elements of a vector space V. Let r be a positive integer $\leq n$. We shall say that $\{v_1, \ldots, v_r\}$ is a *maximal* subset of linearly independent elements if $v_1, \ldots, v_r$ are linearly independent, and if in addition, given any v_i with $i > r$, the elements $v_1, \ldots, v_r, v_i$ are linearly dependent.

The next theorem gives us a useful criterion to determine when a set of elements of a vector space is a basis.

Theorem 1. *Let $\{v_1, \ldots, v_n\}$ be a set of generators of a vector space V. Let $\{v_1, \ldots, v_r\}$ be a maximal subset of linearly independent elements. Then $\{v_1, \ldots, v_r\}$ is a basis of V.*

Proof. We must prove that $v_1, \ldots, v_r$ generate V. We shall first prove that each v_i (for $i > r$) is a linear combination of $v_1, \ldots, v_r$. By hypothesis, given v_i, there exist numbers $x_1, \ldots, x_r, y$ not all 0 such that

$$x_1 v_1 + \cdots + x_r v_r + y v_i = O.$$

Furthermore, $y \neq 0$, because otherwise, we would have a relation of linear dependence for $v_1, \ldots, v_r$. Hence we can solve for v_i, namely

$$v_i = \frac{x_1}{-y} v_1 + \cdots + \frac{x_r}{-y} v_r,$$

thereby showing that v_i is a linear combination of $v_1, \ldots, v_r$.

Next, let v be any element of V. There exist numbers $c_1, \ldots, c_n$ such that

$$v = c_1 v_1 + \cdots + c_n v_n.$$

In this relation, we can replace each v_i $(i > r)$ by a linear combination of $v_1, \ldots, v_r$. If we do this, and then collect terms, we find that we have expressed v as a linear combination of $v_1, \ldots, v_r$. This proves that $v_1, \ldots, v_r$ generate V, and hence form a basis of V.

EXERCISES

1. Show that the following vectors are linearly independent.
   (a) $(1, 1, 1)$ and $(0, 1, -1)$ (b) $(1, 0)$ and $(1, 1)$
   (c) $(-1, 1, 0)$ and $(0, 1, 2)$ (d) $(2, -1)$ and $(1, 0)$
   (e) $(\pi, 0)$ and $(0, 1)$ (f) $(1, 2)$ and $(1, 3)$
   (g) $(1, 1, 0)$, $(1, 1, 1)$ and $(0, 1, -1)$ (h) $(0, 1, 1)$, $(0, 2, 1)$ and $(1, 5, 3)$

2. Express the given vector X as a linear combination of the given vectors A, B, and find the coordinates of X with respect to A, B.
   (a) $X = (1, 0)$, $A = (1, 1)$, $B = (0, 1)$
   (b) $X = (2, 1)$, $A = (1, -1)$, $B = (1, 1)$
   (c) $X = (1, 1)$, $A = (2, 1)$, $B = (-1, 0)$
   (d) $X = (4, 3)$, $A = (2, 1)$, $B = (-1, 0)$

3. Find the coordinates of the vector X with respect to the vectors A, B, C.
   (a) $X = (1, 0, 0)$, $A = (1, 1, 1)$, $B = (-1, 1, 0)$, $C = (1, 0, -1)$
   (b) $X = (1, 1, 1)$, $A = (0, 1, -1)$, $B = (1, 1, 0)$, $C = (1, 0, 2)$
   (c) $X = (0, 0, 1)$, $A = (1, 1, 1)$, $B = (-1, 1, 0)$, $C = (1, 0, -1)$

4. Let (a, b) and (c, d) be two vectors in the plane. If $ad - bc = 0$, show that they are linearly dependent. If $ad - bc \neq 0$, show that they are linearly independent.

5. Consider the vector space of all functions of a variable t. Show that the following pairs of functions are linearly independent.

(a) $1, t$ (b) t, t^2 (c) t, t^4 (d) e^t, t (c) te^t, e^{2t} (f) $\sin t, \cos t$ (g) $t, \sin t$ (h) $\sin t, \sin 2t$ (i) $\cos t, \cos 3t$

6. Consider the vector space of functions defined for $t > 0$. Show that the following pairs of functions are linearly independent.

(a) $t, 1/t$ (b) $e^t, \log t$

7. What are the coordinates of the function $3 \sin t + 5 \cos t = f(t)$ with respect to the basis $\{\sin t, \cos t\}$?

8. Let D be the derivative d/dt. Let $f(t)$ be as in Exercise 7. What are the coordinates of the function $Df(t)$ with respect to the basis of Exercise 7?

9. Let $A_1, \ldots, A_r$ be vectors in $\mathbf{R}^n$ and assume that they are mutually perpendicular (i.e. any two of them are perpendicular), and that none of them is equal to O. Prove that they are linearly independent.

10. Let V be the vector space of continuous functions on the interval $[-\pi, \pi]$. If f, g are two continuous functions on this interval, define their scalar product $\langle f, g \rangle$ to be

$$\langle f, g \rangle = \int_{-\pi}^{\pi} f(t)g(t)\, dt.$$

Show that the functions $\sin nt$ ($n = 1, 2, 3, \ldots$) are mutually perpendicular, i.e. that the scalar product of any two of them is equal to 0.

11. Show that the functions $\sin t, \sin 2t, \sin 3t, \ldots, \sin nt$ are linearly independent, for any integer $n \geq 1$.

Chapter IX

Linear Equations and Bases

You have met linear equations in elementary school. Linear equations are simply equations like

$$2x + y + z = 1,$$
$$5x - y + 7z = 0.$$

You have learned to solve such equations by the successive elimination of the variables. In this chapter, we shall review the theory of such equations, dealing with equations in n variables, and interpreting our results from the point of view of vectors. Several geometric interpretations for the solutions of the equations will be given.

§1. MATRICES

We consider a new kind of object, matrices.

Let n, m be two integers ≥ 1. An array of numbers

$$\begin{pmatrix} a_{11} & a_{12} & a_{13} & \cdots & a_{1n} \\ a_{21} & a_{22} & a_{23} & \cdots & a_{2n} \\ \vdots & \vdots & \vdots & & \vdots \\ a_{m1} & a_{m2} & a_{m3} & \cdots & a_{mn} \end{pmatrix}$$

is called a *matrix*. We can abbreviate the notation for this matrix by writing it (a_{ij}), $i = 1, \ldots, m$ and $j = 1, \ldots, n$. We say that it is an *m by n* matrix, or an $m \times n$ matrix. The matrix has *m rows* and *n columns*. For instance, the first column is

$$\begin{pmatrix} a_{11} \\ a_{21} \\ \vdots \\ a_{m1} \end{pmatrix}$$

and the second row is $(a_{21}, a_{22}, \ldots, a_{2n})$. We call a_{ij} the *ij-entry* or *ij-component* of the matrix.

Example 1. The following is a 2×3 matrix:

$$\begin{pmatrix} 1 & 1 & -2 \\ -1 & 4 & -5 \end{pmatrix}.$$

It has two rows and three columns.

The rows are $(1, 1, -2)$ and $(-1, 4, -5)$. The columns are

$$\begin{pmatrix} 1 \\ -1 \end{pmatrix}, \quad \begin{pmatrix} 1 \\ 4 \end{pmatrix}, \quad \begin{pmatrix} -2 \\ -5 \end{pmatrix}.$$

Thus the rows of a matrix may be viewed as n-tuples, and the columns may be viewed as vertical m-tuples. A vertical m-tuple is also called a *column vector*.

A vector $(x_1, \ldots, x_n)$ is a $1 \times n$ matrix. A column vector

$$\begin{pmatrix} x_1 \\ \vdots \\ x_n \end{pmatrix}$$

is an $n \times 1$ matrix.

When we write a matrix in the form (a_{ij}), then i denotes the row and j denotes the column. In Example 1, we have for instance $a_{11} = 1$, $a_{23} = -5$.

A single number (a) may be viewed as a 1×1 matrix.

Let (a_{ij}), $i = 1, \ldots, m$ and $j = 1, \ldots, n$ be a matrix. If $m = n$, then we say that it is a *square* matrix. Thus

$$\begin{pmatrix} 1 & 2 \\ -1 & 0 \end{pmatrix} \quad \text{and} \quad \begin{pmatrix} 1 & -1 & 5 \\ 2 & 1 & -1 \\ 3 & 1 & -1 \end{pmatrix}$$

are both square matrices.

We have a *zero matrix*, in which $a_{ij} = 0$ for all i, j. It looks like this:

$$\begin{pmatrix} 0 & 0 & 0 & \cdots & 0 \\ 0 & 0 & 0 & \cdots & 0 \\ \vdots & \vdots & \vdots & & \vdots \\ 0 & 0 & 0 & \cdots & 0 \end{pmatrix}.$$

We shall write it O. We note that we have met so far with the zero number, zero vector, and zero matrix.

We shall now define addition of matrices and multiplication of matrices by numbers.

We define addition of matrices only when they have the same size. Thus let m, n be fixed integers ≥ 1. Let $A = (a_{ij})$ and $B = (b_{ij})$ be two $m \times n$ matrices. We define $A + B$ to be the matrix whose entry in the i-th row and j-th column is $a_{ij} + b_{ij}$. In other words, we add matrices of the same size componentwise.

Example 2. Let

$$A = \begin{pmatrix} 1 & -1 & 0 \\ 2 & 3 & 4 \end{pmatrix} \quad \text{and} \quad B = \begin{pmatrix} 5 & 1 & -1 \\ 2 & 1 & -1 \end{pmatrix}.$$

Then

$$A + B = \begin{pmatrix} 6 & 0 & -1 \\ 4 & 4 & 3 \end{pmatrix}.$$

If A, B are both $1 \times n$ matrices, i.e. n-tuples, then we note that our addition of matrices coincides with the addition which we defined in Chapter I for n-tuples.

If O is the zero matrix, then for any matrix A (of the same size, of course), we have $O + A = A + O = A$. This is trivially verified.

We shall now define the multiplication of a matrix by a number. Let c be a number, and $A = (a_{ij})$ be a matrix. We define cA to be the matrix whose ij-component is ca_{ij}. We write $cA = (ca_{ij})$. Thus we multiply each component of A by c.

Example 3. Let A, B be as in Example 2. Let $c = 2$. Then

$$2A = \begin{pmatrix} 2 & -2 & 0 \\ 4 & 6 & 8 \end{pmatrix} \quad \text{and} \quad 2B = \begin{pmatrix} 10 & 2 & -2 \\ 4 & 2 & -2 \end{pmatrix}.$$

We also have:

$$(-1)A = -A = \begin{pmatrix} -1 & 1 & 0 \\ -2 & -3 & -4 \end{pmatrix}.$$

For all matrices A, we find that $A + (-1)A = O$.

We leave it as an exercise to verify that all properties VS 1 through VS 8 are satisfied by our rules for addition of matrices and multiplication of matrices by numbers. The main thing to observe here is that addition of matrices is defined in terms of the components, and for the addition of components, the conditions analogous to VS 1 through VS 4 are satisfied. They are standard properties of numbers. Similarly, VS 5 through VS 8 are true for multiplication of matrices by numbers, because the corresponding properties for the multiplication of numbers are true.

We see that the matrices (of a given size $m \times n$) form a vector space, which we may denote by $\mathfrak{M}_{m,n}$.

We define one more notion related to a matrix. Let $A = (a_{ij})$ be an $m \times n$ matrix. The $n \times m$ matrix $B = (b_{ji})$ such that $b_{ji} = a_{ij}$ is called the *transpose* of A, and is also denoted by ^tA. Taking the transpose of a matrix amounts to changing rows into columns and vice versa. If A is the matrix which we wrote down at the beginning of this section, then ^tA is the matrix

$$\begin{pmatrix} a_{11} & a_{21} & a_{31} & \cdots & a_{m1} \\ a_{12} & a_{22} & a_{32} & \cdots & a_{m2} \\ \vdots & \vdots & \vdots & & \vdots \\ a_{1n} & a_{2n} & a_{3n} & \cdots & a_{mn} \end{pmatrix}.$$

To take a special case:

$$\text{If } A = \begin{pmatrix} 2 & 1 & 0 \\ 1 & 3 & 5 \end{pmatrix} \qquad \text{then} \qquad {}^tA = \begin{pmatrix} 2 & 1 \\ 1 & 3 \\ 0 & 5 \end{pmatrix}.$$

If $A = (2, 1, -4)$ is a *row vector*, then

$${}^tA = \begin{pmatrix} 2 \\ 1 \\ -4 \end{pmatrix}$$

is a *column vector*.

EXERCISES

1. Let

$$A = \begin{pmatrix} 1 & 2 & 3 \\ -1 & 0 & 2 \end{pmatrix} \qquad \text{and} \qquad B = \begin{pmatrix} -1 & 5 & -2 \\ 1 & 1 & -1 \end{pmatrix}.$$

   Find $A + B$, $3B$, $-2B$, $A + 2B$, $2A + B$, $A - B$, $A - 2B$, $B - A$.

2. Let

$$A = \begin{pmatrix} 1 & -1 \\ 2 & 1 \end{pmatrix} \qquad \text{and} \qquad B - \begin{pmatrix} -1 & 1 \\ 0 & -3 \end{pmatrix}.$$

   Find $A + B$, $3B$, $-2B$, $A + 2B$, $A - B$, $B - A$.

3. In Exercise 1, find ${}^tA$ and ${}^tB$.

4. In Exercise 2, find ${}^tA$ and ${}^tB$.

5. If A, B are arbitrary $m \times n$ matrices, show that

$${}^t(A + B) = {}^tA + {}^tB.$$

6. If c is a number, show that ${}^t(cA) = c{}^tA$.

7. If $A = (a_{ij})$ is a square matrix, then the elements a_{ii} are called the *diagonal* elements. How do the diagonal elements of A and ${}^tA$ differ?

8. Find ${}^t(A + B)$ and ${}^tA + {}^tB$ in Exercise 2.

9. Find $A + {}^tA$ and $B + {}^tB$ in Exercise 2.

10. A matrix A is said to be *symmetric* if $A = {}^tA$. Show that for any square matrix A, the matrix $A + {}^tA$ is symmetric.

11. Write down the row vectors and column vectors of the matrices A, B in Exercise 1.

12. Write down the row vectors and column vectors of the matrices A, B in Exercise 2.

§2. HOMOGENEOUS LINEAR EQUATIONS

Let $A = (a_{ij})$, $i = 1, \ldots, m$ and $j = 1, \ldots, n$ be a matrix. Let $b_1, \ldots, b_m$ be numbers. Equations like

(*)
$$a_{11}x_1 + \cdots + a_{1n}x_n = b_1$$
$$\vdots$$
$$a_{m1}x_1 + \cdots + a_{mn}x_n = b_m$$

are called linear equations. We also say that (*) is a system of linear equations. The system is said to be *homogeneous* if all the numbers $b_1, \ldots, b_m$ are equal to 0. The number n is called the number of *unknowns*, and m is the number of equations.

The system of equations

(**)
$$a_{11}x_1 + \cdots + a_{1n}x_n = 0$$
$$\vdots$$
$$a_{m1}x_1 + \cdots + a_{mn}x_n = 0$$

will be called the *homogeneous system associated with* (*). In this section, we study the homogeneous system (**).

The system (**) always has a solution, namely the solution obtained by letting all $x_i = 0$. This solution will be called the *trivial* solution. A solution $(x_1, \ldots, x_n)$ such that some x_i is $\neq 0$ is called *non-trivial*.

We shall be interested in the case when the number of unknowns is greater than the number of equations, and we shall see that in that case, there always exists a non-trivial solution.

Before dealing with the general case, we shall study examples.

First, suppose that we have a single equation, like

$$2x + y - 4z = 0.$$

To find a non-trivial solution, we give all the variables except the first a special value $\neq 0$, say $y = 1$, $z = 1$. We then solve for x. We find $2x - (-y) + 4z = 3$, whence $x = \frac{2}{3}$.

Next, consider a pair of equations, say

(1) $$2x + 3y - z = 0,$$

(2) $$x + y + z = 0.$$

We reduce the problem of solving these simultaneous equations to the preceding case of one equation, by eliminating one variable. Thus we multiply the second equation by 2 and subtract it from the first equation, getting

(3) $$y - 3z = 0.$$

Now we meet one equation in more than one variable. We give z any value $\neq 0$, say $z = 1$, and solve for y, namely $y = 3$. We then solve for x

from the second equation, and obtain $x = -4$. The values which we have obtained for x, y, z are also solutions of the first equation, because the first equation is (in an obvious sense) the sum of equation (2) multiplied by 2, and equation (3).

The procedure which we shall use in general is merely the general formulation of the elimination carried out above on numerical examples.

Consider our system of homogeneous equations (**). Let $A_1, \ldots, A_m$ be the row vectors of the matrix (a_{ij}). Then we can rewrite our equations (**) in the form

(**)
$$
A_1 \cdot X = 0 \\
\vdots \\
A_m \cdot X = 0.
$$

Geometrically, to find a solution of (**) amounts to finding a vector X which is perpendicular to $A_1, \ldots, A_m$. Using the notation of the dot product will make it easier to formulate the proof of our main theorem, namely:

Theorem 1. *Let*

$$
a_{11}x_1 + \cdots + a_{1n}x_n = 0 \\
\vdots \\
a_{m1}x_1 + \cdots + a_{mn}x_n = 0
$$

be a system of m linear equations in n unknowns, and assume that $n > m$. Then the system has a non-trivial solution.

Proof. The proof will be carried out by induction.

Consider first the case of one equation in n unknowns, $n > 1$:

$$
a_1x_1 + \cdots + a_nx_n = 0.
$$

If all coefficients $a_1, \ldots, a_n$ are equal to 0, then any value of the variables will be a solution, and a non-trivial solution certainly exists. Suppose that some coefficient a_i is $\neq 0$. After renumbering the variables and the coefficients, we may assume that it is a_1. Then we give $x_2, \ldots, x_n$ arbitrary values, for instance we let $x_2 = \cdots = x_n = 1$, and solve for x_1, letting

$$
x_1 = \frac{-1}{a_1}(a_2 + \cdots + a_n).
$$

In that manner, we obtain a non-trivial solution for our system of equations.

Let us now assume that our theorem is true for a system of $m - 1$ equations in more than $m - 1$ unknowns. We shall prove that it is true for m equations in n unknowns when $n > m$. We consider the system (**).

If all coefficients (a_{ij}) are equal to 0, we can give any non-zero value to our variables to get a solution. If some coefficient is not equal to 0, then after renumbering the equations and the variables, we may assume that it is a_{11}. We shall subtract a multiple of the first equation from the others to eliminate x_1. Namely, we consider the system of equations

$$\left(A_2 - \frac{a_{21}}{a_{11}} A_1\right) \cdot X = 0$$
$$\vdots$$
$$\left(A_m - \frac{a_{m1}}{a_{11}} A_1\right) \cdot X = 0,$$

which can also be written in the form

$$A_2 \cdot X - \frac{a_{21}}{a_{11}} A_1 \cdot X = 0$$

(***)
$$\vdots$$
$$A_m \cdot X - \frac{a_{m1}}{a_{11}} A_1 \cdot X = 0.$$

In this system, the coefficient of x_1 is equal to 0. Hence we may view (***) as a system of $m - 1$ equations in $n - 1$ unknowns, and $n - 1 > m - 1$.

According to our assumption, we can find a non-trivial solution $(x_2, \ldots, x_n)$ for this system. We can then solve for x_1 in the first equation, namely

$$x_1 = \frac{-1}{a_{11}} (a_{12}x_2 + \cdots + a_{1n}x_n).$$

In that way, we find a solution of $A_1 \cdot X = 0$. But according to (***), we have

$$A_i \cdot X = \frac{a_{i1}}{a_{11}} A_1 \cdot X$$

for $i = 2, \ldots, m$. Hence $A_i \cdot X = 0$ for $i = 2, \ldots, m$, and therefore we have found a non-trivial solution to our original system (**).

The argument we have just given allows us to proceed stepwise from one equation to two equations, then from two to three, and so forth. This concludes the proof.

EXERCISES

1. Let V be a subspace of $\mathbf{R}^n$. Let W be the set of elements of $\mathbf{R}^n$ which are perpendicular to every element of V. Show that W is a subspace of $\mathbf{R}^n$.

2. Let $A_1, \ldots, A_r$ be generators of a substance V of $\mathbf{R}^n$. Let W be the set of all elements of $\mathbf{R}^n$ which are perpendicular to $A_1, \ldots, A_r$. Show that the vectors of W are perpendicular to every element of V.

3. Interpret the solutions of a homogeneous system of linear equations in the light of Exercises 1 and 2.

4. Consider the inhomogeneous system (*) consisting of all X such that $X \cdot A_i = b_i$ for $i = 1, \ldots, m$. If X and X' are two solutions of this system, show that there exists a solution Y of the homogeneous system (**) such that $X' = X + Y$. Conversely, if X is any solution of (*), and Y a solution of (**), show that $X + Y$ is a solution of (*).

§3. INVARIANCE OF DIMENSION

This section consists of applications of Theorem 1.

Theorem 2. *Let V be a vector space, and let $\{v_1, \ldots, v_m\}$ be a basis of V. Let $w_1, \ldots, w_n$ be elements of V and assume that $n > m$. Then $w_1, \ldots, w_n$ are linearly dependent.*

Proof. Since $\{v_1, \ldots, v_m\}$ is a basis, there exist numbers (a_{ij}) such that we can write

$$w_1 = a_{11}v_1 + \cdots + a_{m1}v_m$$
$$\vdots \qquad \vdots \qquad \qquad \vdots$$
$$w_n = a_{1n}v_1 + \cdots + a_{mn}v_m.$$

If $x_1, \ldots, x_n$ are numbers, then

$$x_1w_1 + \cdots + x_nw_n$$
$$= (x_1a_{11} + \cdots + x_na_{1n})v_1 + \cdots + (x_1a_{m1} + \cdots + x_na_{mn})v_m$$

(just add up the coefficients of $v_1, \ldots, v_m$ vertically downward). According to Theorem 1, the system of equations

$$x_1a_{11} + \cdots + x_na_{1n} = 0$$
$$\vdots$$
$$x_1a_{m1} + \cdots + x_na_{mn} = 0$$

has a non-trivial solution, because $n > m$. In view of the preceding remark, such a solution $(x_1, \ldots, x_n)$ is such that

$$x_1w_1 + \cdots + x_nw_n = 0,$$

as desired.

Theorem 3. *Let V be a vector space and suppose that one basis has n elements, and another basis has m elements. Then $m = n$.*

Proof. We apply Theorem 2 to the two bases. Theorem 2 implies that both alternatives $n > m$ and $m > n$ are impossible, and hence $m = n$.

Let V be a vector space having a basis consisting of n elements. We shall say that n is the *dimension* of V. If V consists of O alone, then V does not have a basis, and we shall say that V has dimension 0.

We shall now give criteria which allow us to tell when elements of a vector space constitute a basis.

Let $v_1, \ldots, v_n$ be linearly independent elements of a vector space V. We shall say that they form a *maximal set of linearly independent elements of V* if given any element w of V, the elements $w, v_1, \ldots, v_n$ are linearly dependent.

Theorem 4. *Let V be a vector space, and $\{v_1, \ldots, v_n\}$ a maximal set of linearly independent elements of V. Then $\{v_1, \ldots, v_n\}$ is a basis of V.*

Proof. We must show that $v_1, \ldots, v_n$ generate V, i.e. that every element of V can be expressed as a linear combination of $v_1, \ldots, v_n$. Let w be an element of V. The elements $w, v_1, \ldots, v_n$ of V must be linearly dependent by hypothesis, and hence there exist numbers $x_0, x_1, \ldots, x_n$ not all 0 such that

$$x_0 w + x_1 v_1 + \cdots + x_n v_n = O.$$

We cannot have $x_0 = 0$, because if that were the case, we would obtain a relation of linear dependence among $v_1, \ldots, v_n$. Therefore we can solve for w in terms of $v_1, \ldots, v_n$, namely

$$w = -\frac{x_1}{x_0} v_1 - \cdots - \frac{x_n}{x_0} v_n.$$

This proves that w is a linear combination of $v_1, \ldots, v_n$, and hence that $\{v_1, \ldots, v_n\}$ is a basis.

Theorem 5. *Let V be a vector space of dimension n, and let $v_1, \ldots, v_n$ be linearly independent elements of V. Then $v_1, \ldots, v_n$ constitute a basis of V.*

Proof. According to Theorem 2, $\{v_1, \ldots, v_n\}$ is a maximal set of linearly independent elements of V. Hence it is a basis by Theorem 4.

Theorem 6. *Let V be a vector space having a basis consisting of n elements. Let W be a subspace which does not consist of O alone. Then W has a basis, and the dimension of W is $\leqq n$.*

Proof. Let w_1 be a non-zero element of W. If $\{w_1\}$ is not a maximal set of linearly independent elements of W, we can find an element w_2 of W such that w_1, w_2 are linearly independent. Proceeding in this manner, one element at a time, there must be an integer $m \leqq n$ such that we can find linearly independent elements $w_1, w_2, \ldots, w_m$, and such that $\{w_1, \ldots, w_m\}$ is a maximal set of linearly independent elements of W (by Theorem 2, we cannot go on indefinitely finding linearly independent elements, and the number of such elements is at most n). If we now use Theorem 4, we conclude that $\{w_1, \ldots, w_m\}$ is a basis for W.

EXERCISES

1. What is the dimension of the space of $m \times n$ matrices? Give a basis for this space.

2. What is the dimension of the space of $n \times n$ matrices all of whose components are 0 except possibly the diagonal components?

3. What is the dimension of the space of $n \times n$ matrices which are upper-triangular, i.e. of the following type:

$$\begin{pmatrix} a_{11} & a_{12} & \cdots & a_{1n} \\ 0 & a_{22} & \cdots & a_{2n} \\ \vdots & \vdots & & \vdots \\ 0 & 0 & \cdots & a_{nn} \end{pmatrix}?$$

§4. MULTIPLICATION OF MATRICES

We shall now define the product of matrices. Let $A = (a_{ij})$, $i = 1, \ldots, m$ and $j = 1, \ldots, n$ be an $m \times n$ matrix. Let $B = (b_{jk})$, $j = 1, \ldots, n$ and $k = 1, \ldots, s$ be an $n \times s$ matrix.

$$A = \begin{pmatrix} a_{11} & \cdots & a_{1n} \\ \vdots & & \vdots \\ a_{m1} & \cdots & a_{mn} \end{pmatrix}, \qquad B = \begin{pmatrix} b_{11} & \cdots & b_{1s} \\ \vdots & & \vdots \\ b_{n1} & \cdots & b_{ns} \end{pmatrix}.$$

We define the product AB to be the $m \times s$ matrix whose ik-coordinate is

$$\sum_{j=1}^{n} a_{ij}b_{jk} = a_{i1}b_{1k} + a_{i2}b_{2k} + \cdots + a_{in}b_{nk}.$$

If $A_1, \ldots, A_m$ are the row vectors of the matrix A, and if $B^1, \ldots, B^s$ are the column vectors of the matrix B, then the ik-coordinate of the product AB is equal to $A_i \cdot B^k$. Thus

$$AB = \begin{pmatrix} A_1 \cdot B^1 & \cdots & A_1 \cdot B^s \\ \vdots & & \vdots \\ A_m \cdot B^1 & \cdots & A_m \cdot B^s \end{pmatrix}.$$

Multiplication of matrices is therefore a generalization of the dot product.

Example 1. Let

$$A = \begin{pmatrix} 2 & 1 & 5 \\ 1 & 3 & 2 \end{pmatrix}, \qquad B = \begin{pmatrix} 3 & 4 \\ -1 & 2 \\ 2 & 1 \end{pmatrix}.$$

Then AB is a 2×2 matrix, and computations show that

$$AB = \begin{pmatrix} 2 & 1 & 5 \\ 1 & 3 & 2 \end{pmatrix} \begin{pmatrix} 3 & 4 \\ -1 & 2 \\ 2 & 1 \end{pmatrix} = \begin{pmatrix} 15 & 15 \\ 4 & 12 \end{pmatrix}.$$

Example 2. Let

$$C = \begin{pmatrix} 1 & 3 \\ -1 & -1 \end{pmatrix}.$$

Let A, B be as in Example 1. Then:

$$BC = \begin{pmatrix} 3 & 4 \\ -1 & 2 \\ 2 & 1 \end{pmatrix}\begin{pmatrix} 1 & 3 \\ -1 & -1 \end{pmatrix} = \begin{pmatrix} -1 & 5 \\ -3 & -5 \\ 1 & 5 \end{pmatrix}$$

and

$$A(BC) = \begin{pmatrix} 2 & 1 & 5 \\ 1 & 3 & 2 \end{pmatrix}\begin{pmatrix} -1 & 5 \\ -3 & -5 \\ 1 & 5 \end{pmatrix} = \begin{pmatrix} 0 & 30 \\ -8 & 0 \end{pmatrix}.$$

Compute $(AB)C$. What do you find?

Let A be an $m \times n$ matrix and let B be an $n \times 1$ matrix, i.e. a column vector. Then AB is again a column vector. The product looks like this:

$$\begin{pmatrix} a_{11} & \cdots & a_{1n} \\ \vdots & & \vdots \\ a_{m1} & \cdots & a_{mn} \end{pmatrix}\begin{pmatrix} b_1 \\ \vdots \\ b_n \end{pmatrix} = \begin{pmatrix} c_1 \\ \vdots \\ c_m \end{pmatrix}$$

where

$$c_i = \sum_{j=1}^{n} a_{ij}b_j = a_{i1}b_1 + \cdots + a_{in}b_n.$$

If $X = (x_1, \ldots, x_m)$ is a row vector, i.e. a $1 \times m$ matrix, then we can form the product XA, which looks like this:

$$(x_1, \ldots, x_m)\begin{pmatrix} a_{11} & \cdots & a_{1n} \\ \vdots & & \vdots \\ a_{m1} & \cdots & a_{mn} \end{pmatrix} = (y_1, \ldots, y_n),$$

where

$$y_k = x_1 a_{1k} + \cdots + x_m a_{mk}.$$

In this case, XA is a $1 \times n$ matrix, i.e. a row vector.

If A is a square matrix, then we can form the product AA, which will be a square matrix of the same size as A. It is denoted by A^2. Similarly, we can form A^3, A^4, and in general, A^n for any positive integer n.

We define the unit $n \times n$ matrix to be the matrix having diagonal components all equal to 1, and all other components equal to 0. Thus the unit $n \times n$ matrix, denoted by I_n, looks like this:

$$\begin{pmatrix} 1 & 0 & 0 & \cdots & 0 \\ 0 & 1 & 0 & \cdots & 0 \\ 0 & 0 & 1 & \cdots & 0 \\ \vdots & \vdots & \vdots & \ddots & \vdots \\ 0 & 0 & 0 & 1 & 0 \\ 0 & 0 & 0 & \cdots & 1 \end{pmatrix}$$

We can then define $A^0 = I$ (the unit matrix of the same size as A).

Theorem 7. *Let A, B, C be matrices. Assume that A, B can be multiplied, and A, C can be multiplied, and B, C can be added. Then A, $B + C$ can be multiplied, and we have*

$$A(B + C) = AB + AC.$$

If x is a number, then

$$A(xB) = x(AB).$$

Proof. Let A_i be the i-th row of A, and let B^k, C^k be the k-th column of B and C respectively. Then $B^k + C^k$ is the k-th column of $B + C$. By definition, the ik-component of AB is $A_i \cdot B^k$, the ik-component of AC is $A_i \cdot C^k$, and the ik-component of $A(B + C)$ is $A_i \cdot (B^k + C^k)$. Since

$$A_i \cdot (B^k + C^k) = A_i \cdot B^k + A_i \cdot C^k,$$

our first assertion follows. As for the second, observe that the k-th column of xB is xB^k. Since

$$A_i \cdot xB^k = x(A_i \cdot B^k),$$

our second assertion follows.

Theorem 8. *Let A, B, C be matrices such that A, B can be multiplied and B, C can be multiplied. Then A, BC can be multiplied, so can AB, C, and we have*

$$(AB)C = A(BC).$$

Proof. Let $A = (a_{ij})$ be an $m \times n$ matrix, let $B = (b_{jk})$ be an $n \times r$ matrix, and let $C = (c_{kl})$ be an $r \times s$ matrix. The product AB is an $m \times r$ matrix, whose ik-component is equal to the sum

$$a_{i1}b_{1k} + a_{i2}b_{2k} + \cdots + a_{in}b_{nk}.$$

We shall abbreviate this sum using our $\sum$ notation by writing

$$\sum_{j=1}^{n} a_{ij}b_{jk}.$$

By definition, the *il*-component of $(AB)C$ is equal to

$$\sum_{k=1}^{r}\left[\sum_{j=1}^{n}a_{ij}b_{jk}\right]c_{kl} = \sum_{k=1}^{r}\left[\sum_{j=1}^{n}a_{ij}b_{jk}c_{kl}\right].$$

The sum on the right can also be described as the sum of all terms

$$a_{ij}b_{jk}c_{kl},$$

where j, k range over all integers $1 \leq j \leq n$ and $1 \leq k \leq r$ respectively.

If we had started with the *jl*-component of BC and then computed the *il*-component of $A(BC)$ we would have found exactly the same sum, thereby proving the theorem.

In terms of multiplication of matrices, we can now write a system of linear equations in the form

$$AX = B,$$

where A is an $m \times n$ matrix, X is a column vector of size n, and B is a column vector of size m.

EXERCISES

1. Let I be the unit $n \times n$ matrix. Let A be an $n \times r$ matrix. What is IA? If A is an $m \times n$ matrix, what is AI?

2. Let O be the matrix all of whose coordinates are 0. Let A be a matrix of a size such that the product AO is defined. What is AO?

3. In each one of the following cases, find $(AB)C$ and $A(BC)$.

(a) $A = \begin{pmatrix} 2 & 1 \\ 3 & 1 \end{pmatrix}$, $B = \begin{pmatrix} -1 & 1 \\ 1 & 0 \end{pmatrix}$, $C = \begin{pmatrix} 1 & 4 \\ 2 & 3 \end{pmatrix}$

(b) $A = \begin{pmatrix} 2 & 1 & -1 \\ 3 & 1 & 2 \end{pmatrix}$, $B = \begin{pmatrix} 1 & 1 \\ 2 & 0 \\ 3 & -1 \end{pmatrix}$, $C = \begin{pmatrix} 1 \\ 3 \end{pmatrix}$

(c) $A = \begin{pmatrix} 2 & 4 & 1 \\ 3 & 0 & -1 \end{pmatrix}$, $B = \begin{pmatrix} 1 & 1 & 0 \\ 2 & 1 & -1 \\ 3 & 1 & 5 \end{pmatrix}$, $C = \begin{pmatrix} 1 & 2 \\ 3 & 1 \\ -1 & 4 \end{pmatrix}$

4. Let A, B be square matrices of the same size, and assume that $AB = BA$. Show that $(A + B)^2 = A^2 + 2AB + B^2$, and

$$(A + B)(A - B) = A^2 - B^2,$$

using the properties of matrices stated in Theorem 7.

5. Let

$$A = \begin{pmatrix} 1 & 2 \\ 3 & -1 \end{pmatrix}, \quad B = \begin{pmatrix} 2 & 0 \\ 1 & 1 \end{pmatrix}.$$

Find AB and BA.

6. Let

$$C = \begin{pmatrix} 7 & 0 \\ 0 & 7 \end{pmatrix}.$$

Let A, B be as in Exercise 5. Find CA, AC, CB, and BC. State the general rule including this exercise as a special case.

7. Let $X = (1, 0, 0)$ and let

$$A = \begin{pmatrix} 3 & 1 & 5 \\ 2 & 0 & 1 \\ 1 & 1 & 7 \end{pmatrix}.$$

What is XA?

8. Let $X = (0, 1, 0)$, and let A be an arbitrary 3×3 matrix. How would you describe XA? What if $X = (0, 0, 1)$? Generalize to similar statements concerning $n \times n$ matrices, and their products with unit vectors.

9. Let A, B be the matrices of Exercise 3(a). Verify by computation that $^t(AB) = {}^tB{}^tA$. Do the same for 3(b) and 3(c). Prove the same rule for any two matrices A, B (which can be multiplied). If A, B, C are matrices which can be multiplied, show that $^t(ABC) = {}^tC{}^tB{}^tA$.

10. Let M be an $n \times n$ matrix such that $^tM = M$. Given two row vectors in n-space, say A and B define $\langle A, B \rangle$ to be AM^tB. (Identify a 1×1 matrix with a number.) Show that the conditions of a scalar product are satisfied, except possibly the condition concerning positivity. Give an example of a matrix M and vectors A, B such that AM^tB is negative (taking $n = 2$).

11. (a) Let A be the matrix

$$\begin{pmatrix} 0 & 1 & 1 \\ 0 & 0 & 1 \\ 0 & 0 & 0 \end{pmatrix}.$$

Find A^2, A^3. Generalize to 4×4 matrices.

(b) Let A be the matrix

$$\begin{pmatrix} 1 & 1 & 1 \\ 0 & 1 & 1 \\ 0 & 0 & 1 \end{pmatrix}.$$

Compute A^2, A^3, and A^4.

12. Let X be the indicated column vector, and A the indicated matrix. Find AX as a column vector.

(a) $X = \begin{pmatrix} 3 \\ 2 \\ 1 \end{pmatrix}$, $A = \begin{pmatrix} 1 & 0 & 1 \\ 2 & 1 & 1 \\ 2 & 0 & -1 \end{pmatrix}$ (b) $X = \begin{pmatrix} 1 \\ 1 \\ 0 \end{pmatrix}$, $A = \begin{pmatrix} 2 & 1 & 5 \\ 0 & 1 & 1 \end{pmatrix}$

(c) $X = \begin{pmatrix} x_1 \\ x_2 \\ x_3 \end{pmatrix}$, $A = \begin{pmatrix} 0 & 1 & 0 \\ 0 & 0 & 0 \end{pmatrix}$ (d) $X = \begin{pmatrix} x_1 \\ x_2 \\ x_3 \end{pmatrix}$, $A = \begin{pmatrix} 0 & 0 & 0 \\ 1 & 0 & 0 \end{pmatrix}$

13. Let

$$A = \begin{pmatrix} 2 & 1 & 3 \\ 4 & 1 & 5 \end{pmatrix}.$$

Find AX for each of the following values of X.

(a) $X = \begin{pmatrix} 1 \\ 0 \\ 0 \end{pmatrix}$ (b) $X = \begin{pmatrix} 0 \\ 1 \\ 1 \end{pmatrix}$ (c) $X = \begin{pmatrix} 0 \\ 0 \\ 1 \end{pmatrix}$

14. Let

$$A = \begin{pmatrix} 3 & 7 & 5 \\ 1 & -1 & 4 \\ 2 & 1 & 8 \end{pmatrix}.$$

Find AX for each of the values of X given in Exercise 3.

15. Let

$$X = \begin{pmatrix} 0 \\ 1 \\ 0 \\ 0 \end{pmatrix} \quad \text{and} \quad A \begin{pmatrix} a_{11} & \cdots & a_{14} \\ \vdots & & \vdots \\ a_{m1} & \cdots & a_{m4} \end{pmatrix}.$$

What is AX?

16. Let X be a column vector having all its components equal to 0 except the i-th component which is equal to 1. Let A be an arbitrary matrix, whose size is such that we can form the product AX. What is AX?

17. Let $A = (a_{ij})$, $i = 1, \ldots, m$ and $j = 1, \ldots, n$, be an $m \times n$ matrix. Let $B = (b_{jk})$, $j = 1, \ldots, n$ and $k = 1, \ldots, s$, be an $n \times s$ matrix. Let $AB = C$. Show that the k-th column C^k can be written

$$C^k = b_{1k}A^1 + \cdots + b_{nk}A^n.$$

(This will be useful in finding the determinant of a product.)

18. Let a, b be numbers, and let

$$A = \begin{pmatrix} 1 & a \\ 0 & 1 \end{pmatrix} \quad \text{and} \quad B = \begin{pmatrix} 1 & b \\ 0 & 1 \end{pmatrix}.$$

What is AB? What is A^n where n is a positive integer?

19. If A is a square $n \times n$ matrix, we call a square matrix B an *inverse* for A if $AB = BA = I_n$. Show that if B, C are inverses for A, then $B = C$.

20. Show that the matrix A in Exercise 18 has an inverse. What is this inverse?

21. Show that if A, B are $n \times n$ matrices which have inverses, then AB has an inverse.

22. Determine all 2×2 matrices A such that $A^2 = O$.

23. Let $A = \begin{pmatrix} \cos \theta & -\sin \theta \\ \sin \theta & \cos \theta \end{pmatrix}$. Show that $A^2 = \begin{pmatrix} \cos 2\theta & -\sin 2\theta \\ \sin 2\theta & \cos 2\theta \end{pmatrix}$.

Determine A^n by induction for any positive integer n.

24. Find a 2×2 matrix A such that $A^2 = -I = \begin{pmatrix} -1 & 0 \\ 0 & -1 \end{pmatrix}$.

Chapter X

Linear Mappings

We shall first define the general notion of a mapping, which generalizes the notion of a function. Among mappings, the linear mappings are the most important. A good deal of mathematics is devoted to reducing questions concerning arbitrary mappings to linear mappings. For one thing, they are interesting in themselves, and many mappings are linear. On the other hand, it is often possible to approximate an arbitrary mapping by a linear one, whose study is much easier than the study of the original mapping. (Cf. Chapter XIII.)

§1. MAPPINGS

Let S, S' be two sets. A *mapping* from S to S' is an association which to every element of S associates an element of S'. Instead of saying that F is a mapping from S into S', we shall often write the symbols $F: S \to S'$. A mapping will also be called a *map*, for the sake of brevity.

A function is a special type of mapping, namely it is a mapping from a set into the set of numbers, i.e. into **R**.

We extend to mappings some of the terminology we have used for functions. For instance, if $T: S \to S'$ is a mapping, and if u is an element of S, then we denote by $T(u)$, or Tu, the element of S' associated to u by T. We call $T(u)$ the *value* of T at u, or also the *image* of u under T. The symbols $T(u)$ are read "T of u". The set of all elements $T(u)$, when u ranges over all elements of S, is called the *image* of T. If W is a subset of S, then the set of elements $T(w)$, when w ranges over all elements of W, is called the *image* of W under T, and is denoted by $T(W)$.

Let $F: S \to S'$ be a map from a set S into a set S'. If x is an element of S, we often write

$$x \mapsto F(x)$$

with a special arrow $\mapsto$ to denote the image of x under F. Thus, for instance, we would speak of the map F such that $F(x) = x^2$ as the map $x \mapsto x^2$.

Example 1. Let S and S' be both equal to **R**. Let $f: \mathbf{R} \to \mathbf{R}$ be the function $f(x) = x^2$ (i.e. the function whose value at a number x is x^2). Then f is a mapping from **R** into **R**. Its image is the set of numbers ≥ 0.

Example 2. Let S be the set of numbers ≥ 0, and let $S' = \mathbf{R}$. Let $g: S \to S'$ be the function such that $g(x) = x^{1/2}$. Then g is a mapping from S into **R**.

Example 3. Let S be the set of functions having derivatives of all orders on the interval $0 < t < 1$, and let $S' = S$. Then the derivative $D = d/dt$ is a mapping from S into S. Indeed, our map D associates the function $df/dt = Df$ to the function f. According to our terminology, Df is the value of the mapping D at f.

Example 4. Let S be the set of continuous functions on the interval $[0, 1]$ and let S' be the set of differentiable functions on that interval. We shall define a mapping $\mathscr{I}: S \to S'$ by giving its value at any function f in S. Namely, we let $\mathscr{I}f$ (or $\mathscr{I}(f)$) be the function whose value at x is

$$(\mathscr{I}f)(x) = \int_0^x f(t)\,dt.$$

Then $\mathscr{I}(f)$ is a differentiable function.

Example 5. Let S be the set $\mathbf{R}^3$, i.e. the set of 3-tuples. Let $A = (2, 3, -1)$. Let $L: \mathbf{R}^3 \to \mathbf{R}$ be the mapping whose value at a vector $X = (x, y, z)$ is $A \cdot X$. Then $L(X) = A \cdot X$. If $X = (1, 1, \quad 1)$, then the value of L at X is 6.

Just as we did with functions, we describe a mapping by giving its values. Thus, instead of making the statement in Example 5 describing the mapping L, we would also say: Let $L: \mathbf{R}^3 \to \mathbf{R}$ be the mapping $L(X) = A \cdot X$. This is somewhat incorrect, but is briefer, and does not usually give rise to confusion. More correctly, we can write $X \mapsto L(X)$ or $X \mapsto A \cdot X$ with the special arrow $\mapsto$ to denote the effect of the map L on the element X.

Example 6. Let $F: \mathbf{R}^2 \to \mathbf{R}^2$ be the mapping given by

$$F(x, y) = (2x, 2y).$$

Describe the image under F of the points lying on the circle $x^2 + y^2 = 1$. Let (x, y) be a point on the circle of radius 1. Let $u = 2x$ and $v = 2y$. Then u, v satisfy the relation

$$(u/2)^2 + (v/2)^2 = 1$$

or in other words,

$$\frac{u^2}{4} + \frac{v^2}{4} = 1.$$

Hence (u, v) is a point on the circle of radius 2. Therefore the image under F of the circle of radius 1 is a subset of the circle of radius 2. Conversely, given a point (u, v) such that

$$u^2 + v^2 = 4,$$

let $x = u/2$ and $y = v/2$. Then the point (x, y) satisfies the equation $x^2 + y^2 = 1$, and hence is a point on the circle of radius 1. Furthermore, $F(x, y) = (u, v)$. Hence every point on the circle of radius 2 is the image of some point on the circle of radius 1. We conclude finally that the image of the circle of radius 1 under F is precisely the circle of radius 2.

Note. In general, let S, S' be two sets. To prove that $S = S'$, one frequently proves that S is a subset of S' and that S' is a subset of S. This is what we did in the preceding argument.

Example 7. Let S be a set. A mapping from S into $\mathbf{R}$ will be called a *function*, and the set of such functions will be called the set of functions defined on S. Let f, g be two functions defined on S. We can define their sum just as we did for functions of numbers, namely $f + g$ is the function whose value at an element t of S is $f(t) + g(t)$. We can also define the product of f by a number c. It is the function whose value at t is $cf(t)$. Then the set of mappings from S into $\mathbf{R}$ is a vector space.

Example 8. Let S be a set and let V be a vector space. Let F, G be two mappings from S into V. We can define their sum in the same way as we defined the sum of functions, namely the sum $F + G$ is the mapping whose value at an element t of S is $F(t) + G(t)$. We also define the product of F by a number c to be the mapping whose value at an element t of S is $cF(t)$. It is easy to verify that conditions VS 1 through VS 8 are satisfied.

Example 9. Let $F: \mathbf{R} \rightarrow \mathbf{R}^n$ be a mapping. For each number t, the value of F at t is a vector $F(t)$. The coordinates of $F(t)$ depend on t. Hence there are functions $f_1, \ldots, f_n$ such that

$$F(t) = (f_1(t), \ldots, f_n(t)).$$

Each f_i is a function from $\mathbf{R}$ into $\mathbf{R}$. These functions are called the *coordinate functions* of F.

Let $G: \mathbf{R} \rightarrow \mathbf{R}^n$ be another mapping from $\mathbf{R}$ into $\mathbf{R}^n$, and let $g_1, \ldots, g_n$ be its coordinate functions. Then

$$G(t) = (g_1(t), \ldots, g_n(t)).$$

Then

$$(F + G)(t) = F(t) + G(t) = (f_1(t) + g_1(t), \ldots, f_n(t) + g_n(t))$$

and for any number c,

$$(cF)(t) = cF(t) = \big(cf_1(t), \ldots, cf_n(t)\big).$$

If all the functions $f_1, \ldots, f_n$ are differentiable, then we say that the mapping F above is *differentiable*. The set of all differentiable mappings from $\mathbf{R}$ into $\mathbf{R}^n$ is a subspace of the vector space of all mappings.

If J is an interval and $F: J \to \mathbf{R}^n$ is a mapping, then we see that F is nothing else but what we previously called a parametrized curve.

Let U, V, W be sets. Let $F: U \to V$ and $G: V \to W$ be mappings. Then we can form the composite mapping from U into W, denoted by $G \circ F$. It is by definition the mapping defined by

$$(G \circ F)(t) = G\big(F(t)\big)$$

for all $t \in U$.

Example 10. If $f: \mathbf{R} \to \mathbf{R}$ is a function and $g: \mathbf{R} \to \mathbf{R}$ is also a function, then $g \circ f$ is the composite function we studied long ago. We have also considered composite mappings in Chapter IV, §1, in connection with the chain rule, which gives the formula for the derivative of composite mappings under special circumstances.

The following statement is an important property of mappings.
Let U, V, W, S be sets. Let

$$F: U \to V, \qquad G: V \to W, \qquad and \qquad H: W \to S$$

be mappings. Then

$$H \circ (G \circ F) = (H \circ G) \circ F.$$

Proof. Here again, the proof is very simple. By definition, we have, for any element u of U:

$$\big(H \circ (G \circ F)\big)(u) = H\big((G \circ F)(u)\big) = H\big(G(F(u))\big).$$

On the other hand,

$$\big((H \circ G) \circ F\big)(u) = (H \circ G)(F(u)) = H\big(G(F(u))\big).$$

By definition, this means that $(H \circ G) \circ F = H \circ (G \circ F)$.

Finally, we define inverse mappings. Let $F: S \to S'$ be a mapping from one set into another set. We say that F has an *inverse* if there exists a mapping $G: S' \to S$ such that

$$G \circ F = Id_S \qquad and \qquad F \circ G = Id_{S'}.$$

By this we mean that the composite maps $G \circ F$ and $F \circ G$ are the identity mappings of S and S' respectively.

Example 11. Let $S = S'$ be the set of all numbers ≥ 0. Let

$$f\colon S \to S'$$

be the map such that $f(x) = x^2$. Then f has an inverse mapping, namely the map $g\colon S \to S$ such that $g(x) = \sqrt{x}$.

Example 12. Let $\mathbf{R}^+$ be the set of numbers > 0 and let $f\colon \mathbf{R} \to \mathbf{R}^+$ be the map such that $f(x) = e^x$. Then f has an inverse mapping which is nothing but the logarithm.

Example 13. This example is particularly important in geometric applications. Let V be a vector space, and let u be a fixed element of V. We let

$$T_u\colon V \to V$$

be the map such that $T_u(v) = v + u$. We call T_u the *translation* by u. If S is any subset of V, then $T_u(S)$ is called the translation of S by u, and consists of all vectors $v + u$, with $v \in S$. We often denote it by $S + u$. In the next picture, we draw a set S and its translation by a vector u.

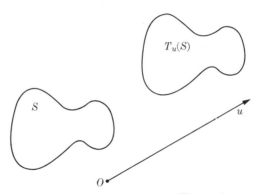

Figure 1

As exercises, we leave the proofs of the following statements to the reader:

If u_1, u_2 are elements of V, then $T_{u_1+u_2} = T_{u_1} \circ T_{u_2}$.
If u is an element of V then $T_u\colon V \to V$ has an inverse mapping which is nothing but the translation T_{-u}.

EXERCISES

1. In Example 3, give Df when f is the function:

   (a) $f(x) = \sin x$ (b) $f(x) = e^x$ (c) $f(x) = \log x$

2. In Example 4, give $\mathcal{G}(f)$ when f is the function:

   (a) $f(x) = e^x$ (b) $f(x) = \dfrac{1}{1 + x^2}$ (c) $f(x) = \cos x$

3. In Example 5, give $L(X)$ when X is the vector:

   (a) $(1, 2, -3)$ (b) $(-1, 5, 0)$ (c) $(2, 1, 1)$

4. Let $F: \mathbf{R} \to \mathbf{R}^2$ be the mapping such that $F(t) = (e^t, t)$. What is $F(1)$, $F(0)$, $F(-1)$?

5. Let $G: \mathbf{R} \to \mathbf{R}^2$ be the mapping such that $G(t) = (t, 2t)$. Let F be as in Exercise 4. What is $(F + G)(1)$, $(F + G)(2)$, $(F + G)(0)$?

6. Let F be as in Exercise 4. What is $(2F)(0)$, $(\pi F)(1)$?

7. Let $A = (1, 1, -1, 3)$. Let $F: \mathbf{R}^4 \to \mathbf{R}$ be the mapping such that for any vector $X = (x_1, x_2, x_3, x_4)$ we have $F(X) = X \cdot A + 2$. What is the value of $F(X)$ when (a) $X = (1, 1, 0, -1)$ and (b) $X = (2, 3, -1, 1)$?

In Exercises 8 through 12, refer to Example 6. In each case, to prove that the image is equal to a certain set S, you must prove that the image is contained in S, and also that every element of S is in the image.

8. Let $F: \mathbf{R}^2 \to \mathbf{R}^2$ be the mapping defined by $F(x, y) = (2x, 3y)$. Describe the image of the points lying on the circle $x^2 + y^2 = 1$.

9. Let $F: \mathbf{R}^2 \to \mathbf{R}^2$ be the mapping defined by $F(x, y) = (xy, y)$. Describe the image under F of the straight line $x = 2$.

10. Let F be the mapping defined by $F(x, y) = (e^x \cos y, e^x \sin y)$. Describe the image under F of the line $x = 1$. Describe more generally the image under F of a line $x = c$, where c is a constant.

11. Let F be the mapping defined by $F(t, u) = (\cos t, \sin t, u)$. Describe geometrically the image of the (t, u)-plane under F.

12. Let F be the mapping defined by $F(x, y) = (x/3, y/4)$. What is the image under F of the ellipse

$$\frac{x^2}{9} + \frac{y^2}{16} = 1\,?$$

13. Prove the statement about translations at the end of the section.

§2. LINEAR MAPPINGS

Let V, V' be two vector spaces. A *linear mapping*

$$T: V \to V'$$

is a mapping which satisfies the following two properties. First, for any elements u, v in V, we have

LM 1. $T(u + v) = T(u) + T(v)$.

Secondly, for any number c, we have

LM 2. $T(cu) = cT(u)$.

Example 1. Let V be the set of functions which have derivatives of all orders. Then the derivative $D: V \to V$ is a linear mapping. This is simply a brief way of summarizing properties of the derivative which we have known for a long time, namely

$$D(f + g) = Df + Dg,$$
$$D(cf) = cD(f).$$

Example 2. Let $V = \mathbf{R}^3$ be the vector space of vectors in 3-space. Let $V' = \mathbf{R}^2$ be the vector space of vectors in 2-space. We can define a mapping

$$F: \mathbf{R}^3 \to \mathbf{R}^2$$

by the projection, namely $F(x, y, z) = (x, y)$. We leave it to you to check that the conditions **LM 1** and **LM 2** are satisfied.

Example 3. Let $A = (1, 2, -1)$. Let $V = \mathbf{R}^3$ and $V' = \mathbf{R}$. We can define a mapping $L = L_A: \mathbf{R}^3 \to \mathbf{R}$ by the rule

$$L(X) = X \cdot A$$

for any vector X in 3-space. The fact that L is linear summarizes two known properties of the scalar product, namely, for any two vectors X, Y we have

$$(X + Y) \cdot A = X \cdot A + Y \cdot A,$$
$$(cX) \cdot A = c(X \cdot A).$$

Example 4. Let V be any vector space. The mapping which associates to any element u of V this element itself is obviously a linear mapping, which is called the *identity* mapping. We denote it by *Id* or simply I. Thus $Id(u) = u$.

Example 5. Let V, V' be any vector spaces. The mapping which associates the element O in V' to any element u of V is called the *zero* mapping and is obviously linear.

Example 6. Let V, V' be two vector spaces. We consider the set of all linear mappings from V into V', and denote this set by $\mathcal{L}$. We shall define the addition of linear mappings and their multiplication by numbers in such a way as to make $\mathcal{L}$ into a vector space.

Let $T: V \to V'$ and let $F: V \to V'$ be two linear mappings. We define their *sum* $T + F$ to be the map whose value at an element u of V is $T(u) + F(u)$. Thus we may write

$$(T + F)(u) = T(u) + F(u).$$

The map $T + F$ is then a linear map. Indeed, it is easy to verify that the two conditions which define a linear map are satisfied. For any elements u, v of V, we have

$$
\begin{aligned}
(T + F)(u + v) &= T(u + v) + F(u + v) \\
&= T(u) + T(v) + F(u) + F(v) \\
&= T(u) + F(u) + T(v) + F(v) \\
&= (T + F)(u) + (T + F)(v).
\end{aligned}
$$

Furthermore, if c is a number, then

$$
\begin{aligned}
(T + F)(cu) &= T(cu) + F(cu) \\
&= cT(u) + cF(u) \\
&= c[T(u) + F(u)] \\
&= c[(T + F)(u)].
\end{aligned}
$$

Hence $T + F$ is a linear map.

If a is a number, and $T: V \to V'$ is a linear map, we define a map aT from V into V' by giving its value at an element u of V, namely $(aT)(u) = aT(u)$. Then it is easily verified that aT is a linear map. We leave this as an exercise.

We have just defined operations of addition and multiplication by numbers in our set $\mathcal{L}$. Furthermore, if $T: V \to V'$ is a linear map, i.e. an element of $\mathcal{L}$, then we can define $-T$ to be $(-1)T$, i.e. the product of the number -1 by T. Finally, we have the *zero-map*, which to every element of V associates the element O of V'. Then $\mathcal{L}$ is a vector space. In other words, the set of linear maps from V into V' is itself a vector space. The verification that the rules VS 1 through VS 8 for a vector space are satisfied is easy and is left to the reader.

Example 7. Let $V = V'$ be the vector space of functions which have derivatives of all orders. Let D be the derivative, and let Id be the identity. If f is in V, then

$$(D + Id)f = Df + f.$$

Thus, when $f(x) = e^x$, then $(D + Id)f$ is the function whose value at x is $e^x + e^x = 2e^x$.

If $f(x) = \sin x$, then $((D + Id)f)(x) = \cos x + \sin x$.

We note that $3 \cdot Id$ is a linear map, whose value at f is $3f$. Thus $(D + 3 \cdot Id)f = Df + 3f$. At any number x, the value of $(D + 3 \cdot Id)f$ is $Df(x) + 3f(x)$. We can also write $(D + 3I)f = Df + 3f$.

Let $T: V \to V'$ be a linear mapping. Let u, v, w be elements of V. Then

$$T(u + v + w) = T(u) + T(v) + T(w).$$

This can be seen stepwise, using the definition of linear mappings. Thus

$$T(u + v + w) = T(u + v) + T(w) = T(u) + T(v) + T(w).$$

Similarly, given a sum of more than three elements, an analogous property is satisfied. For instance, let $u_1, \ldots, u_n$ be elements of V. Then

$$T(u_1 + \cdots + u_n) = T(u_1) + \cdots + T(u_n).$$

The sum on the right can be taken in any order. A formal proof can easily be given by induction, and we omit it.

If $a_1, \ldots, a_n$ are numbers, then

$$T(a_1 u_1 + \cdots + a_n u_n) = a_1 T(u_1) + \cdots + a_n T(u_n).$$

We show this for three elements.

$$\begin{aligned} T(a_1 u + a_2 v + a_3 w) &= T(a_1 u) + T(a_2 v) + T(a_3 w) \\ &= a_1 T(u) + a_2 T(v) + a_3 T(w). \end{aligned}$$

The next theorem will show us how a linear map is determined when we know its value on basis elements.

Theorem 1. *Let V and W be vector spaces. Let $\{v_1, \ldots, v_n\}$ be a basis of V, and let $w_1, \ldots, w_n$ be arbitrary elements of W. Then there exists a unique linear mapping $T: V \to W$ such that*

$$T(v_1) = w_1, \ldots, T(v_n) = w_n.$$

If $x_1, \ldots, x_n$ are numbers, then

$$T(x_1 v_1 + \cdots + x_n v_n) = x_1 w_1 + \cdots + x_n w_n.$$

Proof. We shall prove that a linear map T satisfying the required conditions exists. Let v be an element of V, and let $x_1, \ldots, x_n$ be the unique numbers such that $v = x_1 v_1 + \cdots + x_n v_n$. We let

$$T(v) = x_1 w_1 + \cdots + x_n w_n.$$

We then have defined a mapping T from V into W, and we contend that T is linear. If v' is an element of V, and if $v' = y_1 v_1 + \cdots + y_n v_n$, then

$$v + v' = (x_1 + y_1) v_1 + \cdots + (x_n + y_n) v_n.$$

By definition, we obtain

$$\begin{aligned} T(v + v') &= (x_1 + y_1) w_1 + \cdots + (x_n + y_n) w_n \\ &= x_1 w_1 + y_1 w_1 + \cdots + x_n w_n + y_n w_n \\ &= T(v) + T(v'). \end{aligned}$$

Let c be a number. Then $cv = cx_1 v_1 + \cdots + cx_n v_n$, and hence

$$T(cv) = cx_1 w_1 + \cdots + cx_n w_n = cT(v).$$

We have therefore proved that T is linear, and hence that there exists a linear map as asserted in the theorem.

Such a map is unique, because for any element $x_1v_1 + \cdots + x_nv_n$ of V, any linear map $F: V \to W$ such that $F(v_i) = w_i$ $(i = 1, \ldots, n)$ must also satisfy

$$F(x_1v_1 + \cdots + x_nv_n) = x_1F(v_1) + \cdots + x_nF(v_n)$$
$$= x_1w_1 + \cdots + x_nw_n.$$

This concludes the proof.

EXERCISES

1. Determine which of the following mappings F are linear.

(a) $F: \mathbf{R}^3 \to \mathbf{R}^2$ defined by $F(x, y, z) = (x, z)$.

(b) $F: \mathbf{R}^4 \to \mathbf{R}^4$ defined by $F(X) = -X$.

(c) $F: \mathbf{R}^3 \to \mathbf{R}^3$ defined by $F(X) = X + (0, -1, 0)$.

(d) $F: \mathbf{R}^2 \to \mathbf{R}^2$ defined by $F(x, y) = (2x + y, y)$.

(e) $F: \mathbf{R}^2 \to \mathbf{R}^2$ defined by $F(x, y) = (2x, y - x)$.

(f) $F: \mathbf{R}^2 \to \mathbf{R}^2$ defined by $F(x, y) = (y, x)$.

(g) $F: \mathbf{R}^2 \to \mathbf{R}$ defined by $F(x, y) = xy$.

(h) Let U be an open subset of $\mathbf{R}^3$, and let V be the vector space of differentiable functions on U. Let V' be the vector space of vector fields on U. Then grad: $V \to V'$ is a mapping. Is it linear?

2. Let $T: V \to W$ be a linear map from one vector space into another. Show that $T(O) = O$.

3. Let T be as in Exercise 2. Let u, v be elements of V, and let $Tu = w$. If $Tv = O$, show that $T(u + v)$ is also equal to w.

4. Determine all elements z of V such that $Tz = w$.

5. Let $T: V \to W$ be a linear map. Let v be an element of V. Show that $T(-v) = -T(v)$.

6. Let V be a vector space, and $f: V \to \mathbf{R}$, $g: V \to \mathbf{R}$ two linear mappings. Let $F: V \to \mathbf{R}^2$ be the mapping defined by $F(v) = (f(v), g(v))$. Show that F is linear. Generalize.

7. Let V, W be two vector spaces and let $F: V \to W$ be a linear map. Let U be the subset of V consisting of all elements v such that $F(v) = O$. Prove that U is a subspace of V.

8. Which of the mappings in Exercises 4, 7, 8, 9 of §1 are linear?

9. Let $F: \mathbf{R}^3 \to \mathbf{R}^4$ be a linear map. Let P be a point of $\mathbf{R}^3$, and A a nonzero element of $\mathbf{R}^3$. Describe the image of the straight line $P + tA$ under F. [Distinguish the cases when $F(A) = O$ and $F(A) \neq O$.]

Let V be a vector space, and let v_1, v_2 be two elements of V which are linearly independent. The set of elements of V which can be written in the form $t_1v_1 + t_2v_2$ with numbers t_1, t_2 satisfying

$$0 \leq t_1 \leq 1 \quad \text{and} \quad 0 \leq t_2 \leq 1,$$

is called a *parallelogram*, spanned by v_1, v_2.

10. Let V and W be vector spaces, and let $F: V \to W$ be a linear map. Let v_1, v_2 be linearly independent elements of V, and assume that $F(v_1)$, $F(v_2)$ are linearly independent. Show that the image under F of the parallelogram spanned by v_1 and v_2 is the parallelogram spanned by $F(v_1)$, $F(v_2)$.

11. Let F be a linear map from $\mathbf{R}^2$ into itself such that

$$F(E_1) = (1, 1) \quad \text{and} \quad F(E_2) = (-1, 2).$$

Let S be the square whose corners are at $(0, 0)$, $(1, 0)$, $(1, 1)$, and $(0, 1)$. Show that the image of this square under F is a parallelogram.

12. Let A, B be two non-zero vectors in the plane such that there is no constant $c \neq 0$ such that $B = cA$. Let T be a linear mapping of the plane into itself such that $T(E_1) = A$ and $T(E_2) = B$. Describe the image under T of the rectangle whose corners are $(0, 1)$, $(3, 0)$, $(0, 0)$, and $(3, 1)$.

13. Let A, B be two non-zero vectors in the plane such that there is no constant $c \neq 0$ such that $B = cA$. Describe geometrically the set of points $tA + uB$ for values of t and u such that $0 \le t \le 5$ and $0 \le u \le 2$.

14. Let $T_u: V \to V$ be the translation by a vector u. For which vectors u is T_u a linear map?

15. Let V, W be two vector spaces, and $F: V \to W$ a linear map. Let $w_1, \ldots, w_n$ be elements of W which are linearly independent, and let $v_1, \ldots, v_n$ be elements of V such that $F(v_i) = w_i$ for $i = 1, \ldots, n$. Show that $v_1, \ldots, v_n$ are linearly independent.

16. Let V be a vector space and $F: V \to \mathbf{R}$ a linear map. Let W be the subset of V consisting of all elements v such that $F(v) = O$. Assume that $W \neq V$, and let v_0 be an element of V which does not lie in W. Show that every element of V can be written as a sum $w + cv_0$, with some w in W and some number c.

17. In Exercise 16, show that W is a subspace of V. Let $\{v_1, \ldots, v_n\}$ be a basis of W. Show that $\{v_0, v_1 \ldots, v_n\}$ is a basis of V.

§3. THE KERNEL AND IMAGE OF A LINEAR MAP

Let V, W be vector spaces, and let $F: V \to W$ be a linear map. We contend that the following two conditions are equivalent:

1. If v is an element of V such that $F(v) = O$, then $v = O$.

2. If v, w are elements of V such that $F(v) = F(w)$, then $v = w$.

To prove our contention, assume first that F satisfies the first condition, and suppose that v, w are such that $F(v) = F(w)$. Then

$$F(v - w) = F(v) - F(w) = O.$$

By assumption, $v - w = O$, and hence $v = w$.

Conversely, assume that F satisfies the second condition. If v is such that $F(v) = F(O) = O$, we conclude that $v = O$.

Let $F: V \to W$ be as above. The set of elements v of V such that $F(v) = O$ is called the *kernel* of F. We leave it as an exercise to prove that the kernel of F is a subspace of V (Exercise 7 of §2).

Theorem 2. *Let $F: V \to W$ be a linear map whose kernel is $\{O\}$. If $v_1, \ldots, v_n$ are linearly independent elements of V, then $F(v_1), \ldots, F(v_n)$ are linearly independent elements of W.*

Proof. Let $x_1, \ldots, x_n$ be numbers such that

$$x_1 F(v_1) + \cdots + x_n F(v_n) = O.$$

By linearity, we get

$$F(x_1 v_1 + \cdots + x_n v_n) = O.$$

Hence $x_1 v_1 + \cdots + x_n v_n = O$. Since $v_1, \ldots, v_n$ are linearly independent it follows that $x_i = 0$ for $i = 1, \ldots, n$. This proves our theorem.

Let $F: V \to W$ be a linear map. The *image* of F is the set of elements w in W such that there exists an element v of V such that $F(v) = w$. *The image of F is a subspace of W.* To prove this, observe first that $F(O) = O$, and hence O is in the image. Next, suppose that w_1, w_2 are in the image. Then there exist elements v_1, v_2 of V such that $F(v_1) = w_1$ and $F(v_2) = w_2$. Hence $F(v_1 + v_2) = F(v_1) + F(v_2) - w_1 + w_2$, thereby proving that $w_1 + w_2$ is in the image. If c is a number, then

$$F(cv_1) = cF(v_1) = cw_1.$$

Hence cw_1 is in the image. This proves that the image is a subspace of W.

We often abbreviate kernel and image by writing Ker and Im respectively. The next theorem relates the dimensions of the kernel and image of a linear map, with the dimension of the space on which the map is defined.

Theorem 3. *Let V be a vector space. Let $L: V \to W$ be a linear map of V into another space W. Let n be the dimension of V, q the dimension of the kernel of L, and s the dimension of the image of L. Then $n = q + s$. In other words,*

$$\dim V = \dim \text{Ker } L + \dim \text{Im } L.$$

Proof. If the image of L consists of O only, then our assertion is trivial We may therefore assume that $s > 0$. Let $\{w_1, \ldots, w_s\}$ be a basis of the image of L. Let $v_1, \ldots, v_s$ be elements of V such that $L(v_i) = w_i$ for $i = 1, \ldots, s$. If the kernel of L is not $\{O\}$, let $\{u_1, \ldots, u_q\}$ be a basis of the kernel. If the kernel is $\{O\}$, it is understood that all reference to $\{u_1, \ldots, u_q\}$ is to be omitted in what follows. We contend that

$\{v_1, \ldots, v_s, u_1, \ldots, u_q\}$ is a basis of V. This will suffice to prove our assertion. Let v be any element of V. Then there exist numbers $x_1, \ldots, x_s$ such that

$$L(v) = x_1 w_1 + \cdots + x_s w_s,$$

because $\{w_1, \ldots, w_s\}$ is a basis of the image of L. By linearity,

$$L(v) = L(x_1 v_1 + \cdots + x_s v_s),$$

and again by linearity, subtracting the right-hand side from the left-hand side, it follows that

$$L(v - x_1 v_1 - \cdots - x_s v_s) = O.$$

Hence $v - x_1 v_1 - \cdots - x_s v_s$ lies in the kernel of L, and there exist numbers $y_1, \ldots, y_q$ such that

$$v - x_1 v_1 - \cdots - x_s v_s = y_1 u_1 + \cdots + y_q u_q.$$

Hence

$$v = x_1 v_1 + \cdots + x_s v_s + y_1 u_1 + \cdots + y_q u_q$$

is a linear combination of $v_1, \ldots, v_s, u_1, \ldots, u_q$. This proves that these $s + q$ elements of V generate V.

We now show that they are linearly independent, and hence that they constitute a basis. Suppose that there exists a linear relation.

$$x_1 v_1 + \cdots + x_s v_s + y_1 u_1 + \cdots + y_q u_q = O.$$

Applying L to this relation, and using the fact that $L(u_j) = O$ for $j = 1, \ldots, q$, we obtain

$$x_1 L(v_1) + \cdots + x_s L(v_s) = O.$$

But $L(v_1), \ldots, L(v_s)$ are none other than $w_1, \ldots, w_s$, which have been assumed linearly independent. Hence $x_i = 0$ for $i = 1, \ldots, s$. Hence

$$y_1 u_1 + \cdots + y_q u_q = 0.$$

But $u_1, \ldots, u_q$ constitute a basis of the kernel of L, and in particular, are linearly independent. Hence all $y_j = 0$ for $j = 1, \ldots, q$. This concludes the proof of our assertion.

EXERCISES

1. Let A, B be two vectors in $\mathbf{R}^2$ forming a basis of $\mathbf{R}^2$. Let $F: \mathbf{R}^2 \to \mathbf{R}^n$ be a linear map. Show that either $F(A)$, $F(B)$ are linearly independent, or the image of F has dimension 1, or the image of F is $\{O\}$.

2. Let A be a non-zero vector in $\mathbf{R}^2$. Let $F: \mathbf{R}^2 \to W$ be a linear map such that $F(A) = O$. Show that the image of F is either a straight line or $\{O\}$.

3. Let $F: V \to W$ be a linear map, whose kernel is $\{O\}$. Assume that V and W have both the same dimension n. Show that the image of F is all of W.

4. Let $F: V \to W$ be a linear map and assume that the image of F is all of W. Assume that V and W have the same dimension n. Show that the kernel of F is $\{O\}$.

5. Let $L: V \to W$ be a linear map. Let w be an element of W. Let v_0 be an element of V such that $L(v_0) = w$. Show that any solution of the equation $L(X) = w$ is of type $v_0 + u$, where u is an element of the kernel of L.

6. Let V be the vector space of functions which have derivatives of all orders, and let $D: V \to V$ be the derivative. What is the kernel of D?

7. Let D^2 be the second derivative (i.e. the iteration of D taken twice). What is the kernel of D^2? In general, what is the kernel of D^n (n-th derivative)?

8. Let V be as in Exercise 6. We write the functions as functions of a variable t, and let $D = d/dt$. Let $a_1, \ldots, a_m$ be numbers. Let g be an element of V. Describe how the problem of finding a solution of the differential equation

$$a_m \frac{d^m f}{dt^m} + a_{m-1} \frac{d^{m-1} f}{dt^{m-1}} + \cdots + a_0 f = g$$

can be interpreted as fitting the abstract situation described in Exercise 5.

9. Let V, D be as in Exercise 6. Let $L = D - I$, where I is the identity mapping of V. What is the kernel of L?

10. Same question of $L = D - aI$, where a is a number.

§4. COMPOSITION AND INVERSE OF LINEAR MAPPINGS

In §1 we have mentioned the fact that we can compose arbitrary maps. We can say something additional in the case of linear maps.

Theorem 4. *Let U, V, W be vector spaces. Let*

$$F: U \to V \quad and \quad G: V \to W$$

be linear maps. Then the composite map $G \circ F$ is also a linear map.

Proof. This is very easy to prove. Let u, v be elements of U. Since F is linear, we have $F(u + v) = F(u) + F(v)$. Hence

$$(G \circ F)(u + v) = G(F(u + v)) = G(F(u) + F(v)).$$

Since G is linear, we obtain

$$G(F(u) + F(v)) = G(F(u)) + G(F(v)).$$

Hence

$$(G \circ F)(u + v) = (G \circ F)(u) + (G \circ F)(v).$$

Next, let c be a number. Then

$$(G \circ F)(cu) = G\big(F(cu)\big)$$
$$= G\big(cF(u)\big) \qquad \text{(because } F \text{ is linear)}$$
$$= cG\big(F(u)\big) \qquad \text{(because } G \text{ is linear)}.$$

This proves that $G \circ F$ is a linear mapping.

The next theorem states that some of the rules of arithmetic concerning the product and sum of numbers also apply to the composition and sum of linear mappings.

Theorem 5. *Let U, V, W be vector spaces. Let*

$$F \colon U \to V$$

be a linear mapping, and let G, H be two linear mappings of V into W. Then

$$(G + H) \circ F = G \circ F + H \circ F.$$

If c is a number, then

$$(cG) \circ F = c(G \circ F).$$

If $T \colon U \to V$ is a linear mapping from U into V, then

$$G \circ (F + T) = G \circ F + G \circ T.$$

The proofs are all simple. We shall just prove the first assertion and leave the others as exercises.

Let u be an element of U. We have:

$$((G + H) \circ F)(u) = (G + H)(F(u)) = G\big(F(u)\big) + H\big(F(u)\big)$$
$$= (G \circ F)(u) + (H \circ F)(u).$$

By definition, it follows that $(G + H) \circ F = G \circ F + H \circ F$.

It may happen that $U = V = W$. Let $F \colon U \to U$ and $G \colon U \to U$ be two linear mappings. Then we may form $F \circ G$ and $G \circ F$. It is not always true that these two composite mappings are equal. As an example, let $U = \mathbf{R}^3$. Let F be the linear mapping given by

$$F(x, y, z) = (x, y, 0)$$

and let G be the linear mapping given by

$$G(x, y, z) = (x, z, 0).$$

Then $(G \circ F)(x, y, z) = (x, 0, 0)$, but $(F \circ G)(x, y, z) = (x, z, 0)$.

Theorem 6. *Let $F \colon U \to V$ be a linear map, and assume that this map has an inverse mapping $G \colon V \to U$. Then G is a linear map.*

Proof. This proof will be left as an exercise.

§5. GEOMETRIC APPLICATIONS

Let V be a vector space, and let v, w be elements of V. We define the *straight line segment* between v and w to be the set of all points (Fig. 2)

$$v + t(w - v), \qquad\qquad 0 \leqq t \leqq 1.$$

Observe that we can rewrite the expression for these points in the form

(1) $$(1 - t)v + tw, \qquad\qquad 0 \leqq t \leqq 1,$$

and letting $s = 1 - t$, $t = 1 - s$, we can also write it as

$$sv + (1 - s)w, \qquad\qquad 0 \leqq s \leqq 1.$$

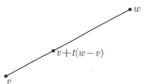

Figure 2

Finally, we can write the points of our line segment in the form

(2) $$t_1 v + t_2 w$$

with t_1, $t_2 \geqq 0$ and $t_1 + t_2 = 1$. Indeed, letting $t = t_2$, we see that every point which can be written in the form (2) satisfies (1). Conversely, we let $t_1 = 1 - t$ and $t_2 = t$ and see that every point of the form (1) can be written in the form (2).

We shall now generalize this discussion to higher dimensional figures.

Let v, w be linearly independent elements of the vector space V. We define the *parallelogram* spanned by v, w to be the set of all points

$$t_1 v + t_2 w, \qquad 0 \leqq t_i \leqq 1 \quad \text{for} \quad i = 1, 2.$$

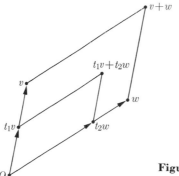

Figure 3

This definition is clearly justified since $t_1 v$ is a point of the segment between O and v (Fig. 3), and $t_2 w$ is a point of the segment between

O and w. For all values of t_1, t_2 ranging independently between 0 and 1, we see geometrically that $t_1v + t_2w$ describes all points of the parallelogram.

At the end of §1 we defined *translations*. We obtain the most general parallelogram (Fig. 4) by taking the translation of the parallelogram just described. Thus if u is an element of V, the translation by u of the parallelogram spanned by v and w consists of all points

$$u + t_1v + t_2w, \quad 0 \le t_i \le 1 \quad \text{for} \quad i = 1, 2.$$

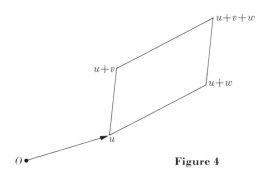

Figure 4

We shall now describe triangles. We begin with triangles located at the origin. Let v, w again be linearly independent. We define the *triangle spanned* by O, v, w to be the set of all points

(3) $t_1v + t_2w, \quad 0 \le t_i \quad \text{and} \quad t_1 + t_2 \le 1.$

We must convince ourselves that this is a reasonable definition. We do this by showing that the triangle defined above coincides with the set of points on all line segments between v and all the points of the segment between O and w. From Fig. 5, this second description of a triangle does coincide with our geometric intuition.

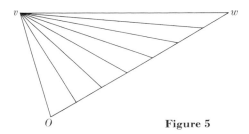

Figure 5

We denote the line segment between O and w by $\overline{Ow}$. A point on $\overline{Ow}$ can then be written tw with $0 \le t \le 1$. The set of points between v and tw is the set of points

(4) $sv + (1 - s)tw, \qquad\qquad 0 \le s \le 1.$

Let $t_1 = s$ and $t_2 = (1 - s)t$. Then

$$t_1 + t_2 = s + (1 - s)t \leqq s + (1 - s) \leqq 1.$$

Hence all points satisfying (4) also satisfy (3). Conversely, suppose given a point $t_1v + t_2w$ satisfying (3), so that $t_1 + t_2 \leqq 1$. Then $t_2 \leqq 1 - t_1$ and we let

$$s = t_1, \qquad t = t_2/(1 - t_1).$$

Then
$$t_1v + t_2w = t_1v + (1 - t_1)\frac{t_2}{(1 - t_1)}w = sv + (1 - s)tw,$$

which shows that every point satisfying (3) also satisfies (4). This justifies our definition of a triangle.

As with parallelograms, an arbitrary triangle is obtained by translating a triangle located at the origin. In fact, we have the following description of a triangle.

Let v_1, v_2, v_3 be elements of V such that $v_1 - v_3$ and $v_2 - v_3$ are linearly independent. Let $v = v_1 - v_3$ and $w = v_2 - v_3$. Let S be the set of points

(5) $$t_1v_1 + t_2v_2 + t_3v_3, \qquad 0 \leqq t_i \quad \text{for} \quad i = 1, 2, 3$$
$$t_1 + t_2 + t_3 = 1.$$

Then S is the translation by v_3 of the triangle spanned by O, v, w. (Cf. Fig. 6.)

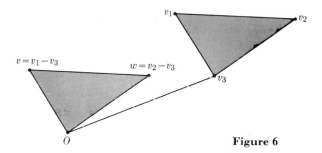

$$v_1 \qquad\qquad v_2$$
$$v = v_1 - v_3 \qquad w = v_2 - v_3$$
$$v_3$$
$$O \qquad\qquad\qquad\qquad \textbf{Figure 6}$$

Proof. Let $P = t_1v_1 + t_2v_2 + t_3v_3$ be a point satisfying (5). Then

$$P = t_1(v_1 - v_3) + t_2(v_2 - v_3) + t_1v_3 + t_2v_3 + t_3v_3$$
$$= t_1v + t_2w + v_3,$$

and $t_1 + t_2 \leqq 1$. Hence our point P is a translation by v_3 of a point satisfying (3). Conversely, given a point satisfying (3), which we translate by v_3, we let $t_3 = 1 - t_2 - t_1$, and we can then reverse the steps we have just taken to see that

$$t_1v + t_2w + v_3 = t_1v_1 + t_2v_2 + t_3v_3.$$

This proves what we wanted.

Actually, it is (5) which is the most useful description of a triangle, because the vertices v_1, v_2, v_3 occupy a symmetric position in this definition. Furthermore, the conditions of (5) are those which generalize to the fruitful concept of convex set which we now discuss.

Let S be a subset of a vector space V. We shall say that S is *convex* if given points P, Q in S the line segment between P and Q is contained in S.

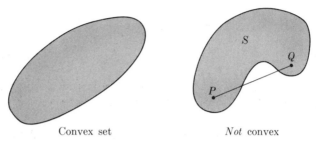

Convex set   *Not* convex

Figure 7

The set on the left is convex. The set on the right is not convex since the line segment between P and Q is not entirely contained in S.

Theorem 7. *Let* $P_1, \ldots, P_n$ *be points of a vector space* V. *Let* S *be the set of all linear combinations*

$$t_1 P_1 + \cdots + t_n P_n$$

with $0 \leq t_i$ *and* $t_1 + \cdots + t_n = 1$. *Then* S *is convex.*

Proof. Let

$$P = t_1 P_1 + \cdots + t_n P_n \qquad \text{and} \qquad Q = s_1 P_1 + \cdots + s_n P_n$$

with $0 \leq t_i$, $0 \leq s_i$, and $t_1 + \cdots + t_n = 1$, $s_1 + \cdots + s_n = 1$. Let $0 \leq t \leq 1$. Then:

$(1 - t)P + tQ$
$$= (1 - t)t_1 P_1 + \cdots + (1 - t)t_n P_n + ts_1 P_1 + \cdots + ts_n P_n$$
$$= [(1 - t)t_1 + ts_1]P_1 + \cdots + [(1 - t)t_n + ts_n]P_n.$$

We have $0 \leq (1 - t)t_i + ts_i$ for all i, and

$(1 - t)t_1 + ts_1 + \cdots + (1 - t)t_n + ts_n$
$$= (1 - t)(t_1 + \cdots + t_n) + t(s_1 + \cdots + s_n)$$
$$= (1 - t) + t$$
$$= 1.$$

This proves our theorem.

From Theorem 7, we see that a triangle, as we have defined it analytically, is convex. The convex set of Theorem 7 is therefore a natural generalization of a triangle. It looks like this:

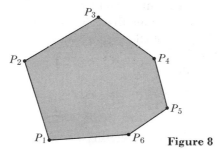

Figure 8

We shall call the convex set of Theorem 7 the convex set *spanned* by $P_1, \ldots, P_n$. Although we shall not need the next result, it shows that this convex set is the smallest convex set containing all the points $P_1, \ldots, P_n$.

Theorem 8. *Let $P_1, \ldots, P_n$ be points of a vector space V. Any convex set S' which contains $P_1, \ldots, P_n$ also contains all linear combinations*

$$t_1 P_1 + \cdots + t_n P_n$$

with $0 \leq t_i$ for all i and $t_1 + \cdots + t_n = 1$.

Proof. We prove this by induction. If $n = 1$, then $t_1 = 1$, and our assertion is obvious. Assume the theorem proved for some integer $n - 1 \geq 1$. We shall prove it for n. Let $t_1, \ldots, t_n$ be numbers satisfying the conditions of the theorem. If $t_n = 1$, then our assertion is trivial because $t_1 = \cdots = t_{n-1} = 0$. Suppose that $t_n \neq 1$. Then the linear combination $t_1 P_1 + \cdots + t_n P_n$ is equal to

$$(1 - t_n)\left(\frac{t_1}{1 - t_n} P_1 + \cdots + \frac{t_{n-1}}{1 - t_n} P_{n-1}\right) + t_n P_n.$$

Let

$$s_i = \frac{t_i}{1 - t_i} \quad \text{for} \quad i = 1, \ldots, n - 1.$$

Then $s_i \geq 0$ and $s_1 + \cdots + s_{n-1} = 1$ so that by induction, we conclude that the point

$$Q = s_1 P_1 + \cdots + s_{n-1} P_{n-1}$$

lies in S'. But then

$$(1 - t_n)Q + t_n P_n = t_1 P_1 + \cdots + t_n P_n$$

lies in S' by definition of a convex set, as was to be shown.

One of the advantages of giving a definition of a triangle as we did it, is that it is then easy to see what happens to a triangle under a linear map, and similarly for parallelograms and convex sets. For instance, let $L: V \to W$ be a linear map, and let v, w be elements of V which are linearly independent. Assume that $L(v)$ and $L(w)$ are also linearly independent. Let S be the triangle spanned by O, v, w. Then the image of S under L, namely $L(S)$, is the triangle spanned by O, $L(v)$, $L(w)$. Indeed, it is the set of all points

$$L(t_1 v + t_2 w) = t_1 L(v) + t_2 L(w)$$

with

$$0 \leq t_i \quad \text{and} \quad t_1 + t_2 \leq 1.$$

Similarly, let R be the parallelogram spanned by v, w. Then the image of R under L, namely $L(R)$, is the set of all points

$$L(t_1 v + t_2 w) = t_1 L(v) + t_2 L(w)$$

with

$$0 \leq t_i \leq 1 \quad \text{for} \quad i = 1, 2.$$

Thus it is also a parallelogram.

Finally, we give an example showing that a certain set is convex. *Let V be a vector space, and let $L: V \to \mathbf{R}$ be a linear map. We contend that the set S of all elements v in V such that $L(v) < 0$ is convex.*

Proof. Let $L(v) < 0$ and $L(w) < 0$. Let $0 < t < 1$. Then

$$L(tv + (1 - t)w) = tL(v) + (1 - t)L(w).$$

Then $tL(v) < 0$ and $(1 - t)L(w) < 0$ so $tL(v) + (1 - t)L(w) < 0$, whence $tv + (1 - t)w$ lies in S. If $t = 0$ or $t = 1$, then $tv + (1 - t)w$ is equal to v or w and thus also lies in S. This proves our assertion.

EXERCISES

1. Show that the image under a linear map of a convex set is convex.

2. Let S_1 and S_2 be convex sets in V. Show that the intersection $S_1 \cap S_2$ is convex.

3. Let $L: \mathbf{R}^n \to \mathbf{R}$ be a linear map. Let S be the set of all points A in $\mathbf{R}^n$ such that $L(A) \geq 0$. Show that S is convex.

4. Let $L: \mathbf{R}^n \to \mathbf{R}$ be a linear map and c a number. Show that the set S consisting of all points A in $\mathbf{R}^n$ such that $L(A) > c$ is convex.

5. Let A be a non-zero vector in $\mathbf{R}^n$ and c a number. Show that the set of points X such that $X \cdot A \geq c$ is convex.

6. Let $L: V \to W$ be a linear map. Let S' be a convex set in W. Let S be the set of all elements P in V such that $L(P)$ is in S'. Show that S is convex.

7. Show that a parallelogram is convex.

8. Let S be a convex set in V and let u be an element of V. Let $T_u: V \to V$ be the translation by u. Show that the image $T_u(S)$ is convex.

9. Let S be a convex set in the vector space V and let c be a number. Let cS denote the set of all elements cv with v in S. Show that cS is convex.

Chapter XI

Linear Maps and Matrices

§1. THE LINEAR MAP ASSOCIATED WITH A MATRIX

Let

$$A = \begin{pmatrix} a_{11} & \cdots & a_{1n} \\ \vdots & & \vdots \\ a_{m1} & \cdots & a_{mn} \end{pmatrix}$$

be an $m \times n$ matrix. We can then associate with A a map

$$L_A : \mathbf{R}^n \to \mathbf{R}^m$$

by letting

$$L_A(X) = AX$$

for every column vector X in $\mathbf{R}^n$. Thus L_A is defined by the association $X \mapsto AX$, the product being the product of matrices. That L_A is linear is simply a special case of Theorem 7, Chapter IX, §4, namely the theorem concerning properties of multiplication of matrices. Indeed, we have

$$A(X + Y) = AX + AY \qquad \text{and} \qquad A(cX) = cAX$$

for all vectors X, Y in $\mathbf{R}^n$ and all numbers c. We call L_A the linear map *associated* with the matrix A.

Example. If

$$A = \begin{pmatrix} 2 & 1 \\ -1 & 5 \end{pmatrix} \qquad \text{and} \qquad X = (3, 7)$$

then

$$L_A(X) = \begin{pmatrix} 2 & 1 \\ -1 & 5 \end{pmatrix} \begin{pmatrix} 3 \\ 7 \end{pmatrix} = \begin{pmatrix} 6 - 7 \\ -3 + 35 \end{pmatrix} = \begin{pmatrix} -1 \\ 32 \end{pmatrix},$$

which we may also write as horizontal vector $(-1, 32)$.

Theorem 1. *If A, B are $m \times n$ matrices and if $L_A = L_B$, then $A = B$. In other words, if matrices A, B give rise to the same linear map, then they are equal.*

Proof. By definition, we have $A_i \cdot X = B_i \cdot X$ for all i, if A_i is the i-th row of A and B_i is the i-th row of B. Hence $(A_i - B_i) \cdot X = 0$ for all i and all X. Hence $A_i - B_i = O$, and $A_i = B_i$ for all i. Hence $A = B$.

We can give a new interpretation for a system of homogeneous linear equations in terms of the linear map associated with a matrix. Indeed, such a system can be written

$$AX = 0,$$

and hence we see that *the set of solutions is the kernel of the linear map L_A.*

EXERCISES

1. In each case, find the vector $L_A(X)$. View X as a column vector.

(a) $A = \begin{pmatrix} 2 & 1 \\ 1 & 0 \end{pmatrix}$, $X = (3, -1)$ (b) $A = \begin{pmatrix} 1 & 0 \\ 0 & 0 \end{pmatrix}$, $X = (5, 1)$

(c) $A = \begin{pmatrix} 1 & 1 \\ 0 & 1 \end{pmatrix}$, $X = (4, 1)$ (d) $A = \begin{pmatrix} 0 & 0 \\ 0 & 1 \end{pmatrix}$, $X = (7, -3)$

§2. THE MATRIX ASSOCIATED WITH A LINEAR MAP

Let $L : \mathbf{R}^n \to \mathbf{R}^m$ be a linear map. As usual, let $E_1, \ldots, E_n$ be the unit vectors in $\mathbf{R}^n$, and let $E'_1, \ldots, E'_m$ be the unit vectors in $\mathbf{R}^m$. We can write any vector X in $\mathbf{R}^n$ as a linear combination

$$X = x_1 E_1 + \cdots + x_n E_n,$$

where x_j is the j-th component of X. We view $E_1, \ldots, E_n$ as column vectors. By linearity, we find that

$$L(X) = x_1 L(E_1) + \cdots + x_n L(E_n)$$

and we can write each $L(E_j)$ in terms of $E'_1, \ldots, E'_m$. In other words, there exist numbers a_{ij} such that

$$L(E_1) = a_{11} E'_1 + \cdots + a_{m1} E'_m$$
$$\vdots \qquad \vdots \qquad \qquad \vdots$$
$$L(E_n) = a_{1n} E'_1 + \cdots + a_{mn} E'_n$$

or in terms of the column vectors,

(*) $$L(E_1) = \begin{pmatrix} a_{11} \\ \vdots \\ a_{m1} \end{pmatrix}, \quad \cdots, \quad L(E_n) = \begin{pmatrix} a_{1n} \\ \vdots \\ a_{mn} \end{pmatrix}.$$

Hence

$$L(X) = x_1(a_{11}E_1' + \cdots + a_{m1}E_m') + \cdots + x_n(a_{1n}E_1' + \cdots + a_{mn}E_n')$$
$$= (a_{11}x_1 + \cdots + a_{1n}x_n)E_1' + \cdots + (a_{m1}x_1 + \cdots + a_{mn}x_n)E_m'.$$

Consequently, if we let $A = (a_{ij})$, then we see that

$$L(X) = AX.$$

Thus $L = L_A$ is the linear map associated with the matrix A. We also call A *the matrix associated with the linear map L*. We know that this matrix is uniquely determined by Theorem 1.

Example 1. Let $F: \mathbf{R}^3 \to \mathbf{R}^2$ be the projection, in other words the mapping such that $F(x_1, x_2, x_3) = (x_1, x_2)$. Then the matrix associated with F is

$$\begin{pmatrix} 1 & 0 & 0 \\ 0 & 1 & 0 \end{pmatrix}.$$

Example 2. Let $F: \mathbf{R}^n \to \mathbf{R}^n$ be the identity. Then the matrix associated with F relative to the usual bases is the matrix

$$\begin{pmatrix} 1 & 0 & 0 & \cdots & 0 \\ 0 & 1 & 0 & \cdots & 0 \\ \vdots & \vdots & \vdots & \ddots & \vdots \\ 0 & 0 & 0 & \cdots & 1 \end{pmatrix},$$

having components equal to 1 on the diagonal, and 0 otherwise.

Example 3. According to Theorem 1 of Chapter X, §2, there exists a unique linear map $L: \mathbf{R}^4 \to \mathbf{R}^2$ such that

$$L(E_1) = \begin{pmatrix} 2 \\ 1 \end{pmatrix}, \quad L(E_2) = \begin{pmatrix} 3 \\ -1 \end{pmatrix}, \quad L(E_3) = \begin{pmatrix} -5 \\ 4 \end{pmatrix}, \quad L(E_4) = \begin{pmatrix} 1 \\ 7 \end{pmatrix}.$$

According to the relations (*), we see that the matrix associated with L is the matrix

$$\begin{pmatrix} 2 & 3 & -5 & 1 \\ 1 & -1 & 4 & 7 \end{pmatrix}.$$

Example 4 (Rotations). We can define a rotation in terms of matrices. Indeed, we call a linear map $L: \mathbf{R}^2 \to \mathbf{R}^2$ a *rotation* if its associated matrix can be written in the form

$$\begin{pmatrix} \cos\theta & -\sin\theta \\ \sin\theta & \cos\theta \end{pmatrix}.$$

The geometric justification for this definition comes from the following picture.

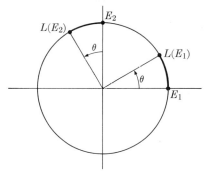

We see that

$$L(E_1) = (\cos \theta)E_1 + (\sin \theta)E_2,$$

$$L(E_2) = (-\sin \theta)E_1 + (\cos \theta)E_2.$$

Thus our definition corresponds precisely to the picture. When the matrix of the rotation is as above, we say that the rotation is by an angle θ. For example, the matrix associated with a rotation by an angle $\pi/2$ is

$$\begin{pmatrix} 0 & -1 \\ 1 & 0 \end{pmatrix}.$$

We observe finally that the operations on matrices correspond to the operations on the associated linear map. For instance, if A, B are $m \times n$ matrices, then

$$L_{A+B} = L_A + L_B$$

and if c is a number, then

$$L_{cA} = cL_A.$$

This is obvious, because

$$(A + B)X = AX + BX \qquad \text{and} \qquad (cA)X = c(AX).$$

Similarly for composition of mappings. Indeed, let

$$F: \mathbf{R}^n \to \mathbf{R}^m \qquad \text{and} \qquad G: \mathbf{R}^m \to \mathbf{R}^s$$

be linear maps, and let A, B be the matrices associated with F and G respectively. Then for any vector X in $\mathbf{R}^n$ we have

$$(G \circ F)(X) = G(F(X)) = B(AX) = (BA)X.$$

Hence the product BA is the matrix associated with the composite linear map $G \circ F$.

EXERCISES

1. Assume that $\mathbf{R}^n$, $\mathbf{R}^m$ have their usual bases. Find the matrix associated with the following linear maps. (Although the vectors are written horizontally, for typographical reasons, view them as column vectors.)

   (a) $F: \mathbf{R}^4 \to \mathbf{R}^2$ given by $F(x_1, x_2, x_3, x_4) = (x_1, x_2)$ (the projection)
   (b) The projection from $\mathbf{R}^4$ to $\mathbf{R}^3$
   (c) $F: \mathbf{R}^2 \to \mathbf{R}^2$ given by $F(x, y) = (3x, 3y)$
   (d) $F: \mathbf{R}^n \to \mathbf{R}^n$ given by $F(X) = 7X$
   (e) $F: \mathbf{R}^n \to \mathbf{R}^n$ given by $F(X) = -X$
   (f) $F: \mathbf{R}^4 \to \mathbf{R}^4$ given by $F(x_1, x_2, x_3, x_4) = (x_1, x_2, 0, 0)$

2. Find the matrix associated with the rotation for each of the following values of θ.

   (a) $\pi/2$ (b) $\pi/4$ (c) π (d) $-\pi$ (e) $-\pi/3$
   (f) $\pi/6$ (g) $5\pi/4$

3. In general, let $\theta > 0$. What is the matrix associated with the rotation by an angle $-\theta$ (i.e. clockwise rotation by θ)?

4. Let $X = (1, 2)$ be a point of the plane. Let F be the rotation through an angle of $\pi/4$. What are the coordinates of $F(X)$ relative to the usual basis $\{E_1, E_2\}$?

5. Same question when $X = (-1, 3)$, and F is the rotation through $\pi/2$.

6. Let $F: \mathbf{R}^n \to \mathbf{R}^n$ be a linear map which is invertible. Show that if A is the matrix associated with F, then A^{-1} is the matrix associated with the inverse of F.

7. Let F be a rotation through an angle θ. Show that for any vector X in $\mathbf{R}^2$ we have $\|X\| = \|F(X)\|$ (i.e. F preserves norms).

8. Let c be a number, and let $L: \mathbf{R}^n \to \mathbf{R}^n$ be the linear map such that $L(X) = cX$. What is the matrix associated with this linear map?

9. Let F_θ be one rotation by an angle θ. If θ, φ are numbers, compute the matrix of the linear map $F_\theta \circ F_\varphi$ and show that it is the matrix of $F_{\theta + \varphi}$.

Chapter XII

Determinants

We have worked with vectors for some time, and we have often felt the need of a method to determine when vectors are linearly independent. Up to now, the only method available to us was to solve a system of linear equations by the elimination method. In this chapter, we shall exhibit a very efficient computational method to solve linear equations, and determine when vectors are linearly independent.

§1. DETERMINANTS OF ORDER 2

Before stating the general properties of an arbitrary determinant, we shall consider a special case.

Let

$$A = \begin{pmatrix} a & b \\ c & d \end{pmatrix}$$

be a 2×2 matrix. We define its determinant to be $ad - cb$. Thus the determinant is a number.

The determinant can be viewed as a function of the matrix A. It can also be viewed as a function of its two columns. Let these be A^1 and A^2 as usual. Then we write the determinant as

$$D(A), \qquad \text{Det}(A), \qquad \text{or} \qquad D(A^1, A^2).$$

The following properties are easily verified by direction computation, which you should carry out completely.

As a function of the column vectors, the determinant is linear. This means: let b', d' be two numbers. Then

$$\text{Det}\begin{pmatrix} a & b + b' \\ c & d + d' \end{pmatrix} = \text{Det}\begin{pmatrix} a & b \\ c & d \end{pmatrix} + \text{Det}\begin{pmatrix} a & b' \\ c & d' \end{pmatrix}.$$

Furthermore, *if t is a number, then*

$$\text{Det}\begin{pmatrix} a & tb \\ c & td \end{pmatrix} = t\,\text{Det}\begin{pmatrix} a & b \\ c & d \end{pmatrix}.$$

The analogous properties also hold with respect to the first column.

If the two columns are equal, then the determinant is equal to 0.

If A is the unit matrix,

$$A = \begin{pmatrix} 1 & 0 \\ 0 & 1 \end{pmatrix},$$

then $\text{Det}(A) = 1$.

The determinant also satisfies the following additional properties.

If one adds a multiple of one column to the other, then the value of the determinant does not change.

In other words, let t be a number. The determinant of the matrix

$$\begin{pmatrix} a + tb & b \\ c + td & d \end{pmatrix}$$

is the same as $D(A)$, and similarly when we add a multiple of the first column to the second.

If the two columns are interchanged, then the determinant changes by a sign.

In other words, we have

$$\text{Det} \begin{pmatrix} a & b \\ c & d \end{pmatrix} = -\text{Det} \begin{pmatrix} b & a \\ d & c \end{pmatrix}.$$

The determinant of A is equal to the determinant of its transpose, i.e. $D(A) = D({}^t A)$.

Explicitly, we have

$$\text{Det} \begin{pmatrix} a & b \\ c & d \end{pmatrix} = \text{Det} \begin{pmatrix} a & c \\ b & d \end{pmatrix}.$$

The vectors $\begin{pmatrix} a \\ c \end{pmatrix}$ *and* $\begin{pmatrix} b \\ d \end{pmatrix}$ *are linearly dependent if and only if the determinant* $ad - bc$ *is equal to* 0.

In the next section, we shall consider determinants of $n \times n$ matrices, and the analogous properties will give us a method for computing the determinant in general.

§2. PROPERTIES OF DETERMINANTS

Let A be an $n \times n$ matrix. It would be possible to define its determinant by a sum, just as we defined the determinant of a 2×2 matrix. However, to write such a sum is a little complicated, and it turns out that to find the value of a determinant, it is not necessary to have this expression. What is needed is a set of properties which can be used to compute it.

Some of these properties are already contained in the following theorem.

Theorem 1. *To each $n \times n$ matrix A we can associate a number, called its determinant, and denoted by $D(A)$, or $D(A^1, \ldots, A^n)$, if $A^1, \ldots, A^n$ are the columns of A, satisfying the following properties:*

1. *As a function of each column vector, the determinant is linear, i.e. if the j-th column A^j is equal to a sum of two column vectors, say $A^j = C + C'$, then*

$$D(A^1, \ldots, C + C', \ldots, A^n)$$
$$= D(A^1, \ldots, C, \ldots, A^n) + D(A^1, \ldots, C', \ldots, A^n).$$

Furthermore, if t is a number, then

$$D(A^1, \ldots, tA^j, \ldots, A^n) = tD(A^1, \ldots, A^j, \ldots, A^n).$$

2. *If two adjacent columns are equal, i.e. if $A^j = A^{j+1}$ for some $j = 1, \ldots, n - 1$, then the determinant $D(A)$ is equal to 0.*

3. *If I is the unit matrix, then $D(I) = 1$.*
Determinants are uniquely determined by the above three properties.

We shall prove in §4 that determinants exist. Here, we shall prove more simple properties which follow from (1), (2), and (3). We shall also use the notation $\text{Det}(A)$ instead of $D(A)$. Furthermore, the determinant of the matrix (a_{ij}) is also denoted by two vertical bars surrounding the matrix:

$$D(A) = \begin{vmatrix} a_{11} & \cdots & a_{1n} \\ & \cdots & \\ a_{n1} & \cdots & a_{nn} \end{vmatrix}$$

4. *Let j be some integer, $1 \leqq j < n$. If the j-th and $(j + 1)$-th columns are interchanged, then the determinant changes by a sign.*

Proof. In the matrix A, we replace the j-th and $(j + 1)$-th columns by $A^j + A^{j+1}$. We obtain a matrix with two equal adjacent columns and by (2) we have:

$$0 = D(\ldots, A^j + A^{j+1}, A^j + A^{j+1}, \ldots).$$

Expanding out using (1) repeatedly yields

$$0 = D(\ldots, A^j, A^j, \ldots) + D(\ldots, A^{j+1}, A^j, \ldots)$$
$$+ D(\ldots, A^j, A^{j+1}, \ldots) + D(\ldots, A^{j+1}, A^{j+1}, \ldots).$$

Using (2), we see that two of these four terms are equal to 0, and hence that

$$0 = D(\ldots, A^{j+1}, A^j, \ldots) + D(\ldots, A^j, A^{j+1}, \ldots).$$

In this last sum, one term must be equal to minus the other, as desired.

5. *If two columns A^j, A^i of A are equal, $j \neq i$, then the determinant of A is equal to 0.*

Proof. Assume that two columns of the matrix A are equal. We can change the matrix by a successive interchange of adjacent columns until we obtain a matrix with equal adjacent columns. (This could be proved formally by induction.) Each time that we make such an adjacent interchange, the determinant changes by a sign, which does not affect its being 0 or not. Hence we conclude by (2) that $D(A) = 0$ if two columns are equal.

6. *If one adds a scalar multiple of one column to another then the value of the determinant does not change.*

Proof. Consider two distinct columns, say the k-th and j-th columns A^k and A^j with $k \neq j$. Let t be a scalar. We add tA^j to A^k. By (1), the determinant becomes

$$D(\ldots, \underset{\underset{k}{\uparrow}}{A^k + tA^j}, \ldots) = D(\ldots, \underset{\underset{k}{\uparrow}}{A^k}, \ldots) + D(\ldots, \underset{\underset{k}{\uparrow}}{tA^j}, \ldots)$$

(the k points to the k-th column). In both terms on the right, the indicated column occurs in the k-th place. But $D(\ldots, A^k, \ldots)$ is simply $D(A)$. Furthermore,

$$D(\ldots, \underset{\underset{k}{\uparrow}}{tA^j}, \ldots) = tD(\ldots, \underset{\underset{k}{\uparrow}}{A^j}, \ldots).$$

Since $k \neq j$, the determinant on the right has two equal columns, because A^j occurs in the k-th place and also in the j-th place. Hence it is equal to 0. Hence

$$D(\ldots, A^k + tA^j, \ldots) = D(\ldots, A^k, \ldots),$$

thereby proving our property (6).

EXERCISE

1. Let c be a number and let A be an $n \times n$ matrix. Show that

$$D(cA) = c^n D(A).$$

§3. CRAMER'S RULE

The properties of the preceding section are already sufficient to prove a well-known rule used in solving linear equations.

Theorem 2. *Let $A^1, \ldots, A^n$ be column vectors such that*

$$D(A^1, \ldots, A^n) \neq 0.$$

Let B be a column vector. If $x_1, \ldots, x_n$ are numbers such that

$$x_1 A^1 + \cdots + x_n A^n = B,$$

then for each $j = 1, \ldots, n$ we have

$$x_j = \frac{D(A^1, \ldots, B, \ldots, A^n)}{D(A^1, \ldots, A_n)},$$

where B occurs in the j-th column instead of A^j. In other words,

$$x_j = \frac{\begin{vmatrix} a_{11} & \cdots & b_1 & \cdots & a_{1n} \\ a_{21} & \cdots & b_2 & \cdots & a_{2n} \\ \vdots & & \vdots & & \vdots \\ a_{n1} & \cdots & b_n & \cdots & a_{nn} \end{vmatrix}}{\begin{vmatrix} a_{11} & \cdots & a_{ij} & \cdots & a_{1n} \\ a_{21} & \cdots & a_{2j} & \cdots & a_{2n} \\ \vdots & & \vdots & & \vdots \\ a_{n1} & \cdots & a_{nj} & \cdots & a_{nn} \end{vmatrix}}.$$

(The numerator is obtained from A by replacing the j-th column A^j by B. The denominator is the determinant of the matrix A.)

Theorem 2 gives us an explicit way of finding the coordinates of B with respect to $A^1, \ldots, A^n$. In the language of linear equations, Theorem 2 allows us to solve explicitly in terms of determinants the system of n linear equations in n unknowns:

$$x_1 a_{11} + \cdots + x_n a_{1n} = b_1,$$
$$\cdots$$
$$x_1 a_{n1} + \cdots + x_n a_{nn} = b_n.$$

We now prove Theorem 2.

Let B be written as in the statement of the theorem, and consider the determinant of the matrix obtained by replacing the j-th column of A by B. Then

$$D(A^1, \ldots, B, \ldots, A^n) = D(A^1, \ldots, x_1 A_1^1 + \cdots + x_n A_n^1, \ldots, A^n).$$

We use property (1) and obtain a sum:

$$D(A^1, \ldots, x_1 A^1, \ldots, A^n) + \cdots + D(A^1, \ldots, x_j A^j, \ldots, A^n)$$
$$+ \cdots + D(A^1, \ldots, x_n A^n, \ldots, A^n),$$

which by property (1) again, is equal to

$$x_1 D(A^1, \ldots, A^1, \ldots, A^n) + \cdots + x_j D(A^1, \ldots, A^n)$$
$$+ \cdots + x_n D(A^1, \ldots, A^n, \ldots, A^n).$$

In every term of this sum except the j-th term, two column vectors are equal. Hence every term except the j-th term is equal to 0, by property (5). The j-th term is equal to

$$x_j D(A^1, \ldots, A^n),$$

and is therefore equal to the determinant we started with, namely $D(A^1, \ldots, B, \ldots, A^n)$. We can solve for x_j, and obtain precisely the expression given in the statement of the theorem.

The rule of Theorem 2, giving us the solution to the system of linear equations by means of determinants, is known as *Cramer's rule*.

Example. Solve the system of linear equations:

$$3x + 2y + 4z = 1,$$
$$2x - y + z = 0,$$
$$x + 2y + 3z = 1.$$

We have:

$$x = \frac{\begin{vmatrix} 1 & 2 & 4 \\ 0 & -1 & 1 \\ 1 & 2 & 3 \end{vmatrix}}{\begin{vmatrix} 3 & 2 & 4 \\ 2 & -1 & 1 \\ 1 & 2 & 3 \end{vmatrix}}, \quad y = \frac{\begin{vmatrix} 3 & 1 & 4 \\ 2 & 0 & 1 \\ 1 & 1 & 3 \end{vmatrix}}{\begin{vmatrix} 3 & 2 & 4 \\ 2 & -1 & 1 \\ 1 & 2 & 3 \end{vmatrix}}, \quad z = \frac{\begin{vmatrix} 3 & 2 & 1 \\ 2 & -1 & 0 \\ 1 & 2 & 1 \end{vmatrix}}{\begin{vmatrix} 3 & 2 & 4 \\ 2 & -1 & 1 \\ 1 & 2 & 3 \end{vmatrix}}.$$

Observe how the column

$$B = \begin{pmatrix} 1 \\ 0 \\ 1 \end{pmatrix}$$

shifts from the first column when solving for x, to the second column when solving for y, to the third column when solving for z. The denominator in all three expressions is the same, namely it is the determinant of the matrix of coefficients of the equations.

In the next section we shall give a method for computing the determinant. One then finds $x = -\frac{1}{5}$, $y = 0$, $z = \frac{2}{5}$.

Determinants also allow us to determine when vectors are linearly independent.

Theorem 3. *Let $A^1, \ldots, A^n$ be column vectors (of dimension n). If they are linearly dependent, then*

$$D(A^1, \ldots, A^n) = 0.$$

If $D(A^1, \ldots, A^n) \neq 0$, then $A^1, \ldots, A^n$ are linearly independent.

Proof. The second assertion is merely an equivalent formulation of the first. It will therefore suffice to prove the first. Assume that $A^1, \ldots, A^n$ are linearly dependent. We can find numbers $x_1, \ldots, x_n$ not all 0 such that

$$x_1 A^1 + \cdots + x_n A^n = O.$$

Suppose $x_j \neq 0$. Then

$$x_j A^j = -x_1 A^1 - \cdots - x_n A^n = \sum_{k \neq j} x_k A^k,$$

it being understood that the j-th term on the right-hand side does not appear. Dividing by x_j, we obtain A^j as a linear combination of $A^1, \ldots, A^n$ (omitting A^j). In other words, there are numbers $y_1, \ldots, y_n$ such that

$$A^j = y_1 A^1 + \cdots + y_n A^n = -\sum_{k \neq j} y_k A^k,$$

the j-th term in the sum being omitted. We get:

$$D(A^1, \ldots, A^n) = D(A^1, \ldots, y_1 A^1 + \cdots + y_n A^n, \ldots, A^n),$$

which we can expand out using property (1). This yields

$$y_1 D(A^1, \ldots, A^1, \ldots, A^n) + \cdots + y_n D(A^1, \ldots, A^n, \ldots, A^n).$$

Here again, the j-term is omitted. In the other terms, we always have two equal columns, and hence each such term is equal to 0 by property (5). This proves Theorem 3.

Corollary. *If $A^1, \ldots, A^n$ are column vectors of $\mathbf{R}^n$ such that $D(A^1, \ldots, A^n) \neq 0$, and if B is a column vector of $\mathbf{R}^n$, then there exist numbers $x_1, \ldots, x_n$ such that*

$$x_1 A^1 + \cdots + x_n A^n = B.$$

Proof. According to the theorem, $A^1, \ldots, A^n$ are linearly independent, and hence form a basis of $\mathbf{R}^n$. Hence any vector of $\mathbf{R}^n$ can be written as a linear combination of $A^1, \ldots, A^n$.

EXERCISE

1. Solve the following systems of linear equations after you have read the next section.

(a) $3x + y - z = 0$
  $x + y + z = 0$
    $y - z = 1$

(b) $2x - y + z = 1$
  $x + 3y - 2z = 0$
  $4x - 3y + z = 2$

(c) $4x + y + z + w = 1$
  $x - y + 2z - 3w = 0$
  $2x + y + 3z + 5w = 0$
  $x + y - z - w = 2$

(d) $x + 2y - 3z + 5w = 0$
  $2x + y - 4z - w = 1$
  $x + y + z + w = 0$
  $-x - y - z + w = 4$

§4. EXISTENCE OF DETERMINANTS

We come to the question of existence, and the problem of computing determinants. We shall define determinants by induction, and give a formula for computing them at the same time. We first deal with the 3×3 case.

We have already defined 2×2 determinants. Let

$$A = (a_{ij}) = \begin{pmatrix} a_{11} & a_{12} & a_{13} \\ a_{21} & a_{22} & a_{23} \\ a_{31} & a_{32} & a_{33} \end{pmatrix}$$

be a 3×3 matrix. We define its determinant according to the formula known as the expansion by a row, say the first row. That is, we define

$$(*) \quad \text{Det}(A) = a_{11} \begin{vmatrix} a_{22} & a_{23} \\ a_{32} & a_{33} \end{vmatrix} - a_{12} \begin{vmatrix} a_{21} & a_{23} \\ a_{31} & a_{33} \end{vmatrix} + a_{13} \begin{vmatrix} a_{21} & a_{22} \\ a_{31} & a_{32} \end{vmatrix}.$$

We may describe this sum as follows. Let A_{ij} be the matrix obtained from A by deleting the i-th row and j-th column. Then the sum expressing $\text{Det}(A)$ can be written

$$a_{11} \, \text{Det}(A_{11}) - a_{12} \, \text{Det}(A_{12}) + a_{13} \, \text{Det}(A_{13}).$$

In other words, each term consists of the product of an element of the first row and the determinant of the 2×2 matrix obtained by deleting the first row and the j-th column, and putting the appropriate sign to this term as shown.

Example 1. Let

$$A = \begin{pmatrix} 2 & 1 & 0 \\ 1 & 1 & 4 \\ -3 & 2 & 5 \end{pmatrix}.$$

Then

$$A_{11} = \begin{pmatrix} 1 & 4 \\ 2 & 5 \end{pmatrix}, \qquad A_{12} = \begin{pmatrix} 1 & 4 \\ -3 & 5 \end{pmatrix}, \qquad A_{13} = \begin{pmatrix} 1 & 1 \\ -3 & 2 \end{pmatrix}$$

and our formula for the determinant of A yields

$$\mathrm{Det}(A) = 2 \begin{vmatrix} 1 & 4 \\ 2 & 5 \end{vmatrix} - 1 \begin{vmatrix} 1 & 4 \\ -3 & 5 \end{vmatrix} + 0 \begin{vmatrix} 1 & 1 \\ -3 & 2 \end{vmatrix}$$
$$= 2(5 - 8) - 1(5 + 12) + 0$$
$$= -23.$$

A direct computation shows that the definition of the determinant by (*) satisfies the three properties of Theorem 1, and consequently the other properties proved in §1 from these three. For instance, suppose that the first column is a sum of two columns:

$$A^1 = B + C, \qquad \text{that is,} \qquad \begin{pmatrix} a_{11} \\ a_{21} \\ a_{31} \end{pmatrix} = \begin{pmatrix} b_1 \\ b_2 \\ b_3 \end{pmatrix} + \begin{pmatrix} c_1 \\ c_2 \\ c_3 \end{pmatrix}.$$

Substituting in each term of (*), we see that each term splits into a sum of two terms corresponding to B and C. For instance,

$$a_{11} \begin{vmatrix} a_{22} & a_{23} \\ a_{31} & a_{33} \end{vmatrix} = b_1 \begin{vmatrix} a_{22} & a_{23} \\ a_{31} & a_{33} \end{vmatrix} + c_1 \begin{vmatrix} a_{22} & a_{23} \\ a_{31} & a_{33} \end{vmatrix},$$

$$a_{12} \begin{vmatrix} b_2 + c_2 & a_{23} \\ b_3 + c_3 & a_{33} \end{vmatrix} = a_{12} \begin{vmatrix} b_2 & a_{23} \\ b_3 & a_{33} \end{vmatrix} + a_{12} \begin{vmatrix} c_2 & a_{23} \\ c_3 & a_{33} \end{vmatrix},$$

and similarly for the third term. The proof with respect to the other columns is analogous. Furthermore, if t is a number, then

$$\mathrm{Det}(tA^1, A^2, A^3) = ta_{11} \begin{vmatrix} a_{22} & a_{23} \\ a_{32} & a_{33} \end{vmatrix} - a_{12} \begin{vmatrix} ta_{21} & a_{23} \\ ta_{31} & a_{33} \end{vmatrix} + a_{13} \begin{vmatrix} ta_{21} & a_{22} \\ ta_{31} & a_{32} \end{vmatrix}$$

$$= t \, \mathrm{Det}(A^1, A^2, A^3)$$

because each 2×2 determinant is linear in the first column, and we can take t outside each one of the second and third terms. Again the proof is similar with respect to the other columns. A direct substitution shows that if two adjacent columns are equal, then formula (*) yields 0 for the determinant. Finally, one sees at once that if A is the unit matrix, then $\mathrm{Det}(A) = 1$. Thus the three properties are verified.

In the above proof, we see that the properties of 2×2 determinants are used to prove the properties of 3×3 determinants.

Furthermore, there is no particular reason why we selected the expansion according to the first row. We could also have used the second row, and write a similar sum, namely:

$$-a_{21} \begin{vmatrix} a_{12} & a_{13} \\ a_{32} & a_{33} \end{vmatrix} + a_{22} \begin{vmatrix} a_{11} & a_{13} \\ a_{31} & a_{33} \end{vmatrix} - a_{23} \begin{vmatrix} a_{11} & a_{12} \\ a_{31} & a_{32} \end{vmatrix}$$

$$= -a_{21} \operatorname{Det}(A_{21}) + a_{22} \operatorname{Det}(A_{22}) - a_{23} \operatorname{Det}(A_{23}).$$

Again, each term is the product of a_{2j}, the determinant of the 2×2 matrix obtained by deleting the second row and j-th column, and putting the appropriate sign in front of each term. This sign is determined according to the pattern:

$$\begin{pmatrix} + & - & + \\ - & + & - \\ + & - & + \end{pmatrix}.$$

One can see directly that the determinant can be expanded according to any row by multiplying out all the terms, and expanding the 2×2 determinants, thus obtaining:

(**) $\operatorname{Det}(A) = a_{11}a_{22}a_{33} - a_{11}a_{32}a_{23} - a_{12}a_{21}a_{33} + a_{12}a_{23}a_{31}$

$$+ a_{13}a_{21}a_{32} - a_{13}a_{22}a_{31}.$$

Furthermore, we can also expand according to columns following the same principle. For instance, expanding out according to the first column:

$$a_{11} \begin{vmatrix} a_{22} & a_{23} \\ a_{32} & a_{33} \end{vmatrix} - a_{21} \begin{vmatrix} a_{12} & a_{13} \\ a_{32} & a_{33} \end{vmatrix} + a_{31} \begin{vmatrix} a_{12} & a_{13} \\ a_{22} & a_{23} \end{vmatrix}$$

yields precisely the same six terms as in (**). Thus in the case of 3×3 determinants, we have the following result.

Theorem 4. Determinants satisfy the rule for expansion according to rows and columns, and $\operatorname{Det}(A) = \operatorname{Det}({}^{t}A)$. *In other words, the determinant of a matrix is equal to the determinant of its transpose.*

This last assertion follows because taking the transpose of a matrix changes rows into columns and vice versa. We shall see in the next section that the proofs given here for the 3×3 case apply in the general case.

With the above means at our disposal, we can now compute 3×3 determinants very efficiently. In doing so, we apply the operations described in property (6), which we now see are valid for rows or columns, since $\operatorname{Det}(A) = \operatorname{Det}({}^{t}A)$. We try to make as many entries in the matrix A

equal to 0. We try especially to make all but one element of a column (or row) equal to 0, and then expand according to that column (or row). The expansion will contain only one term, and reduces our computation to a 2×2 determinant.

Example 2. Compute the determinant

$$\begin{vmatrix} 3 & 0 & 1 \\ 1 & 2 & 5 \\ -1 & 4 & 2 \end{vmatrix}.$$

We already have 0 in the first row. We subtract twice the second row from the third row. Our determinant is then equal to

$$\begin{vmatrix} 3 & 0 & 1 \\ 1 & 2 & 5 \\ -3 & 0 & -8 \end{vmatrix}.$$

We expand according to the second column. The expansion has only one term $\neq 0$, with a $+$ sign, and that is:

$$2 \begin{vmatrix} 3 & 1 \\ -3 & -8 \end{vmatrix}.$$

The 2×2 determinant can be evaluated by our definition $ad - bc$, and we find $2(-24 - (-3)) = -42$.

In the sequel, we deal mostly with 2×2 and 3×3 matrices, so that the reader may omit the discussion of the general case, or simply read the statement of the definitions and properties, and omit the proofs.

The general case of $n \times n$ determinants is done by induction. Suppose that we have been able to define determinants of $n \times n$ matrices for all integers $< n$, satisfying our properties. Let i, j be a pair of integers between 1 and n. If we cross out the i-th row and j-th column in the $n \times n$ matrix A, we obtain an $(n - 1) \times (n - 1)$ matrix, which we denote by A_{ij}. It looks like this:

$$i\begin{array}{c} \\ \end{array}\begin{pmatrix} a_{11} & \cdots & \vline & \cdots & a_{1n} \\ \vdots & & \vline & & \vdots \\ \hline & & a_{ij} & & \\ \vdots & & \vline & & \vdots \\ a_{n1} & \cdots & \vline & \cdots & a_{nn} \end{pmatrix}.$$

We give an expression for the determinant of an $n \times n$ matrix in terms of determinants of $(n-1) \times (n-1)$ matrices. Let i be an integer, $1 \leq i \leq n$. We define

$$D(A) = (-1)^{i+1}a_{i1}\operatorname{Det}(A_{i1}) + \cdots + (-1)^{i+n}a_{in}\operatorname{Det}(A_{in}).$$

Each A_{ij} is an $(n-1) \times (n-1)$ matrix.

This sum can be described in words. For each element of the i-th row, we have a contribution of one term in the sum. This term is equal to $+$ or $-$ the product of this element, times the determinant of the matrix obtained from A by deleting the i-th row and the corresponding column. The sign $+$ or $-$ is determined according to the chess-board pattern:

$$\begin{pmatrix} + & - & + & - & \cdots \\ - & + & - & + & \cdots \\ + & - & + & - & \cdots \\ & & \cdots & & \end{pmatrix}$$

This sum is called the *expansion of the determinant according to the i-th row*. We shall prove that this function D satisfies properties (1), (2), and (3).

Note that $D(A)$ is a sum of terms

$$(-1)^{i+j}a_{ij}\operatorname{Det}(A_{ij})$$

as j ranges from 1 to n.

1. Consider D as a function of the k-th column, and consider any term

$$(-1)^{i+j}a_{ij}\operatorname{Det}(A_{ij}).$$

If $j \neq k$, then a_{ij} does not depend on the k-th column, and $\operatorname{Det}(A_{ij})$ depends linearly on the k-th column. If $j = k$, then a_{ij} depends linearly on the k-th column, and $\operatorname{Det}(A_{ij})$ does not depend on the k-th column. In any case, our term depends linearly on the k-th column. Since $D(A)$ is a sum of such terms, it depends linearly on the k-th column, and property (1) follows.

2. Suppose two adjacent columns of A are equal, namely $A^k = A^{k+1}$. Let j be an index $\neq k$ or $k+1$. Then the matrix A_{ij} has two adjacent equal columns, and hence its determinant is equal to 0. Thus the term corresponding to an index $j \neq k$ or $k+1$ gives a zero contribution to $D(A)$. The other two terms can be written

$$(-1)^{i+k}a_{ik}\operatorname{Det}(A_{ik}) + (-1)^{i+k+1}a_{i,k+1}\operatorname{Det}(A_{i,k+1}).$$

The two matrices A_{ik} and $A_{i,k+1}$ are equal because of our assumption that the k-th column of A is equal to the $(k + 1)$-th column. Similarly, $a_{ik} = a_{i,k+1}$. Hence these two terms cancel since they occur with opposite signs. This proves property (2).

3. Let A be the unit matrix. Then $a_{ij} = 0$ unless $i = j$, in which case $a_{ii} = 1$. Each A_{ij} is the unit $(n - 1) \times (n - 1)$ matrix. The only term in the sum which gives a non-zero contribution is

$$(-1)^{i+i} a_{ii} \operatorname{Det}(A_{ii}),$$

which is equal to 1. This proves property (3).

Example 3. We wish to compute the determinant

$$\begin{vmatrix} 1 & 2 & 1 \\ -1 & 3 & 1 \\ 0 & 1 & 5 \end{vmatrix}.$$

We use the expansion according to the third row (because it has a zero in it), and only two non-zero terms occur:

$$(-1) \begin{vmatrix} 1 & 1 \\ -1 & 1 \end{vmatrix} + (-5) \begin{vmatrix} 1 & 2 \\ -1 & 3 \end{vmatrix}.$$

We can compute explicitly the 2×2 determinants as in §1, and thus we get the value -27 for the determinant of our 3×3 matrix.

It will be shown in a subsequent section that the determinant of a matrix A is equal to the determinant of its transpose. When we have proved this result, we will obtain:

Theorem 4_n. *Determinants satisfy the rule for expansion according to rows and columns. For any column A^j of the matrix $A = (a_{ij})$, we have*

$$D(A) = (-1)^{1+j} a_{1j} D(A_{1j}) + \cdots + (-1)^{n+j} a_{nj} D(A_{nj}).$$

In practice, the computation of a determinant is always done by using an expansion according to some row or column.

Example 4. We wish to compute the determinant

$$\begin{vmatrix} 1 & 3 & 1 & 1 \\ 2 & 1 & 5 & 2 \\ 1 & -1 & 2 & 3 \\ 4 & 1 & -3 & 7 \end{vmatrix}.$$

We add the third row to the second row, and then add the third row to the fourth row. This yields

$$\begin{vmatrix} 1 & 3 & 1 & 1 \\ 3 & 0 & 7 & 5 \\ 1 & -1 & 2 & 3 \\ 4 & 1 & -3 & 7 \end{vmatrix} = \begin{vmatrix} 1 & 3 & 1 & 1 \\ 3 & 0 & 7 & 5 \\ 1 & -1 & 2 & 3 \\ 5 & 0 & -1 & 10 \end{vmatrix}.$$

We then add three times the third row to the first row and get

$$\begin{vmatrix} 4 & 0 & 7 & 10 \\ 3 & 0 & 7 & 5 \\ 1 & -1 & 2 & 3 \\ 5 & 0 & -1 & 10 \end{vmatrix}$$

which we expand according to the third row. There is only one term, namely

$$\begin{vmatrix} 4 & 7 & 10 \\ 3 & 7 & 5 \\ 5 & -1 & 10 \end{vmatrix}$$

We subtract twice the second row from the first row, and then from the third row, yielding

$$\begin{vmatrix} -2 & -7 & 0 \\ 3 & 7 & 5 \\ -1 & -15 & 0 \end{vmatrix}$$

which we expand according to the third column, and get

$$-5(30 - 7) = -5(23) = -115.$$

EXERCISES

1. Compute the following determinants.

$$\text{(a)} \begin{vmatrix} 2 & 1 & 2 \\ 0 & 3 & -1 \\ 4 & 1 & 1 \end{vmatrix} \quad \text{(b)} \begin{vmatrix} 3 & -1 & 5 \\ -1 & 2 & 1 \\ -2 & 4 & 3 \end{vmatrix} \quad \text{(c)} \begin{vmatrix} 2 & 4 & 3 \\ -1 & 3 & 0 \\ 0 & 2 & 1 \end{vmatrix}$$

$$\text{(d)} \begin{vmatrix} 1 & 2 & -1 \\ 0 & 1 & 1 \\ 0 & 2 & 7 \end{vmatrix} \quad \text{(e)} \begin{vmatrix} -1 & 5 & 3 \\ 4 & 0 & 0 \\ 2 & 7 & 8 \end{vmatrix}$$

2. Compute the following determinants.

(a) $\begin{vmatrix} 1 & 1 & -2 & 4 \\ 0 & 1 & 1 & 3 \\ 2 & -1 & 1 & 0 \\ 3 & 1 & 2 & 5 \end{vmatrix}$
(b) $\begin{vmatrix} -1 & 1 & 2 & 0 \\ 0 & 3 & 2 & 1 \\ 0 & 4 & 1 & 2 \\ 3 & 1 & 5 & 7 \end{vmatrix}$
(c) $\begin{vmatrix} 3 & 1 & 1 \\ 2 & 5 & 5 \\ 8 & 7 & 7 \end{vmatrix}$

(d) $\begin{vmatrix} 4 & -9 & 2 \\ 4 & -9 & 2 \\ 3 & 1 & 0 \end{vmatrix}$
(e) $\begin{vmatrix} 4 & -1 & 1 \\ 2 & 0 & 0 \\ 1 & 5 & 7 \end{vmatrix}$
(f) $\begin{vmatrix} 2 & 0 & 0 \\ 1 & 1 & 0 \\ 8 & 5 & 7 \end{vmatrix}$

(g) $\begin{vmatrix} 4 & 0 & 0 \\ 0 & 1 & 0 \\ 0 & 0 & 27 \end{vmatrix}$
(h) $\begin{vmatrix} 5 & 0 & 0 \\ 0 & 3 & 0 \\ 0 & 0 & 9 \end{vmatrix}$

3. In general, what is the determinant of a diagonal matrix

$$\begin{vmatrix} a_{11} & 0 & 0 & \cdots & 0 \\ 0 & a_{22} & 0 & \cdots & 0 \\ \vdots & \vdots & & & \vdots \\ 0 & 0 & & \ddots & 0 \\ 0 & 0 & 0 & \cdots & a_{nn} \end{vmatrix} ?$$

4. Compute the determinant $\begin{vmatrix} \cos \theta & -\sin \theta \\ \sin \theta & \cos \theta \end{vmatrix}$.

5. (a) Let x_1, x_2, x_3 be numbers. Show that

$$\begin{vmatrix} 1 & x_1 & x_1^2 \\ 1 & x_2 & x_2^2 \\ 1 & x_3 & x_3^2 \end{vmatrix} = (x_2 - x_1)(x_3 - x_1)(x_3 - x_2).$$

(b) If $x_1, \ldots, x_n$ are numbers, then show by induction that

$$\begin{vmatrix} 1 & x_1 & \cdots & x_1^{n-1} \\ 1 & x_2 & \cdots & x_2^{n-1} \\ & & \cdots & \\ 1 & x_n & \cdots & x_n^{n-1} \end{vmatrix} = \prod_{i<j} (x_j - x_i),$$

the symbol on the right meaning that it is the product of all terms $x_j - x_i$ with $i < j$ and i, j integers from 1 to n. This determinant is called the *Vandermonde* determinant V_n. To do the induction easily, multiply each column by x_1 and subtract it from the next column on the right, starting from the right-hand side. You will find that

$$V_n = (x_n - x_1) \cdots (x_2 - x_1)V_{n-1}.$$

6. Let A be a triangular $n \times n$ matrix, say a matrix such that all components below the diagonal are equal to 0.

$$A = \begin{pmatrix} a_{11} & & & & \\ 0 & a_{22} & & * & \\ 0 & 0 & \ddots & & \\ \vdots & \vdots & & \ddots & \\ 0 & 0 & \cdots & & a_{nn} \end{pmatrix}$$

What is $D(A)$?

7. If $a(t)$, $b(t)$, $c(t)$, $d(t)$ are functions of t, one can form the determinant

$$\begin{vmatrix} a(t) & b(t) \\ c(t) & d(t) \end{vmatrix},$$

just as with numbers. Write out in full the determinant

$$\begin{vmatrix} \sin t & \cos t \\ -\cos t & \sin t \end{vmatrix}.$$

8. Write out in full the determinant

$$\begin{vmatrix} t + 1 & t - 1 \\ t & 2t + 5 \end{vmatrix}.$$

9. Let $f(t)$, $g(t)$ be two functions having derivatives of all orders. Let $\varphi(t)$ be the function obtained by taking the determinant

$$\varphi(t) = \begin{vmatrix} f(t) & g(t) \\ f'(t) & g'(t) \end{vmatrix}.$$

Show that

$$\varphi'(t) = \begin{vmatrix} f(t) & g(t) \\ f''(t) & g''(t) \end{vmatrix},$$

i.e. the derivative is obtained by taking the derivative of the bottom row.

10. Let

$$A(t) = \begin{pmatrix} b_1(t) & c_1(t) \\ b_2(t) & c_2(t) \end{pmatrix}$$

be a 2×2 matrix of differentiable functions. Let $B(t)$ and $C(t)$ be its column vectors. Let

$$\varphi(t) = \text{Det}(A(t)).$$

Show that

$$\varphi'(t) = D\big(B'(t), C(t)\big) + D\big(B(t), C'(t)\big).$$

11. Let $\alpha_1, \ldots, \alpha_n$ be distinct numbers, $\neq 0$. Show that the functions

$$e^{\alpha_1 t}, \ldots, e^{\alpha_n t}$$

are linearly independent over the complex numbers. [*Hint:* Suppose we have a linear relation

$$c_1 e^{\alpha_1 t} + \cdots + c_n e^{\alpha_n t} = 0$$

with constants c_i, valid for all t. If not all c_i are 0, without loss of generality, we may assume that none of them is 0. Differentiate the above relation $n - 1$ times. You get a system of linear equations. The determinant of its coefficients must be zero. (Why?) Get a contradiction from this.]

12. For this exercise, we assume that the reader is acquainted with polynomials. If he is not, he can do it after reading further into the book.
    (a) Let P_{ij} $(i, j = 1, \ldots, n)$ be polynomials. Assume that all polynomials in a given column in the matrix

$$\begin{pmatrix} P_{11} & \cdots & P_{1n} \\ \vdots & & \vdots \\ P_{n1} & \cdots & P_{nn} \end{pmatrix}$$

have the same degree, and let $d_1, \ldots, d_n$ be these degrees. Let c_{ij} $(\neq 0)$ be the leading coefficient of P_{ij}. Let Q be the determinant of the above matrix. Show that Q has an expression

$$Q(t) = ct^d + \text{terms of degree} < d$$

where $c = \text{Det}(c_{ij})$. Hence if $\text{Det}(c_{ij}) \neq 0$, we see that $Q \neq 0$. (If you wish, do this only for $n = 2$, and then $n = 3$ using the expansion according to a column. The general case can be done by induction. Similarly, you may assume $n = 2$ or 3 in the subsequent parts of the exercise.)

    (b) Let D denote the derivative, $D = d/dt$. Let P be a polynomial, and α a number, $\alpha \neq 0$. Show that

$$D\big(P(t)e^{\alpha t}\big) = (D + \alpha)P(t)e^{\alpha t},$$

and by induction,

$$D^k\big(P(t)e^{\alpha t}\big) = (D + \alpha)^k P(t)e^{\alpha t}.$$

    (c) Let $\alpha_1, \ldots, \alpha_n$ be distinct numbers $\neq 0$. Show that the functions $e^{\alpha_1 t}, \ldots, e^{\alpha_n t}$ are linearly independent over the polynomials, i.e. that if $P_1, \ldots, P_n$ are polynomials such that

$$P_1(t)e^{\alpha_1 t} + \cdots + P_n(t)e^{\alpha_n t} = 0$$

for all t, then $P_1, \ldots, P_n$ are the zero polynomials. [*Hint:* Differentiate the above expression $n - 1$ times. Prove that if $\alpha \neq 0$, then

$$\deg(D + \alpha)^k P = \deg P$$

for any polynomial P, and integer $k \geq 0$. You obtain a system of linear equations

$$P_{k1}(t)e^{\alpha_1 t} + \cdots + P_{kn}(t)e^{\alpha_n t} = 0$$

with $k = 0, \ldots, n - 1$. Hence the determinant $\text{Det}(P_{kj})$ must be 0. Apply part (a) to get a contradiction. You should recognize the determinant of leading coefficients as being a special kind of determinant.]

§5. PERMUTATIONS

(*Note.* The reader who is allergic to combinatorial arguments is advised to understand only the statements of the propositions, and to omit their proofs.)

We shall deal only with permutations of the set of integers $\{1, \ldots, n\}$, which we denote by J_n. By definition, a *permutation* of this set is a map

$$\sigma: \{1, \ldots, n\} \rightarrow \{1, \ldots, n\}$$

of J_n into itself such that, if $i, j \in J_n$ and $i \neq j$ then $\sigma(i) \neq \sigma(j)$. If σ is such a permutation, then the set of integers

$$\{\sigma(1), \ldots, \sigma(n)\}$$

has n distinct elements, and hence consists again of the integers $1, \ldots, n$ in a different arrangement. Thus to each integer $j \in J_n$ there exists a unique integer k such that $\sigma(k) = j$. We can define the *inverse permutation*, denoted by σ^{-1}, as the map

$$\sigma^{-1}: J_n \rightarrow J_n$$

such that $\sigma^{-1}(k) =$ unique integer $j \in J_n$ such that $\sigma(j) = k$. If σ, τ are permutations of J_n, then we can form their composite map

$$\sigma \circ \tau,$$

and this map will again be a permutation. We shall usually omit the small circle, and write $\sigma\tau$ for the composite map. Thus

$$(\sigma\tau)(i) = \sigma(\tau(i)).$$

By definition, for any permutation σ, we have

$$\sigma\sigma^{-1} = id \qquad \text{and} \qquad \sigma^{-1}\sigma = id,$$

where id is the identity permutation, that is, the permutation such that $id(i) = i$ for all $i = 1, \ldots, n$.

If $\sigma_1, \ldots, \sigma_r$ are permutations of J_n, then the inverse of the composite map

$$\sigma_1 \cdots \sigma_r$$

is the permutation

$$\sigma_r^{-1} \cdots \sigma_1^{-1}.$$

This is trivially seen by direct multiplication.

A *transposition* is a permutation which interchanges two numbers and leaves the others fixed. The inverse of a transposition is obviously a transposition.

Proposition 1. *Every permutation of J_n can be expressed as a product of transpositions.*

Proof. We shall prove our assertion by induction on n. For $n = 1$, there is nothing to prove. Let $n > 1$ and assume the assertion proved for $n - 1$. Let σ be a permutation of J_n. Let $\sigma(n) = k$. Let τ be the transposition of J_n such that $\tau(k) = n$, $\tau(n) = k$. Then $\tau\sigma$ is a permutation such that

$$\tau\sigma(n) = \tau(k) = n.$$

In other words, $\tau\sigma$ leaves n fixed. We may therefore view $\tau\sigma$ as a permutation of J_{n-1}, and by induction, there exist transpositions $\tau_1, \ldots, \tau_s$ of J_{n-1}, leaving n fixed, such that

$$\tau\sigma = \tau_1 \cdots \tau_s.$$

We can now write

$$\sigma = \tau^{-1}\tau_1 \cdots \tau_s = \tau\tau_1 \cdots \tau_s,$$

thereby proving our proposition.

Example 1. A permutation σ of the integers $\{1, \ldots, n\}$ is denoted by

$$\begin{bmatrix} 1 & \cdots & n \\ \sigma(1) & \cdots & \sigma(n) \end{bmatrix}.$$

Thus

$$\begin{bmatrix} 1 & 2 & 3 \\ 2 & 1 & 3 \end{bmatrix}$$

denotes the permutation σ such that $\sigma(1) = 2$, $\sigma(2) = 1$, and $\sigma(3) = 3$. This permutation is in fact a transposition. If σ' is the permutation

$$\begin{bmatrix} 1 & 2 & 3 \\ 3 & 1 & 2 \end{bmatrix},$$

then $\sigma\sigma' = \sigma \circ \sigma'$ is the permutation such that

$$\sigma\sigma'(1) = \sigma(\sigma'(1)) = \sigma(3) = 3,$$
$$\sigma\sigma'(2) = \sigma(\sigma'(2)) = \sigma(1) = 2,$$
$$\sigma\sigma'(3) = \sigma(\sigma'(3)) = \sigma(2) = 1,$$

so that we can write

$$\sigma\sigma' = \begin{bmatrix} 1 & 2 & 3 \\ 3 & 2 & 1 \end{bmatrix}.$$

Example 2. We wish to express the permutation

$$\sigma = \begin{bmatrix} 1 & 2 & 3 \\ 3 & 1 & 2 \end{bmatrix}$$

as a product of permutations. Let τ be the transposition which inter-changes 3 and 1, and leaves 2 fixed. Then using the definition, we find that

$$\tau\sigma = \begin{bmatrix} 1 & 2 & 3 \\ 1 & 3 & 2 \end{bmatrix}$$

so that $\tau\sigma$ is a transposition, which we denote by τ'. We can then write $\tau\sigma = \tau'$, so that

$$\sigma = \tau^{-1}\tau' = \tau\tau'$$

because $\tau^{-1} = \tau$. This is the desired product.

Example 3. Express the permutation

$$\sigma = \begin{bmatrix} 1 & 2 & 3 & 4 \\ 2 & 3 & 4 & 1 \end{bmatrix}$$

as a product of transpositions.

Let τ_1 be the transposition which interchanges 1 and 2, and leaves 3, 4 fixed. Then

$$\tau_1\sigma = \begin{bmatrix} 1 & 2 & 3 & 4 \\ 1 & 3 & 4 & 2 \end{bmatrix}.$$

Now let τ_2 be the transposition which interchanges 2 and 3, and leaves 1, 4 fixed. Then

$$\tau_2\tau_1\sigma = \begin{bmatrix} 1 & 2 & 3 & 4 \\ 1 & 2 & 4 & 3 \end{bmatrix}$$

and we see that $\tau_2\tau_1\sigma$ is a transposition, which we may denote by τ_3. Then we get $\tau_2\tau_1\sigma = \tau_3$ so that

$$\sigma = \tau_1\tau_2\tau_3.$$

The proof of the next proposition is the only long one of this section, and can be omitted without harm.

Proposition 2. *To each permutation σ of J_n it is possible to assign a sign 1 or -1, denoted by $\epsilon(\sigma)$, satisfying the following conditions:*
(a) If τ is a transposition, then $\epsilon(\tau) = -1$.
(b) If σ, σ' are permutations of J_n, then

$$\epsilon(\sigma\sigma') = \epsilon(\sigma)\epsilon(\sigma').$$

Proof. Let $x_1, \ldots, x_n$ be variables, and let σ be a permutation of J_n. Let P^+ be the set of pairs (i, j) with $1 \leq i < j \leq n$ such that $\sigma(i) < \sigma(j)$. Let P^- be the set of pairs (i, j) with $1 \leq i < j \leq n$ such that $\sigma(i) > \sigma(j)$. Let m be the number of pairs in P^-. This number m is called the number of *inversions* of σ. We let P be the set of all pairs (i, j) with $1 \leq i < j \leq n$. Then P is the union of P^+ and P^-, and P^+, P^- have no elements in common.

We consider the expression

$$\Delta_\sigma = \prod_{(i,j)\in P} [x_{\sigma(j)} - x_{\sigma(i)}].$$

The product symbol means that we must take the product over all pairs in P, of the terms $x_{\sigma(j)} - x_{\sigma(i)}$. Then we may decompose our product into two products, the first taken over all pairs in P^+, and the second taken over all pairs in P^-. Thus we may write our product in the form

$$\Delta_\sigma = \prod_{(i,j)\in P^+} [x_{\sigma(j)} - x_{\sigma(i)}] \prod_{(k,l)\in P^-} [x_{\sigma(l)} - x_{\sigma(k)}].$$

Inverting each factor in the second product, we find

$$\Delta_\sigma = \prod_{(i,j)\in P^+} [x_{\sigma(j)} - x_{\sigma(i)}] (-1)^m \prod_{(k,l)\in P^-} [x_{\sigma(k)} - x_{\sigma(l)}].$$

The pairs $(\sigma(i), \sigma(j))$ with $(i, j) \in P^+$ are all distinct, and similarly, the pairs $(\sigma(l), \sigma(k))$ with $(k, l) \in P^-$ are all distinct because σ is a permutation.

Furthermore, no pair $(\sigma(l), \sigma(k))$ with $(k, l) \in P^-$ can be equal to a pair $(\sigma(i), \sigma(j))$ with $(i, j) \in P^+$, for otherwise, $l = i$ and $k = j$, contradicting the fact that $k < l$. Hence the set of pairs

$$S = \left\{ \begin{matrix} (\sigma(i), \sigma(j)) & \text{with} & (i, j) \in P^+ \\ (\sigma(k), \sigma(l)) & \text{with} & (k, l) \in P^- \end{matrix} \right\}$$

has as many elements as there are pairs in the union $P = P^+ \cup P^-$. But $P^+ \cup P^-$ is the set of all pairs of integers (i, j) with $1 \leq i < j \leq n$. Hence $S = P$.

We define $\epsilon(\sigma)$ to be $(-1)^m$, where m is the number of inversions of σ.

Then our products for Δ_σ may be rewritten

$$\prod_{(i,j)\in P} [x_{\sigma(j)} - x_{\sigma(i)}] = \epsilon(\sigma) \prod_{(i,j)\in P} [x_j - x_i].$$

Let σ' be a permutation. Substitute $\sigma'(\lambda)$ for x_λ, for each value $\lambda = 1, \ldots, n$. Then on the one hand,

$$\prod_{i<j} [\sigma'(\sigma(j)) - \sigma'(\sigma(i))] = \epsilon(\sigma) \prod_{i<j} [\sigma'(j) - \sigma'(i)]$$

$$= \epsilon(\sigma)\epsilon(\sigma') \prod_{i<j} (j - i),$$

and on the other hand, the product on the left is equal to

$$\epsilon(\sigma'\sigma) \prod_{i<j} (j - i).$$

From this we conclude that $\epsilon(\sigma'\sigma) = \epsilon(\sigma')\epsilon(\sigma)$.

To determine the sign of a transposition, we consider the set of pairs P^- associated with a transposition σ. Suppose that $1 \leq \alpha < \beta \leq n$ and that σ is a transposition such that $\sigma(\alpha) = \beta$ and $\sigma(\beta) = \alpha$. Then P^- consists of all pairs

$$(\alpha, l) \quad \text{with} \quad \alpha + 1 \leq l \leq \beta,$$
$$(k, \beta) \quad \text{with} \quad \alpha + 1 \leq k \leq \beta - 1.$$

Hence P^- will contain an odd number of pairs, whence the sign of the transposition is -1. This proves our proposition.

Corollary 1. *If a permutation σ of J_n is expressed as a product of transpositions,*

$$\sigma = \tau_1 \cdots \tau_s,$$

where each τ_i is a transposition, then s is even or odd according as $\epsilon(\sigma) = 1$ or -1.

Proof. We have

$$\epsilon(\sigma) = (-1)^s,$$

whence our assertion is clear.

Corollary 2. *If σ is a permutation of J_n, then*

$$\epsilon(\sigma) = \epsilon(\sigma^{-1}).$$

Proof. We have

$$1 = \epsilon(id) = \epsilon(\sigma\sigma^{-1}) = \epsilon(\sigma)\epsilon(\sigma^{-1}).$$

Hence either $\epsilon(\sigma)$ and $\epsilon(\sigma^{-1})$ are both equal to 1, or both equal to -1, as desired.

As a matter of terminology, a permutation is called *even* if its sign is 1, and it is called *odd* if its sign is -1. Thus every transposition is odd.

Example 4. The sign of the permutation σ in Example 2 is equal to 1 because $\sigma = \tau\tau'$. The sign of the permutation σ in Example 3 is equal to -1 because $\sigma = \tau_1\tau_2\tau_3$.

EXERCISES

1. Determine the sign of the following permutations.

(a) $\begin{bmatrix} 1 & 2 & 3 \\ 2 & 3 & 1 \end{bmatrix}$ (b) $\begin{bmatrix} 1 & 2 & 3 \\ 3 & 1 & 2 \end{bmatrix}$ (c) $\begin{bmatrix} 1 & 2 & 3 \\ 3 & 2 & 1 \end{bmatrix}$

(d) $\begin{bmatrix} 1 & 2 & 3 & 4 \\ 2 & 3 & 1 & 4 \end{bmatrix}$ (e) $\begin{bmatrix} 1 & 2 & 3 & 4 \\ 2 & 1 & 4 & 3 \end{bmatrix}$ (f) $\begin{bmatrix} 1 & 2 & 3 & 4 \\ 3 & 2 & 4 & 1 \end{bmatrix}$

(g) $\begin{bmatrix} 1 & 2 & 3 & 4 \\ 4 & 2 & 1 & 3 \end{bmatrix}$ (h) $\begin{bmatrix} 1 & 2 & 3 & 4 \\ 3 & 1 & 4 & 2 \end{bmatrix}$ (i) $\begin{bmatrix} 1 & 2 & 3 & 4 \\ 2 & 4 & 1 & 3 \end{bmatrix}$

2. In each one of the cases of Exercise 1, write the inverse of the permutation.

3. Show that the number of odd permutations of $\{1, \ldots, n\}$ for $n \geq 2$ is equal to the number of even permutations.

§6. UNIQUENESS

Before proceeding with the main part of the argument, we make some remarks on repeated linear maps, as in property (1). Consider first the case $n = 2$. If we have to expand

$$D(3A + 5B, 2A - B),$$

where A, B are 2-vectors, then using property (1), we obtain a sum of four terms, namely

$$D(3A, 2A - B) + D(5B, 2A - B)$$
$$= D(3A, 2A) + D(3A, -B) + D(5B, 2A) + D(5B, -B)$$
$$= 6D(A, A) - 3D(A, B) + 10D(B, A) - 5D(B, B).$$

Observe that we have used the fact that when $c = -1$ in property (1),

$$D(A, -B) = -D(A, B).$$

In such an expression, we note that $D(A, A) = 0$ and $D(B, B) = 0$. Thus only two terms remain to give a contribution which is not *a priori* equal to 0.

To give another example, let us expand $D(2A + B - C, 3E + F)$ where A, B, C, E, F are vectors. Using (1) repeatedly, we obtain six terms, namely

$$6D(A, E) + 2D(A, F) + 3D(B, E) + D(B, F) - 3D(C, E) - D(C, F).$$

More generally, suppose that we have a determinant

$$D(x_1 A^1 + \cdots + x_n A^n, y_1 B^1 + \cdots + y_m B^m)$$

with numbers $x_1, \ldots, x_n, y_1, \ldots, y_m$ and vectors

$$A^1, \ldots, A^n, B^1, \ldots, B^m.$$

Using (1) repeatedly, this determinant is equal to

$$D(x_1 A^1, y_1 B^1 + \cdots + y_m B^m) + \cdots + D(x_n A^n, y_1 B^1 + \cdots + y_m B^m).$$

Each expression can then be further expanded, and our determinant is equal to a double sum,

$$D(x_1 A^1, y_1 B^1) + \cdots + D(x_1 A^1, y_m B^m)$$
$$\vdots \qquad\qquad\qquad \vdots$$
$$+ D(x_n A^n, y_1 B^1) + \cdots + D(x_n A^n, y_m B^m).$$

The principle involved in expanding such a determinant is the following. We select one term from the first sum, one term from the second sum, and take the sum over all such terms. Thus our double sum may be written

$$\sum_{i=1}^{n} \sum_{j=1}^{m} x_i y_j D(A^i, B^j).$$

The same principle applies when we deal with more general expansions.

We shall find an explicit expression of a determinant satisfying conditions (1), (2) and (3) in terms of the components of the matrix. Since properties (4), (5) and (6) are consequences of (1), (2), and (3), we may use them freely.

We shall now give the uniqueness proof in the case of 2×2 determinants. Let

$$A = \begin{pmatrix} a & b \\ c & d \end{pmatrix}$$

be a 2×2 matrix, and let

$$A^1 = \begin{pmatrix} a \\ c \end{pmatrix}, \qquad A^2 = \begin{pmatrix} b \\ d \end{pmatrix}$$

be its column vectors. We can write

$$A^1 = aE^1 + cE^2 \qquad \text{and} \qquad A^2 = bE^1 + dE^2,$$

where E^1, E^2 are the unit column vectors. Then

$$
\begin{aligned}
D(A) = D(A^1, A^2) &= D(aE^1 + cE^2, bE^1 + dE^2) \\
&= ab D(E^1, E^1) + cb D(E^2, E^1) + ad D(E^1, E^2) + cd D(E^2, E^2) \\
&= -bc D(E^1, E^2) + ad D(E^1, E^2) \\
&= ad - bc.
\end{aligned}
$$

This proves that any function D satisfying the basic properties of a determinant is given by the formula of §1, namely $ad - bc$.

The proof in general is entirely similar, taking into account the n components. It is based on an expansion similar to the one we have just used in the 2×2 case. We can formulate it in a lemma.

Lemma. *Let $X^1, \ldots, X^n$ be n vectors in n-space. Let $B = (b_{ij})$ be an $n \times n$ matrix, and let*

$$
\begin{aligned}
A^1 &= b_{11}X^1 + \cdots + b_{n1}X^n \\
&\ \ \vdots \qquad\qquad\quad \vdots \\
A^n &= b_{1n}X^1 + \cdots + b_{nn}X^n.
\end{aligned}
$$

Then

$$
D(A^1, \ldots, A^n) = \sum_\sigma \epsilon(\sigma) b_{\sigma(1),1} \cdots b_{\sigma(n),n} D(X^1, \ldots, X_n),
$$

where the sum is taken over all permutations σ of $\{1, \ldots, n\}$.

Proof. We must compute

$$
D(b_{11}X^1 + \cdots + b_{n1}X^n, \ldots, b_{1n}X^1 + \cdots + b_{nn}X^n).
$$

Using property (1), we can express this as a sum of terms

$$
D(b_{\sigma(1),1}X^{\sigma(1)}, \ldots, b_{\sigma(n),n}X^{\sigma(n)}),
$$

where $\sigma(1), \ldots, \sigma(n)$ denote a choice of an integer between 1 and n for each value of $1, \ldots, n$. Thus σ is a mapping of the set of integers $\{1, \ldots, n\}$ into itself. By property (1), each one of the above terms can also be written

$$
b_{\sigma(1),1} \cdots b_{\sigma(n),n} D(X^{\sigma(1)}, \ldots, X^{\sigma(n)}).
$$

If some σ assigns the same integer to distinct values i, j between 1 and n, then the determinant on the right has two equal columns, and hence is equal to 0. Consequently we can take our sum only for those σ which are such that $\sigma(i) \neq \sigma(j)$ whenever $i \neq j$, namely *permutations*. Instead of saying that we take the sum for all permutations σ, we abbreviate the notation with the usual $\sum$ symbol. Thus we can write

$$
D(A^1, \ldots, A^n) = \sum_\sigma b_{\sigma(1),1} \cdots b_{\sigma(n),n} D(X^{\sigma(1)}, \ldots, X^{\sigma(n)}).
$$

The vectors $X^{\sigma(1)}, \ldots, X^{\sigma(n)}$ occur in a permutation of the standard arrangement $X^1, \ldots, X^n$. If we interchange any two distinct columns, this corresponds to a transposition of $\{1, \ldots, n\}$, and thus the determinant changes by a sign. By a succession of interchanges of adjacent columns, we can reestablish the standard order for the vectors. If $m(\sigma)$ is the number of transpositions of adjacent column vectors which have to be carried out to reestablish the standard ordering of the unit vectors, then

$$D(X^{\sigma(1)}, \ldots, X^{\sigma(n)}) = (-1)^{m(\sigma)} D(X^1, \ldots, X^n)$$
$$= \epsilon(\sigma) D(X^1, \ldots, X^n).$$

Substituting this for our expression of $D(A^1, \ldots, A^n)$ obtained above, we find the desired expression of the lemma.

Theorem 5. *Determinants are uniquely determined by properties* (1), (2), *and* (3). *Let* $A = (a_{ij})$. *This determinant satisfies the expression*

$$D(A^1, \ldots, A^n) = \sum_{\sigma} \epsilon(\sigma) a_{\sigma(1),1} \cdots a_{\sigma(n),n},$$

where the sum is taken over all permutations of the integers $\{1, \ldots, n\}$.

Proof. We let $X^j = E^j$ be the unit vector having 1 in the j-th component, and we let $b_{ij} = a_{ij}$ in the Lemma. Since by hypothesis we have $D(E^1, \ldots, E^n) = 1$, we see that the formula of Theorem 5 drops out at once.

EXERCISES

1. Let $A^1, \ldots, A^n$ be column vectors of dimension n and assume that they are linearly independent. Show that $D(A^1, \ldots, A^n) \neq 0$. [*Hint:* Express each one of the standard unit vectors $E^1, \ldots, E^n$ viewed as column vectors as linear combinations of $A^1, \ldots, A^n$. Using the fact that $D(E^1, \ldots, E^n) = 1$, and properties (1) and (2), prove the assertion.] Thus in view of Theorem 3, we can now say that $A^1, \ldots, A^n$ are linearly dependent if and only if $D(A^1, \ldots, A^n) = 0$.

2. Let V, V' be vector spaces. Suppose that we have a product, defined between pairs of elements of V, and denoted by $v \wedge w$ for v, w elements of V. We assume that the values of the product lie in the space V', that is $v \wedge w$ is an element of V' for all v, w in V. Assume that the product satisfies the following conditions:

   AP 1. *We have* $(u + v) \wedge w = u \wedge w + v \wedge w$ *and*

   $$u \wedge (v + w) = u \wedge v + u \wedge w$$

   for all u, v, w *in* V. *Also for any number* c,

   $$(cu) \wedge v = c(u \wedge v) = u \wedge (cv).$$

AP 2. *We have* $u \wedge u = 0$ *for all u in V.*

Prove the following statements:

(a) We have $u \wedge v = -v \wedge u$.

(b) Let z be an element of V', and assume that $V = \mathbf{R}^2$. Let e^1, e^2 be the two unit vectors of $\mathbf{R}^2$. Show that a product satisfying AP 1, AP 2, and the condition that $e^1 \wedge e^2 = z$ is uniquely determined by these three conditions.

(c) Let z_1, z_2, z_3 be elements of V' and let $V = \mathbf{R}^3$. Let e^1, e^2, e^3 be the three unit vectors of $\mathbf{R}^3$. Show that a product satisfying AP 1, AP 2, and the conditions

$$e^1 \wedge e^2 = z_1, \qquad e^1 \wedge e^3 = z_2, \qquad e^2 \wedge e^3 = z_3$$

is uniquely determined. [*Hint:* Write arbitrary elements of V in terms of the unit vectors and expand.]

Compare (c) with the formulas for the cross product given in Chapter I. Observe that the cross product satisfies AP 1 and AP 2. A product satisfying these conditions is called an *alternating product*.

3. Let V, V' be vector spaces, and consider a product as described in Exercise 2, satisfying conditions AP 1, and AP 2.

(a) Assume that dim $V = 2$. Show that the set of all elements $v \wedge w$ with v, w in V is a subspace of V', of dimension 0 or 1.

(b) Assume that dim $V = 3$. Let U' be the subspace of V' generated by all elements $v \wedge w$ with v, w in V. Show that U' has dimension ≤ 3.

§7. DETERMINANT OF A TRANSPOSE

Theorem 6. *Let A be a square matrix. Then* $\mathrm{Det}(A) = \mathrm{Det}({}^t A)$.

Proof. In Theorem 5, we had

(*) $$\mathrm{Det}(A) = \sum_\sigma \epsilon(\sigma) a_{\sigma(1),1} \cdots a_{\sigma(n),n}.$$

Let σ be a permutation of $\{1, \ldots, n\}$. If $\sigma(j) = k$, then $\sigma^{-1}(k) = j$. We can therefore write

$$a_{\sigma(j),j} = a_{k,\sigma^{-1}(k)}.$$

In a product

$$a_{\sigma(1),1} \cdots a_{\sigma(n),n}$$

each integer k from 1 to n occurs precisely once among the integers $\sigma(1), \ldots, \sigma(n)$. Hence this product can be written

$$a_{1,\sigma^{-1}(1)} \cdots a_{n,\sigma^{-1}(n)},$$

and our sum (*) is equal to

$$\sum_\sigma \epsilon(\sigma^{-1}) a_{1,\sigma^{-1}(1)} \cdots a_{n,\sigma^{-1}(n)},$$

because $\epsilon(\sigma) = \epsilon(\sigma^{-1})$. In this sum, each term corresponds to a permutation σ. However, as σ ranges over all permutations, so does σ^{-1} because a permutation determines its inverse uniquely. Hence our sum is equal to

(**) $$\sum_{\sigma} \epsilon(\sigma) a_{1,\sigma(1)} \cdots a_{n,\sigma(n)}.$$

The sum (**) is precisely the sum giving the expanded form of the determinant of the transpose of A. Hence we have proved what we wanted.

§8. DETERMINANT OF A PRODUCT

We shall prove the important rule:

Theorem 7. *Let A, B be two $n \times n$ matrices. Then*

$$\mathrm{Det}(AB) = \mathrm{Det}(A)\,\mathrm{Det}(B).$$

The determinant of a product is equal to the product of the determinants.

Proof. Let $A = (a_{ij})$ and $B = (b_{jk})$:

$$\begin{pmatrix} a_{11} & \cdots & a_{1n} \\ \vdots & & \vdots \\ a_{n1} & \cdots & a_{nn} \end{pmatrix} \begin{pmatrix} b_{11} & \cdots & b_{1k} & \cdots & b_{1n} \\ \vdots & & \vdots & & \vdots \\ b_{n1} & \cdots & b_{nk} & \cdots & b_{nn} \end{pmatrix}.$$

Let $AB = C$, and let C^k be the k-th column of C. Then by definition,

$$C^k = b_{1k}A^1 + \cdots + b_{nk}A^n.$$

Thus

$$D(AB) = D(C^1, \ldots, C^n)$$
$$= D(b_{11}A^1 + \cdots + b_{n1}A^n, \ldots, b_{1n}A^1 + \cdots + b_{nn}A^n).$$

If we expand this out using the Lemma before Theorem 5, we find a sum

$$\sum_{\sigma} D(b_{\sigma(1),1}A^{\sigma(1)}, \ldots, b_{\sigma(n),n}A^{\sigma(n)})$$
$$= \sum_{\sigma} b_{\sigma(1),1} \cdots b_{\sigma(n),n} D(A^{\sigma(1)}, \ldots, A^{\sigma(n)})$$
$$= \sum_{\sigma} \epsilon(\sigma) b_{\sigma(1),1} \cdots b_{\sigma(n),n} D(A^1, \ldots, A^n).$$

According to the formula for determinants which we found, this is equal to $D(B)D(A)$, as was to be shown.

Corollary. *Let A be an invertible $n \times n$ matrix. Then*

$$\mathrm{Det}(A^{-1}) = \mathrm{Det}(A)^{-1}.$$

Proof. We have $1 = D(I) = D(AA^{-1}) = D(A)D(A^{-1})$. This proves what we wanted.

§9. INVERSE OF A MATRIX

Let A be an $n \times n$ matrix. If B is a matrix such that $AB = I$ and $BA = I$ ($I = $ unit $n \times n$ matrix), then we called B an *inverse* of A, and we write $B = A^{-1}$. If there exists an inverse of A, then it is unique. Indeed, let C be an inverse of A. Then $CA = I$. Multiplying by B on the right, we obtain $CAB = B$. But $CAB = C(AB) = CI = C$. Hence $C = B$. A similar argument works for $AC = I$.

Theorem 8. *Let $A = (a_{ij})$ be an $n \times n$ matrix, and assume that $D(A) \neq 0$. Then A is invertible. Let E^j be the j-th column unit vector, and let*

$$b_{ij} = \frac{D(A^1, \ldots, E^j, \ldots, A^n)}{D(A)},$$

where E^j occurs in the i-th place. Then the matrix $B = (b_{ij})$ is an inverse for A.

Proof. Let $X = (X_{ij})$ be an unknown $n \times n$ matrix. We wish to solve for the components x_{ij}, so that they satisfy $AX = I$. From the definition of products of matrices, this means that for each j, we must solve

$$E^j = x_{1j}A^1 + \cdots + x_{nj}A^n.$$

This is a system of linear equations, which can be solved uniquely by Cramer's rule, and we obtain

$$x_{ij} = \frac{D(A^1, \ldots, E^j, \ldots, A^n)}{D(A)},$$

which is the formula given in the theorem.

We must still prove that $XA = I$. Note that $D({}^t A) \neq 0$. Hence by what we have already proved, we can find a matrix Y such that ${}^t A Y = I$. Taking transposes, we obtain ${}^t Y A = I$. Now we have

$$I = {}^t Y(AX)A = {}^t YA(XA) = XA,$$

thereby proving what we want, namely that $X = B$ is an inverse for A.

We can write out the components of the matrix B in Theorem 8 as follows:

$$b_{ij} = \frac{\begin{vmatrix} a_{11} & \cdots & 0 & \cdots & a_{1n} \\ \vdots & & \vdots & & \vdots \\ a_{j1} & \cdots & 1 & \cdots & a_{jn} \\ \vdots & & \vdots & & \vdots \\ a_{n1} & \cdots & 0 & \cdots & a_{nn} \end{vmatrix}}{\text{Det}(A)}.$$

If we expand the determinant in the numerator according to the i-th column, then all terms but one are equal to 0, and hence we obtain the numerator of b_{ij} as a subdeterminant of $\text{Det}(A)$. Let A_{ij} be the matrix obtained from A by deleting the i-th row and the j-th column. Then

$$b_{ij} = \frac{(-1)^{i+j}\,\text{Det}(A_{ji})}{\text{Det}(A)}$$

(note the reversal of indices!) and thus we have the formula

$$A^{-1} = \text{transpose of}\left(\frac{(-1)^{i+j}\,\text{Det}(A_{ij})}{\text{Det}(A)}\right).$$

A square matrix whose determinant is $\neq 0$, or equivalently which admits an inverse, is called *non-singular*.

EXERCISES

1. Find the inverses of the matrices in Exercise 1, §4.
2. Using the fact that if A, B are two $n \times n$ matrices then

$$\text{Det}(AB) = \text{Det}(A)\,\text{Det}(B),$$

prove that a matrix A such that $\text{Det}(A) = 0$ does not have an inverse.
3. Write down explicitly the inverse of a 2×2 matrix

$$\begin{pmatrix} a & b \\ c & d \end{pmatrix}.$$

Chapter XIII

Applications to Functions of Several Variables

Having acquired the language of linear maps and matrices, we shall be able to define the derivative of a mapping, or rather, of a differentiable mapping. The theoretical considerations involved in the proof of the general chain rule of §3 become of course a little abstract. But you should note that it is precisely the availability of the notion of linear mapping which allows us to give a statement of the chain rule, and a proof, which runs exactly parallel to the proof for functions of one variable, as given in the *First Course*. The analysis profits from algebra, and conversely, the algebra of linear mappings finds a neat application which enhances its attractiveness.

§1. THE DERIVATIVE AS A LINEAR MAP

We shall interpret our notion of differentiability given in Chapter III in terms of linear mappings.

Let U be an open set in $\mathbf{R}^n$. Let f be a function defined on U. Let P be a point of U, and assume that f is differentiable at P. Then there is a vector A, and a function g such that for all small vectors H we can write

$$(1) \qquad f(P + H) = f(P) + A \cdot H + \|H\|g(H),$$

and

$$(2) \qquad \lim_{\|H\| \to 0} g(H) = 0.$$

The vector A, expressed in terms of coordinates, is none other than the vector of partial derivatives:

$$A = \operatorname{grad} f(P) = \big(D_1 f(P), \ldots, D_n f(P)\big).$$

We have seen that there is a linear map $L = L_A$ such that

$$L(H) = A \cdot H.$$

Our condition that f is differentiable may therefore be expressed by saying that there is a linear map $L: \mathbf{R}^n \to \mathbf{R}$ and a function g defined for sufficiently small H, such that

$$(3) \qquad f(P + H) = f(P) + L(H) + \|H\|g(H)$$

and

$$\lim_{\|H\| \to 0} g(H) = 0.$$

In the case of functions of one variable, we have of course the same kind of formula, namely

$$f(a + h) = f(a) + ch + |h|g(h)$$

where

$$\lim_{h \to 0} g(h) = 0.$$

Here, a, h are numbers, and so is the ordinary derivative c. But the map $L_c: \mathbf{R} \to \mathbf{R}$ such that $L_c(h) = ch$ (multiplication by the number c) is a linear map, so that also in this case, we can write

$$f(a + h) = f(a) + L_c(h) + |h|g(h).$$

Up to now, we did not define the notion of derivative for functions of several variables. We now define the derivative of f at P to be this linear map, which we shall denote by $Df(P)$ or also $f'(P)$. This notation is therefore entirely similar to the notation used for functions of one variable. We could not make the definition before we knew what a linear map is. All the theory developed in Chapters II through VII could be carried out knowing only dot products, and this is the reason we postponed making the general definition of derivative until now.

If L is a linear map from one vector space into another, then it will be useful to omit some parentheses in order to simplify the notation. Thus we shall sometimes write Lv instead of $L(v)$. With this convention, we can write (3) in the form

$$(4) \qquad f(P + H) = f(P) + Df(P)H + \|H\|g(H),$$

or also

$$(5) \qquad f(P + H) = f(P) + f'(P)H + \|H\|g(H).$$

These ways of expressing differentiability are those which generalize to arbitrary mappings.

Let U be an open set in $\mathbf{R}^n$. Let $F: U \to \mathbf{R}^m$ be a mapping. Let P be a point of U. We shall say that F is *differentiable* at P if there exists a linear map

$$L: \mathbf{R}^n \to \mathbf{R}^m$$

and a mapping G defined for all vectors H sufficiently small, such that we have

$$(6) \qquad F(P + H) = F(P) + LH + \|H\|G(H)$$

and

$$(7) \qquad \lim_{\|H\| \to 0} G(H) = O.$$

If such a linear mapping L exists, then we interpret (6) as saying that L approximates F up to an error term whose magnitude is small, near the point P.

A linear map L satisfying conditions (6) and (7) will be said to be *tangent* to F at P. It is also said to be the best linear approximation to F at P.

Just as before, we define a map ψ defined for small H to be $o(H)$ ("little oh of H") if

$$\lim_{\|H\| \to 0} \frac{\psi(H)}{\|H\|} = O.$$

Then we can write our definition of differentiability in the form

$$F(P + H) = F(P) + L(H) + o(H),$$

where L is a linear map.

Theorem 1. *Suppose that there exist linear maps L, M which are tangent to F at P. Then $L = M$. In other words, if there exists one linear map which is tangent to F at P, then there is only one.*

Proof. Suppose that there are two mappings G_1, G_2 such that for all sufficiently small H, we have

$$F(P + H) = F(P) + LH + \|H\|G_1(H),$$
$$F(P + H) = F(P) + MH + \|H\|G_2(H),$$

and

$$\lim_{\|H\| \to 0} G_1(H) = O, \qquad \lim_{\|H\| \to 0} G_2(H) = O.$$

We must show that for any vector Y we have $LY = MY$. Let t range over small positive numbers. Then tY is small, and $P + tY$ lies in U. Thus $F(P + tY)$ is defined. By hypothesis, we have

$$F(P + tY) = F(P) + L(tY) + \|tY\|G_1(tY),$$
$$F(P + tY) = F(P) + M(tY) + \|tY\|G_2(tY).$$

Subtracting, we obtain

$$O = L(tY) - M(tY) + \|tY\|[G_1(tY) - G_2(tY)].$$

Let $G = G_1 - G_2$. Since L, M are linear, we can write $L(tY) = tL(Y)$ and $M(tY) = tM(Y)$. Consequently, we obtain

$$tM(Y) - tL(Y) = t\|Y\|G(tY).$$

Take $t \neq 0$. Dividing by t yields

$$M(Y) - L(Y) = \|Y\|G(tY).$$

As t approaches 0, $G(tY)$ approaches O also. Hence the right-hand side of this last equation approaches O. But $M(Y) - L(Y)$ is a fixed vector. The only way this is possible is that $M(Y) - L(Y) = O$, in other words, $M(Y) = L(Y)$, as was to be shown.

If there exists a linear map tangent to F at P, we shall denote this linear map by $F'(P)$, or $DF(P)$ and call it the *derivative* of F at P. We may therefore write

$$F(P + H) = F(P) + F'(P)H + \|H\|G(H)$$

instead of (6).

In the next section, we shall see how the linear map $F'(P)$ can be computed, or rather how its matrix can be computed when we deal with vectors as n-tuples.

EXERCISES

1. Let $f: \mathbf{R} \to \mathbf{R}$ be a function, and let a be a number. Assume that there exists a linear map L tangent to f at a. Show that

$$L(1) = \lim_{h \to 0} \frac{f(a + h) - f(a)}{h}.$$

2. Conversely, assume that the limit

$$\lim_{h \to 0} \frac{f(a + h) - f(a)}{h}$$

exists and is equal to a number b. Let L_b be the linear map such that $L_b(x) = bx$ for all numbers x. Show that L_b is tangent to f at a. It is customary to identify the number b and the linear map L_b, and to call either one the derivative of f at a.

3. Let $L: \mathbf{R} \to V$ be a linear map from the reals into some vector space V. Show that there is some element v in V such that $L(x) = xv$ for all numbers x.

4. Going back to Chapter II, let $X(t)$ be a curve, defined for all numbers t, say. Discuss in a manner analogous to Exercises 1 and 2 the derivative dX/dt, and the linear map $L_t: \mathbf{R} \to \mathbf{R}^n$ which is tangent to X at t.

§2. THE JACOBIAN MATRIX

Throughout this section, all our vectors will be vertical vectors. We let $D_1, \ldots, D_n$ be the usual partial derivatives. Thus $D_i = \partial/\partial x_i$.

Let $F: \mathbf{R}^n \to \mathbf{R}^m$ be a mapping. We can represent F by coordinate functions. In other words, there exist functions $f_1, \ldots, f_m$ such that

$$F(X) = \begin{pmatrix} f_1(X) \\ f_2(X) \\ \vdots \\ f_m(X) \end{pmatrix} = {}^t(f_1(X), \ldots, f_m(X)).$$

To simplify the typography, we shall sometimes write a vertical vector as the transpose of a horizontal vector, as we have just done.

We view X as a column vector, $X = {}^t(x_1, \ldots, x_n)$.

Let us assume that the partial derivatives of each function f_i $(i = 1, \ldots, m)$ exist. We can then form the matrix of partial derivatives:

$$\left(\frac{\partial f_i}{\partial x_j} \right) = \begin{pmatrix} \dfrac{\partial f_1}{\partial x_1} & \dfrac{\partial f_1}{\partial x_2} & \cdots & \dfrac{\partial f_1}{\partial x_n} \\ \dfrac{\partial f_2}{\partial x_1} & \dfrac{\partial f_2}{\partial x_2} & \cdots & \dfrac{\partial f_2}{\partial x_n} \\ \vdots & \vdots & & \vdots \\ \dfrac{\partial f_m}{\partial x_1} & \dfrac{\partial f_m}{\partial x_2} & \cdots & \dfrac{\partial f_m}{\partial x_n} \end{pmatrix} = \begin{matrix} D_1 f_1(X) & \cdots & D_n f_1(X) \\ \vdots & & \vdots \\ D_1 f_m(X) & \cdots & D_n f_m(X) \end{matrix}$$

$i = 1, \ldots, m$ and $j = 1, \ldots, n$. This matrix is called the *Jacobian* matrix of F, and is denoted by $J_F(X)$.

In the case of two variables (x, y), say F is given by functions (f, g), so that

$$F(x, y) = \big(f(x, y), g(x, y)\big),$$

then Jacobian matrix is

$$J_F(x, y) = \begin{pmatrix} \dfrac{\partial f}{\partial x} & \dfrac{\partial f}{\partial y} \\ \dfrac{\partial g}{\partial x} & \dfrac{\partial g}{\partial y} \end{pmatrix}.$$

(As we have done just now, we sometimes write the vectors horizontally, although to be strictly correct, they should be written vertically.)

Example 1. Let $F: \mathbf{R}^2 \to \mathbf{R}^2$ be the mapping defined by

$$F(x, y) = \begin{pmatrix} x^2 + y^2 \\ e^{xy} \end{pmatrix} = \begin{pmatrix} f(x, y) \\ g(x, y) \end{pmatrix}.$$

Find the Jacobian matrix $J_F(P)$ for $P = (1, 1)$.

The Jacobian matrix at an arbitrary point (x, y) is

$$\begin{pmatrix} \dfrac{\partial f}{\partial x} & \dfrac{\partial f}{\partial y} \\[2mm] \dfrac{\partial g}{\partial x} & \dfrac{\partial g}{\partial y} \end{pmatrix} = \begin{pmatrix} 2x & 2y \\ ye^x & xe^y \end{pmatrix}.$$

Hence when $x = 1$, $y = 1$, we find:

$$J_F(1, 1) = \begin{pmatrix} 2 & 2 \\ e & e \end{pmatrix}.$$

Example 2. Let $F: \mathbf{R}^2 \to \mathbf{R}^3$ be the mapping defined by

$$F(x, y) = \begin{pmatrix} xy \\ \sin x \\ x^2 y \end{pmatrix}.$$

Find $J_F(P)$ at the point $P = (\pi, \pi/2)$.

The Jacobian matrix at an arbitrary point (x, y) is

$$\begin{pmatrix} y & x \\ \cos x & 0 \\ 2xy & x^2 \end{pmatrix}.$$

Hence

$$J_F\left(\pi, \frac{\pi}{2}\right) = \begin{pmatrix} \pi/2 & \pi \\ -1 & 0 \\ \pi^2 & \pi^2 \end{pmatrix}.$$

Theorem 2. *Let U be an open set in $\mathbf{R}^n$. Let $F: U \to \mathbf{R}^m$ be a mapping, having coordinate functions $f_1, \ldots, f_m$. Assume that each function f_i is differentiable at a point X of U. Then F is differentiable at X, and the matrix representing the linear map $DF(X) = F'(X)$ is the Jacobian matrix $J_F(X)$.*

Proof. For each integer i between 1 and n, there is a function g_i such that

$$\lim_{\|H\| \to 0} g_i(H) = 0,$$

and such that we can write

$$f_i(X + H) = f_i(X) + \operatorname{grad} f_i(X) \cdot H + \|H\| g_i(H).$$

We view X and $F(X)$ as vertical vectors. By definition, we can then write

$$F(X + H) = {}^t(f_1(X + H), \ldots, f_m(X + H)).$$

Hence

$$F(X + H) = \begin{pmatrix} f_1(X) \\ \vdots \\ f_m(X) \end{pmatrix} + \begin{pmatrix} \text{grad } f_1\,(X) \cdot H \\ \vdots \\ \text{grad } f_m\,(X) \cdot H \end{pmatrix} + \|H\| \begin{pmatrix} g_1(H) \\ \vdots \\ g_m(H) \end{pmatrix}.$$

The term in the middle, involving the gradients, is precisely equal to the product of the Jacobian matrix, times H, i.e. to

$$J_F(X)H.$$

Let $G(H) = {}^t\big(g_1(H), \ldots, g_m(H)\big)$ be the vector on the right. Then

$$F(X + H) = F(X) + J_F(X)H + \|H\|G(H).$$

As $\|H\|$ approaches 0, each coordinate of $G(H)$ approaches 0. Hence $G(H)$ approaches O; in other words,

$$\lim_{\|H\| \to 0} G(H) = O.$$

Hence the linear map represented by the matrix $J_F(X)$ is tangent to F at X. Since such a linear map is unique, we have proved our theorem.

Let U be open in $\mathbf{R}^n$ and $F: U \to \mathbf{R}^n$ be a differentiable map into the same dimensional space. Then the Jacobian matrix $J_F(X)$ is a square matrix, and its determinant is called the *Jacobian determinant* of F at X. We denote it by

$$\Delta_F(X).$$

Example 3. Let F be as in Example 2, $F(x, y) = (x^2 + y^2, e^{xy})$. Then the Jacobian determinant is equal to

$$\Delta_F(x, y) = \begin{vmatrix} 2x & 2y \\ ye^x & xe^y \end{vmatrix} = 2x^2 e^y - 2y^2 e^x.$$

In particular,

$$\Delta_F(1, 1) = 2e - 2e = 0,$$
$$\Delta_F(1, 2) = 2e^2 - 8e.$$

Example 4. An important map is given by the polar coordinates, $F: \mathbf{R}^2 \to \mathbf{R}^2$ such that $F(r, \theta) = (r \cos \theta, r \sin \theta)$. We can view the map as defined on all of $\mathbf{R}^2$, although when selecting polar coordinates, we take $r > 0$. We see that F maps a rectangle into a circular sector (Fig. 1).

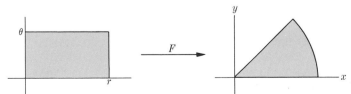

Figure 1

EXERCISES

1. In each of the following cases, compute the Jacobian matrix of F.

   (a) $F(x, y) = (x + y, x^2 y)$ (b) $F(x, y) = (\sin x, \cos xy)$
   (c) $F(x, y) = (e^{xy}, \log x)$ (d) $F(x, y, z) = (xz, xy, yz)$
   (e) $F(x, y, z) = (xyz, x^2 z)$ (f) $F(x, y, z) = (\sin xyz, xz)$

2. Find the Jacobian matrix of the mappings in Exercise 1 evaluated at the following points.

   (a) $(1, 2)$ (b) $(\pi, \pi/2)$ (c) $(1, 4)$
   (d) $(1, 1, -1)$ (e) $(2, -1, -1)$ (f) $(\pi, 2, 4)$

3. Let $L: \mathbf{R}^n \to \mathbf{R}^m$ be a linear map. Show that for each point X of $\mathbf{R}^n$ we have $L'(X) = L$.

4. Find the Jacobian matrix of the following maps.

   (a) $F(x, y) = (xy, x^2)$ (b) $F(x, y, z) = (\cos xy, \sin xy, xz)$

5. Find the Jacobian determinant of the map in Exercise 1(a). Determine all points where the Jacobian determinant is equal to 0.

6. Find the Jacobian determinant of the map in Exercise 1(b).

7. Let $F: \mathbf{R}^2 \to \mathbf{R}^2$ be the map defined by

   $$F(r, \theta) = (r \cos \theta, r \sin \theta),$$

   in other words the polar coordinates map

   $$x = r \cos \theta, \qquad y = r \sin \theta.$$

   Find the Jacobian matrix and Jacobian determinant of this mapping. Determine all points (r, θ) where the Jacobian determinant vanishes.

8. Let $F: \mathbf{R}^3 \to \mathbf{R}^3$ be the mapping defined by

   $$F(r, \varphi, \theta) = (r \sin \varphi \cos \theta, r \sin \varphi \sin \theta, r \cos \varphi)$$

   or in other words

   $$x = r \sin \varphi \cos \theta, \qquad y = r \sin \varphi \sin \theta, \qquad z = r \cos \varphi.$$

   Find the Jacobian matrix and Jacobian determinant of this mapping.

9. Find the Jacobian matrix and determinant of the map

   $$F(r, \theta) = (e^r \cos \theta, e^r \sin \theta).$$

   Show that the Jacobian determinant is never 0. Show that there exist two distinct points (r_1, θ_1) and (r_2, θ_2) such that

   $$F(r_1, \theta_1) = F(r_2, \theta_2).$$

§3. THE CHAIN RULE

In the *First Course*, we proved a chain rule for composite functions. Earlier in this book, a chain rule was given for a composite of a function and a map defined for real numbers, but having values in $\mathbf{R}^n$. In this section, we give a general formulation of the chain rule for arbitrary compositions of mappings.

Let U be an open set in $\mathbf{R}^n$, and let V be an open set in $\mathbf{R}^m$. Let $F: U \to \mathbf{R}^m$ be a mapping, and assume that all values of F are contained in V. Let $G: V \to \mathbf{R}^s$ be a mapping. Then we can form the composite mapping $G \circ F$ from U into $\mathbf{R}^s$.

Let X be a point of U. Then $F(X)$ is a point of V by assumption. Let us assume that F is differentiable at X, and that G is differentiable at $F(X)$. We know that $F'(X)$ is a linear map from $\mathbf{R}^n$ into $\mathbf{R}^m$, and $G'(F(X))$ is a linear map from $\mathbf{R}^m$ into $\mathbf{R}^s$. Thus we may compose these two linear maps to give a linear map $G'(F(X)) \circ F'(X)$ from $\mathbf{R}^n$ into $\mathbf{R}^s$.

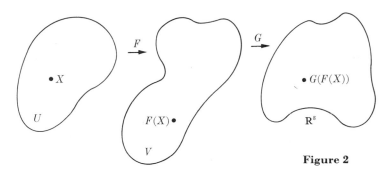

Figure 2

The next theorem tells us what the derivative of $G \circ F$ is in terms of the derivative of F at X, and the derivative of G at $F(X)$. Please observe how the statement and proof of the theorem will be entirely parallel to the statement and proof of the theorem for the chain rule in the *First Course*.

Theorem 3. *Let U be an open set in $\mathbf{R}^n$, let V be an open set in $\mathbf{R}^m$. Let $F: U \to \mathbf{R}^m$ be a mapping such that all values of F are contained in V. Let $G: V \to \mathbf{R}^s$ be a mapping. Let X be a point of U such that F is differentiable at X. Assume that G is differentiable at $F(X)$. Then the composite mapping $G \circ F$ is differentiable at X, and its derivative is given by*

$$(G \circ F)'(X) = G'(F(X)) \circ F'(X).$$

Proof. By definition of differentiability, there exists a mapping Φ_1 such that

$$\lim_{\|H\| \to 0} \Phi_1(H) = O$$

and

$$F(X + H) = F(X) + F'(X)H + \|H\|\Phi_1(H).$$

Similarly, there exists a mapping Φ_2 such that

$$\lim_{\|K\| \to 0} \Phi_2(K) = O,$$

and

$$G(Y + K) = G(Y) + G'(Y)K + \|K\|\Phi_2(K).$$

We let $K = K(H)$ be

$$K = F(X + H) - F(X) = F'(X)H + \|H\|\Phi_1(H).$$

Then

$$G(F(X + H)) = G(F(X) + K)$$
$$= G(F(X)) + G'(F(X))K + o(K).$$

Using the fact that $G'(F(X))$ is linear, and

$$K = F(X + H) - F(X) = F'(X)H + \|H\|\Phi_1(H),$$

we can write

$$(G \circ F)(X + H) = (G \circ F)(X) + G'(F(X))F'(X)H$$
$$+ \|H\|G'(F(X))\Phi_1(H) + o(K).$$

Using simple estimates which we do not give in detail, we conclude that

$$(G \circ F)(X + H) = (G \circ F)(X) + G'(F(X))F'(X)H + o(H).$$

This proves that the linear map

$$G'(F(X))F'(X)$$

is tangent to $G \circ F$ at X. It must therefore be equal to $(G \circ F)'(X)$, as was to be shown.

§4. INVERSE MAPPINGS AND IMPLICIT FUNCTIONS

Let U be open in $\mathbf{R}^n$ and let $F: U \to \mathbf{R}^n$ be a map, given by coordinate functions:

$$F(X) = (f_1(X), \ldots, f_n(X)).$$

If all the partial derivatives of all functions f_i exist and are continuous, we say that F is a C^1-map. We say that F is C^1-invertible on U if the image $F(U)$ is an open set V, and if there exists a C^1-map $G: V \to U$ such that $G \circ F$ and $F \circ G$ are the respective identity mappings on U and V.

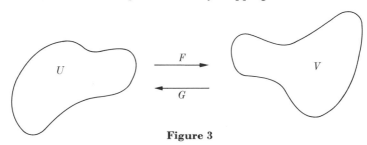

Figure 3

Example 1. Let A be a fixed vector, and let $F: \mathbf{R}^n \to \mathbf{R}^n$ be the translation by A, namely $F(X) = X + A$. Then F is C^1-invertible, its inverse being translation by $-A$.

Example 2. Let U be the subset of $\mathbf{R}^2$ consisting of all pairs (r, θ) with $r > 0$ and $0 < \theta < \pi$. Let

$$F(r, \theta) = (r \cos \theta, r \sin \theta).$$

Let $x = r \cos \theta$ and $y = r \sin \theta$. Then the image of U is the upper half-plane consisting of all (x, y) such that $y > 0$, and arbitrary x (Fig. 4).

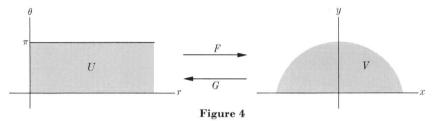

Figure 4

We can solve for the inverse map G, namely:

$$r = \sqrt{x^2 + y^2} \qquad \text{and} \qquad \theta = \arccos \frac{x}{r}$$

so that

$$G(x, y) = \left(\sqrt{x^2 + y^2}, \arccos \frac{x}{r} \right).$$

In many applications, a map is not necessarily invertible, but has still a useful property locally. Let P be a point of U. We say that F is *locally C^1-invertible at P* if there exists an open set U_1 contained in U and containing P such that F is C^1-invertible on U_1.

Example 3. If we view $F(r, \theta) = (r \cos \theta, r \sin \theta)$ as defined on all of $\mathbf{R}^2$, then F is not C^1-invertible on all of $\mathbf{R}^2$, but given any point, it is locally invertible at that point. One could see this by giving an explicit inverse map as we did in Example 1. At any rate, from Example 1, we see that F is C^1-invertible on the set $r > 0$ and $0 < \theta < \pi$.

In most cases, it is not possible to define an inverse map by explicit formulas. However, there is a very important theorem which allows us to conclude that a map is locally invertible at a point.

Inverse mapping theorem. *Let $F: U \to \mathbf{R}^n$ be a C^1-map. Let P be a point of U. If the Jacobian determinant $\Delta_F(P)$ is not equal to 0, then F is locally C^1-invertible at P.*

A proof of this theorem is too involved to be given in this book. However, we make the following comment. The fact that the determinant $\Delta_F(P)$ is not 0 implies (and in fact is equivalent with) the fact that the

Jacobian matrix is invertible, and the Jacobian matrix represents the linear map $F'(P)$. Thus the inverse mapping theorem asserts that if the derivative $F'(P)$ is invertible, then the map F itself is locally invertible at P. Since it is usually very easy to determine whether the Jacobian determinant vanishes or not, we see that the inverse mapping theorem gives us a simple criterion for local invertibility.

Example 4. Consider the case of one variable, $y = f(x)$. In the *First Course*, we proved that if $f'(x_0) \neq 0$ at a point x_0, then there is an inverse function defined near $y_0 = f(x_0)$. Indeed, say $f'(x_0) > 0$. By continuity, assuming that f' is continuous (i.e. f is C^1), we know that $f'(x) > 0$ for x close to x_0. Hence f is strictly increasing, and an inverse function exists near x_0. In fact, we determined the derivative. If g is the inverse function, then we proved that

$$g'(y_0) = f'(x_0)^{-1}.$$

Example 5. The formula for the derivative of the inverse function in the case of one variable can be generalized to the case of the inverse mapping theorem. Suppose that the map $F: U \to V$ has a C^1-inverse $G: V \to U$. Let X be a point of U. Then $G \circ F = I$ is the identity, and since I is linear, we see directly from the definition of the derivative that $I'(X) = I$. Using the chain rule, we find that

$$I = (G \circ F)'(X) = G'(F(X)) \circ F'(X)$$

for all X in U. In particular, this means that if $Y = F(X)$, then

$$\boxed{G'(Y) = F'(X)^{-1}}$$

where the inverse in this last expression is to be understood as the inverse of the linear map $F'(X)$. Thus we have generalized the formula for the derivative of an inverse function.

Example 6. Let $F(x, y) = (e^x \cos y, e^x \sin y)$. Show that F is locally invertible at every point.

We find that

$$J_F(x, y) = \begin{pmatrix} e^x \cos y & -e^x \sin y \\ e^x \sin y & e^x \cos y \end{pmatrix}, \quad \text{whence} \quad \Delta_F(x, y) = e^x \neq 0.$$

Since the Jacobian determinant is not 0, it follows that F is locally invertible at (x, y) for all x, y.

Example 7. Let U be open in $\mathbf{R}^2$ and let $f: U \to \mathbf{R}$ be a C^1-*function.* Let (a, b) be a point of U. Assume that $D_2 f(a, b) \neq 0$. Then the map F

given by

$$(x, y) \mapsto F(x, y) = (x, f(x, y))$$

is locally invertible at (a, b).

Proof. All we have to do is compute the Jacobian matrix and determinant. We have

$$J_F(x, y) = \begin{pmatrix} 1 & 0 \\ \dfrac{\partial f}{\partial x} & \dfrac{\partial f}{\partial y} \end{pmatrix}$$

so that

$$J_F(a, b) = \begin{pmatrix} 1 & 0 \\ D_1 f(a, b) & D_2 f(a, b) \end{pmatrix}$$

and hence

$$\Delta_F(a, b) = D_2 f(a, b).$$

By assumption, this is not 0, and the inverse mapping theorem implies what we want.

The result of Example 7 can be used to discuss implicit functions. Again let $f: U \to \mathbf{R}$ be as in Example 7, and assume that $f(a, b) = c$. We ask whether there is some differentiable function $y = \varphi(x)$ defined near $x = a$ such that $\varphi(a) = b$ and

$$f(x, \varphi(x)) = c$$

for all x near a. If such a function φ exists, then we say that $y = \varphi(x)$ is the *function determined implicitly by* f.

Theorem 4   (Implicit function theorem).   *Let U be open in* $\mathbf{R}^2$ *and let* $f: U \to \mathbf{R}$ *be a* C^1-function. *Let* (a, b) *be a point of U, and let* $f(a, b) - c$. *Assume that* $D_2 f(a, b) \neq 0$. *Then there exists an implicit function* $y = \varphi(x)$ *which is* C^1 *in some interval containing a, and such that* $\varphi(a) = b$.

Proof. We apply Example 7 and use the notation of that exercise. Thus we let

$$F(x, y) = (x, f(x, y)).$$

We know that $F(a, b) = (a, c)$ and that there exists a C^1-inverse G defined locally near (a, c). The inverse map G has two coordinate functions, and we can write $G(x, z) = (x, g(x, z))$ for some function g. Thus we put $y = g(x, z)$, and $z = f(x, y)$. We define

$$\varphi(x) = g(x, c).$$

Then on the one hand,

$$F(x, \varphi(x)) = F(x, g(x, c)) = F(G(x, c)) = (x, c),$$

and on the other hand,

$$F(x, \varphi(x)) = (x, f(x, \varphi(x))).$$

This proves that $f(x, \varphi(x)) = c$. Furthermore, by definition of an inverse map, $G(a, c) = (a, b)$ so that $\varphi(a) = b$. This proves the implicit function theorem.

Example 8. Let $f(x, y) = x^2 + y^2$ and let $(a, b) = (1, 1)$.   Then $c = f(1, 1) = 2$. We have $D_2 f(x, y) = 2y$ so that

$$D_2 f(1, 1) = 2 \neq 0,$$

so the implicit function $y = \varphi(x)$ near $x = 1$ exists. In this case, we can of course solve explicitly for y, namely

$$y = \sqrt{2 - x^2}.$$

Example 9. We take $f(x, y) = x^2 + y^2$ as in Example 8, and $(a, b) = (-1, -1)$. Then again $c = f(-1, -1) = 2$, and

$$D_2 f(-1, -1) = -2 \neq 0.$$

In this case we can still solve for y in terms of x, namely

$$y = -\sqrt{2 - x^2}.$$

In general, the equation $f(x, y) = c$ defines some curve as in the following picture.

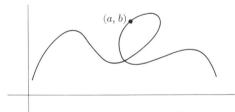

Figure 5

Near the point (a, b) as indicated in the picture, we see that there is an implicit function:

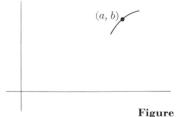

Figure 6

but that one could not define the implicit function for all x, only for those x near a.

Example 10. Let $f(x, y) = x^2 y + 3y^3 x^4 - 4$.   Take $(a, b) = (1, 1)$ so that $f(a, b) = 0$. Then $D_2 f(x, y) = x^2 + 9y^2 x^4$ and

$$D_2 f(1, 1) = 10 \neq 0.$$

Hence the implicit function $y = \varphi(x)$ exists, but there is no simple way to solve for it. We can also determine the derivative $\varphi'(1)$. Indeed, differentiating the equation $f(x, y) = 0$, knowing that $y = \varphi(x)$ is a differentiable function, we find

$$2xy + x^2 y' + 12y^3 x^3 + 9y^2 y' x^4 = 0,$$

whence we can solve for $y' = \varphi'(x)$, namely

$$\varphi'(x) = y' = -\frac{2xy + 12y^3 x^3}{x^2 + 9y^2 x^4}.$$

Hence

$$\varphi'(1) = -\frac{2 + 12}{1 + 9} = -\frac{7}{5}.$$

In Exercise 4 we give the general formula for an arbitrary function f.

Example 11. In general, given any function $f(x, y) = 0$ and $y = \varphi(x)$ we can find $\varphi'(x)$ by differentiating in the usual way. For instance, suppose

$$x^3 + 4y \sin(xy) = 0.$$

Then taking the derivative with respect to x, we find

$$3x^2 + 4y' \sin(xy) + 4y \cos(xy)(y + xy').$$

We then solve for y' as

$$y' = -\frac{4y^2 \cos(xy) + 3x^2}{4 \sin(xy) + 4xy \cos(xy)}$$

whenever $4 \sin(xy) + 4xy \cos(xy) \neq 0$. Similarly, we can solve for y'' by differentiating either of the last two expressions. In the present case, this gets complicated.

EXERCISES

1. Determine whether the following mappings are locally C^1-invertible at the given point.
   (a) $F(x, y) = (x^2 - y^2, 2xy)$ at $(x, y) \neq (0, 0)$
   (b) $F(x, y) = (x^3 y + 1, x^2 + y^2)$ at $(1, 2)$
   (c) $F(x, y) = (x + y, y^{1/4})$ at $(1, 16)$
   (d) $F(x, y) = \left(\dfrac{x}{x^2 + y^2}, \dfrac{y}{x^2 + y^2}\right)$ at $(x, y) \neq (0, 0)$
   (e) $F(x, y) = (x + x^2 + y, x^2 + y^2)$ at $(x, y) = (5, 8)$

2. Determine whether the mappings of Exercises 1, 2 of §2 are locally C^1-invertible at the indicated point.

3. Show that the map defined by $F(x, y) = (e^x \cos y, e^x \sin y)$ is not invertible on all of $\mathbf{R}^2$, even though it is locally invertible everywhere.

4. Let $y = \varphi(x)$ be an implicit function satisfying $f(x, \varphi(x)) = 0$, both f, φ being C^1. Show that

$$\varphi'(x) = - \frac{D_1 f(x, \varphi(x))}{D_2 f(x, \varphi(x))}$$

wherever $D_2 f(x, \varphi(x)) \neq 0$.

5. Find an expression for $\varphi''(x)$ by differentiating the preceding expression for $\varphi'(x)$.

6. Let $f(x, y) = (x - 2)^3 y + x e^{y-1}$. Is $D_2 f(a, b) \neq 0$ at the following points (a, b)?

   (a) $(1, 1)$ (b) $(0, 0)$ (c) $(2, 1)$

7. Let f be a C^1-function of 3 variables (x, y, z) defined on an open set U of $\mathbf{R}^3$. Let (a, b, c) be a point of U, and assume $f(a, b, c) = 0$, $D_3 f(a, b, c) \neq 0$. Show that there exists a C^1-function $\varphi(x, y)$ defined near (a, b) such that

$$f(x, y, \varphi(x, y)) = 0 \quad \text{and} \quad \varphi(a, b) = c.$$

We call φ the implicit function $z = \varphi(x, y)$ determined by f at (a, b).

8. In Exercise 7, show that

$$D_1 \varphi(a, b) = - \frac{D_1 f(a, b, c) + D_2 f(a, b, c)}{D_3 f(a, b, c)}.$$

9. For each of the following functions f, show that $f(x, y) = 0$ defines an implicit function $y = \varphi(x)$ at the given point (a, b), and find $\varphi'(a)$.

   (a) $f(x, y) = x^2 - xy + y^2 - 3$ at $(1, 2)$
   (b) $f(x, y) = x \cos xy$ at $(1, \pi/2)$
   (c) $f(x, y) = 2e^{x+y} - x + y$ at $(1, -1)$
   (d) $f(x, y) = xe^y - y + 1$ at $(-1, 0)$
   (e) $f(x, y) = x + y + x \sin y$ at $(0, 0)$
   (f) $f(x, y) = x^5 + y^5 + xy + 4$ at $(2, -2)$

10. For each of the following functions $f(x, y, z)$, show that $f(x, y, z) = 0$ defines an implicit function $z = \varphi(x, y)$ at the given point (a, b, c) and find $D_1 \varphi(a, b)$ and $D_2 \varphi(a, b)$.

    (a) $f(x, y, z) = x + y + z + \cos xyz$ at $(0, 0, -1)$
    (b) $f(x, y, z) = z^3 - z - xy \sin z$ at $(0, 0, 0)$
    (c) $f(x, y, z) = x^3 + y^3 + z^3 - 3xyz - 4$ at $(1, 1, 2)$
    (d) $f(x, y, z) = x + y + z - e^{xyz}$ at $(0, \frac{1}{2}, \frac{1}{2})$

11. Let $f(x, y, z) = x^3 - 2y^2 + z^2$. Show that $f(x, y, z) = 0$ defines an implicit function $x = \varphi(y, z)$ at the point $(1, 1, 1)$. Find $D_1 \varphi$ and $D_2 \varphi$ at the point $(1, 1)$.

12. In Exercise 10, show that $f(x, y, z) = 0$ also determines y as an implicit function of (x, z) and z as an implicit function of (x, y) at the given point. Find the partial derivatives of these implicit functions at the given point.

13. Show that the equation $x^2/4 + y^2 + z^2/9 = 0$ defines an implicit function $z = \varphi(x, y)$ at the point $(1, \sqrt{11}/6, 2)$, and an implicit function $y = \psi(x, z)$ at this point. Find the first partial derivatives of these functions at the given point.

Chapter XIV

Multiple Integrals

When studying functions of one variable, it was possible to give essentially complete proofs for the existence of an integral of a continuous function over an interval. The investigation of the integral involved lower sums and upper sums.

In order to develop a theory of integration for functions of several variables, it becomes necessary to have techniques whose degree of sophistication is somewhat greater than that which is available to us. Hence we shall only state results, and omit most of the proofs, except in special cases. These results will allow us to compute multiple integrals.

We shall also list various formulas giving double and triple integrals in terms of polar coordinates, and we give a geometric argument to make them plausible. Here again, the general formula for changing variables in a multiple integral can be handled theoretically (and elegantly) only when much more machinery is available than we have at present. The proofs properly belong to an advanced calculus course. (Cf. *Analysis I.*)

§1. DOUBLE INTEGRALS

We begin by discussing the analogue of upper and lower sums associated with partitions.

Let R be a region of the plane (Fig. 1), and let f be a function defined on R. We shall say that f is *bounded* if there exists a number M such that $|f(X)| \leq M$ for all X in R.

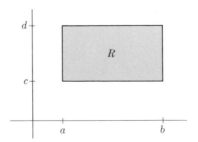

Figure 1

Let a, b be two numbers with $a \leq b$, and let c, d be two numbers with $c \leq d$. We consider the closed interval $[a, b]$ on the x-axis and the closed interval $[c, d]$ on the y-axis. These determine a rectangle R in the plane, consisting of all pairs of points (x, y) with $a \leq x \leq b$ and $c \leq y \leq d$.

536

The rectangle R above will be denoted by $[a, b] \times [c, d]$.

Let I denote the interval $[a, b]$. By a partition P_I of I we mean a sequence of numbers

$$x_1 = a \leq x_2 \leq \cdots \leq x_m = b$$

which we also write as $P_I = (x_1, \ldots, x_m)$. Similarly, by a partition P_J of the interval $J = [c, d]$ we mean a sequence of numbers

$$y_1 = c \leq y_2 \leq \cdots \leq y_n = d$$

which we write as $P_J = (y_1, \ldots, y_n)$.

Each pair of small intervals $[x_i, x_{i+1}]$ and $[y_j, y_{j+1}]$ determines a rectangle

$$S_{ij} = [x_i, x_{i+1}] \times [y_j, y_{j+1}].$$

(Cf. Fig. 2(a).) We denote symbolically by $P = P_I \times P_J$ the partition of R into rectangles S_{ij} and we call such S_{ij} a *subrectangle* of the *partition* (Fig. 2(b)).

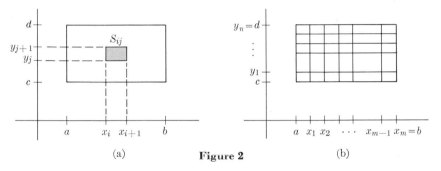

(a)   Figure 2   (b)

Let S be a set and f a function on S (with values which are real, as usual). Assume that f is bounded. By

$$\sup_S f = \sup_{v \in S} f(v)$$

we mean the least upper bound of all values $f(v)$ for v in S. We take it as a known property of the real numbers that any bounded set of numbers has a least upper bound, and also a greatest lower bound. Similarly, we denote by

$$\inf_S f = \inf_{v \in S} f(v)$$

the greatest lower bound of all values of f on S.

If R is a rectangle as above, we define its 2-dimensional volume (that is, its area) to be the obvious thing, namely

$$\mathrm{Vol}(R) = (d - c)(b - a).$$

Thus the volume of each subrectangle S_{ij} is $(y_{j+1} - y_j)(x_{i+1} - x_i)$.

We then form sums which are analogous to the lower and upper sums used to define the integral of functions of one variable. If P denotes the partition as above, and f is a bounded function on R, we define:

$$L(P, f) = \sum_{S} (\inf_S f) \operatorname{Vol}(S),$$

$$U(P, f) = \sum_{S} (\sup_S f) \operatorname{Vol}(S).$$

The symbol $\sum_S$ means that we must take the sum over all subrectangles of the partition. In terms of the indices i, j, we can rewrite say the lower sum as

$$L(P, f) = \sum_{i=1}^{m} \sum_{j=1}^{n} (\inf_{S_{ij}} f)(y_{j+1} - y_j)(x_{i+1} - x_i)$$

and similarly for the upper sum.

Just as in the case of functions of one variable, we can then take refinements of partitions. If P_I' is a partition of I, we say that P_I' is a refinement of P_I if every number of P_I is among the numbers of P_I'. If P_J' is a refinement of P_J, then we call $P_I' \times P_J' = P'$ a refinement of P.

We omit the proof of the following lemma, which is entirely similar to the one variable case.

Lemma. *If P' is a refinement of P, then*

$$L(P,f) \leqq L(P',f) \leqq U(P',f) \leqq U(P,f).$$

In other words, the lower sums increase under refinements of the partition, while the upper sums decrease.

We define f to be *integrable* on R if there exists a unique number which is greater than or equal to every lower sum, and less than or equal to every upper sum. Formulated in another way, we can say that f is integrable on R if and only if the least upper bound of all lower sums is equal to the greatest lower bound of all upper sums. If this number exists, we call it the *integral* of f, and denote it by

$$\int_R f \quad \text{or} \quad \iint_R f(x, y) \, dy \, dx.$$

We can interpret the integral as a volume under certain conditions. Namely, suppose that $f(x, y) \geqq 0$ for all (x, y) in R. The value $f(x, y)$ may be viewed as a height above the point (x, y), and we may consider the integral of f as the volume of the 3-dimensional region lying above the rectangle R and bounded from above by the graph of f (Fig. 3).

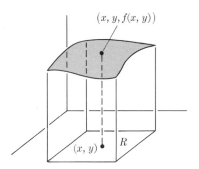

Figure 3

Each term

$$(\inf_S f)\,\text{Vol}(S)$$

is the volume of a rectangular box whose base is the rectangle S in the (x, y)-plane, and whose height is $\inf_S f$. The volume of such a box is precisely $(\inf_S f)\,\text{Vol}(S)$, where, as we said above, $\text{Vol}(S)$ is the 2-dimensional volume of S, that is its area. This box lies below the 3-dimensional region bounded from above by the graph of f. Similarly, the term

$$(\sup_S f)\,\text{Vol}(S)$$

is the volume of a box whose base is S and whose height is $\sup_S f$. This box lies above the above region. This makes our interpretation of the integral as volume clear.

Also, as in one variable, a positive function on a region may be viewed as a density of mass, and thus if $f \geqq 0$ on R, then we also interpret

$$\iint_R f(x, y)\,dy\,dx$$

as the *mass* of R.

Theorem 1. *Assume that f, g are bounded functions on the rectangle R, and are integrable. Then $f + g$ is integrable. If k is a number, then kf is integrable. We have:*

$$\int_R (f + g) = \int_R f + \int_R g \qquad \text{and} \qquad \int_R (kf) = k\int_R f.$$

In other words, integrable functions form a vector space, and the integral is a linear map on this vector space.

Proof. Let P be a partition of R and let S be a subrectangle of the partition. For any point v in S we have

$$\inf_S f \leqq f(v) \qquad \text{and} \qquad \inf_S g \leqq g(v),$$

whence

$$\inf_S f + \inf_S g \leqq f(v) + g(v).$$

Thus $\inf_S f + \inf_S g$ is a lower bound for all values $f(v) + g(v)$. Hence by definition of a greatest lower bound, we obtain the inequality

$$\inf_S f + \inf_S g \leq \inf_{v \in S} (f(v) + g(v)) = \inf_S (f + g).$$

Consequently we get

$$L(P, f) + L(P, g) = \sum_S (\inf_S f) \operatorname{Vol}(S) + \sum_S (\inf_S g) \operatorname{Vol}(S)$$
$$= \sum_S (\inf_S f + \inf_S g) \operatorname{Vol}(S)$$
$$\leq \sum_S \inf_S (f + g) \operatorname{Vol}(S)$$
$$= L(P, f + g).$$

By a similar argument, we find that

$$L(P, f) + L(P, g) \leq L(P, f + g) \leq U(P, f + g) \leq U(P, f) + U(P, g).$$

Since $L(P, f)$ and $U(P, f)$ are arbitrarily close together for suitable partitions, and $L(P, g)$, $U(P, g)$ are arbitrarily close together for suitable partitions, we see by the usual squeezing process of limits that $L(P, f + g)$ and $U(P, f + g)$ are arbitrarily close together for suitable partitions. This proves that $f + g$ is integrable.

As for the constant k, we note that

$$\inf_S (kf) = \inf_{v \in S} (kf(v)) = k \cdot \inf_{v \in S} f(v).$$

Hence k comes out as a factor in each term of the lower sum, and similarly for the upper sum, so that

$$kL(P, f) = L(P, kf) \leq U(P, kf) = kU(P, f).$$

From this our second assertion follows.

Theorem 2. *If f, g are integrable on R, and $f \leq g$, then*

$$\int_R f \leq \int_R g.$$

Proof. We have for each subrectangle S of a partition P:

$$\inf_S f \leq f(v) \leq g(v)$$

for all v in S. Hence $\inf_S f$ is a lower bound for the values of g on S, and hence

$$\inf_S f \leq \inf_S g.$$

Consequently

$$L(P, f) = \sum_S (\inf_S f) \operatorname{Vol}(S) \leq \sum_S (\inf_S g) \operatorname{Vol}(S) = L(P, g) \leq \int_R g.$$

Since $\int_R g$ is an upper bound for $L(P, f)$ it follows that the least upper bound of all lower sums for f is $\leqq \int_R g$, in other words

$$\int_R f \leqq \int_R g,$$

as was to be shown.

We need some criterion for functions to be integrable. The next theorem gives such a criterion, and we shall state it without proof. We need some terminology.

Let s, t be numbers with $s \leqq t$. Let f be a function defined on the closed interval $[s, t]$. If f is differentiable, and if its derivative is continuous, we shall say that f is *smooth*. Let f, g be two functions defined on $[s, t]$. If both f and g are smooth, then the set of points $(f(x), g(x))$ as x ranges over the interval will be called a *smooth curve*. [In preceding chapters we had considered curves arising possibly from open intervals, but for this chapter, we change our meaning and deal only with closed intervals. If the interval consists of a single point, we *define* any function of that point to be differentiable, and we agree to say that its derivative is 0. If $s < t$, then at the end points, the derivative is meant to be the right or left derivative respectively.]

Any curve which the reader draws will consist of a finite number of smooth curves. For instance, a line segment is a smooth curve. We draw a finite number of smooth curves in the next picture.

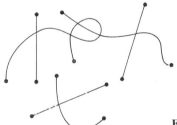

Figure 4

Let A be a region in the plane. We say as usual that A is *bounded* if there exists a number M such that $\|X\| \leqq M$ for all points X in A. Any bounded region is contained in some rectangle.

The set of boundary points of a region A will be called the *boundary* of A. We shall say that the boundary of A is *smooth* if it consists of a finite number of smooth curves.

Let A be a region in the plane, and let f be a function defined on A. As usual, we say that f is *continuous* at a point P of A if

$$\lim_{X \to P} f(X) = f(P).$$

We say that f is continuous on A if it is continuous at every point of A.

Theorem 3. *Let R be a rectangle, and let f be a function defined on R, bounded and continuous except possibly at the points lying on a finite number of smooth curves. Then f is integrable on R.*

This is the promised criterion. Since most functions which arise in practice are of the type described in Theorem 3, we see that most functions are integrable.

Theorem 3 also allows us to integrate on more general sets than rectangles. Let A be a region in the plane, contained in a rectangle R (Fig. 5). Let f be a function defined on A. We denote by f_A the function which has the same values as f at points of A, and such that $f_A(Q) = 0$ if Q is a point not in A. Then f_A is defined on the rectangle R, and we define

$$\int_A f = \int_R f_A$$

provided that f_A is integrable. By Theorem 3, we note that if the boundary of A is smooth, and if f is continuous on A, then f_A is continuous except at all points lying on the boundary of A, and hence f_A is integrable.

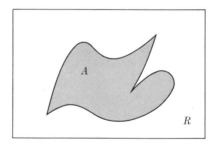

Figure 5

We now have one more property of the integral, corresponding to linearity for regions.

Theorem 4. *Let A be a bounded region in the plane, expressed as a union of two regions A_1 and A_2 having no points in common except possibly boundary points. Assume that the boundaries of A, A_1, A_2 are smooth. If f is a function defined on A and continuous except at a finite number of smooth curves, then*

$$\int_A f = \int_{A_1} f + \int_{A_2} f.$$

The proof of Theorem 4 is left as an exercise with hints (Exercise 3).

In the next section, we shall determine an effective way for computing integrals. Theorem 4 can be used in conjunction with these ways to make such computations easier. Indeed, a region can sometimes be decomposed into other regions A_1, A_2 over which it is easier to find the integral separately. Examples of this will be given later.

EXERCISES

1. Let f be a bounded function on a rectangle R, and assume that f is integrable. Let M be a number such that $|f(v)| \leq M$ for all v in R. Show that

$$\left| \int_R f \right| \leq M \operatorname{Vol}(R).$$

2. Let ψ denote the constant function taking the value 1 for all points of the plane. If A is a region in the plane, denote by ψ_A the function taking the value 1 at points of A, and the value 0 at points not in A. If A is the union of two sets A_1, A_2 which have no point in common, show that

$$\psi_A = \psi_{A_1} + \psi_{A_2}.$$

In this case, show how to deduce Theorem 4 from Theorem 1. [*Hint:* Show that $f_A = \psi_A f$.] Generalize to the union of three disjoint sets.

3. (a) Let A be the union of two sets A_1, A_2. Show that A is the union of the sets (Fig. 6)

$$A_1 - (A_1 \cap A_2), \qquad (A_1 \cap A_2), \qquad A_2 - (A_1 \cap A_2),$$

and that no two of these sets have elements in common. Here we use the following notation: If A, B are sets, then $A - B$ denotes the set of elements of A which are not elements of B.

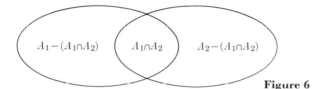

Figure 6

(b) Let A be the union of two sets A_1, A_2. Assuming that all functions occurring in the following formula are integrable, prove the formula:

$$\int_A f = \int_{A_1} f + \int_{A_2} f - \int_{A_1 \cap A_2} f.$$

§2. REPEATED INTEGRALS

To compute the integral we shall investigate double integrals.

Let f be a function defined on our rectangle. For each x in the interval $[a, b]$ we have a function f_x of y given by $f_x(y) = f(x, y)$, and this function f_x is defined on the interval $[c, d]$. Assume that for each x the function f_x is integrable over this interval (in the old sense of the word, for functions of one variable). We may then form the integral

$$\int_c^d f_x(y)\, dy = \int_c^d f(x, y)\, dy.$$

The expression we obtain depends on the particular value of x chosen in the interval $[a, b]$, and is thus a function of x. Assume that this function is integrable over the interval $[a, b]$. We can then take the integral

$$\int_a^b \left[\int_c^d f(x, y)\, dy \right] dx, \qquad \text{also written} \qquad \int_a^b \int_c^d f(x, y)\, dy\, dx,$$

which is called the *repeated integral* of f.

Example 1. Let $f(x, y) = x^2 y$. Find the repeated integral of f over the rectangle determined by the intervals $[1, 2]$ on the x-axis and $[-3, 4]$ on the y-axis.

We must find the repeated integral

$$\int_1^2 \int_{-3}^4 f(x, y)\, dy\, dx.$$

To do this, we first compute the integral with respect to y, namely

$$\int_{-3}^4 x^2 y\, dy.$$

For a fixed value of x, we can take x^2 out of the integral, and hence this inner integral is equal to

$$x^2 \int_{-3}^4 y\, dy = x^2 \frac{y^2}{2} \Big|_{-3}^4 = \frac{7x^2}{2}.$$

We then integrate with respect to x, namely

$$\int_1^2 \frac{7x^2}{2}\, dx = \frac{49}{6}.$$

Thus the integral of f over the rectangle is equal to $\frac{49}{6}$.

The repeated integral is useful in computing a double integral because of the following theorem, which will be proved after discussing some examples.

Theorem 5. *Let R be a rectangle $[a, b] \times [c, d]$, and let f be integrable on R. Assume that for each x in $[a, b]$ the function f_x given by*

$$f_x(y) = f(x, y)$$

is integrable on $[c, d]$. Then the function

$$x \mapsto \int_c^d f(x, y)\, dy$$

is integrable on $[a, b]$, and

$$\int_R f = \int_a^b \left[\int_c^d f(x, y)\, dy \right] dx.$$

Geometrically speaking, the inner integral for a fixed value of x gives the area of a cross section as indicated in the following figure. Then integrating such areas yields the volume of the 3-dimensional figure bounded below by the rectangle R, and above by the graph of f.

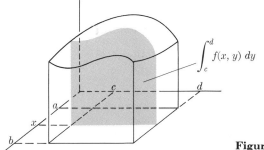

$$\int_c^d f(x, y)\, dy$$

Figure 7

The following situation will arise frequently in practice.

Let g_1, g_2 be two smooth functions on a closed interval $[a, b]$ $(a \leqq b)$ such that $g_1(x) \leqq g_2(x)$ for all x in that interval. Let c, d be numbers such that

$$c < g_1(x) \leqq g_2(x) < d$$

for all x in the interval $[a, b]$. Then g_1, g_2 determine a region A lying between $x - a$, $x - b$, and the two curves $y - g_1(x)$ and $y = g_2(x)$. (Cf. Fig. 8.)

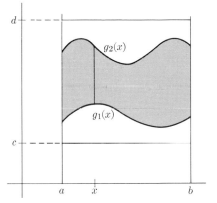

Figure 8

Let f be a function which is continuous on the region A, and define f on the rectangle $[a, b] \times [c, d]$ to be equal to 0 at any point of the rectangle not lying in the region A. For any value x in the interval $[a, b]$ the integral

$$\int_c^d f(x, y)\, dy$$

can be written as a sum:

$$\int_{c}^{g_1(x)} f(x, y)\, dy + \int_{g_1(x)}^{g_2(x)} f(x, y)\, dy + \int_{g_2(x)}^{d} f(x, y)\, dy.$$

Since $f(x, y) = 0$ whenever $c \leqq y < g_1(x)$ and $g_2(x) < y \leqq d$, it follows that the two extreme integrals are equal to 0. Thus the repeated integral of f over the rectangle is in fact equal to the repeated integral

$$\int_{a}^{b}\left[\int_{g_1(x)}^{g_2(x)} f(x, y)\, dy\right] dx.$$

Regions of the type described by two functions g_1, g_2 as above are the most common type of regions with which we deal.

From Theorem 5 and the preceding discussion, we obtain:

Corollary. *Let g_1, g_2 be two smooth functions defined on a closed interval $[a, b]$ ($a \leqq b$) such that $g_1(x) \leqq g_2(x)$ for all x in that interval. Let f be a continuous function on the region A lying between $x = a$, $x = b$, and the two curves $y = g_1(x)$ and $y = g_2(x)$. Then*

$$\int_{A} f = \int_{a}^{b}\left[\int_{g_1(x)}^{g_2(x)} f(x, y)\, dy\right] dx;$$

in other words, the double integral is equal to the repeated integral.

We shall give the proof of Theorem 5 below. Before doing that, we first give examples showing how to apply Theorem 5, or rather its corollary.

Example 2. Let $f(x, y) = x^2 + y^2$. Find the integral of f over the region A bounded by the straight line $y = x$ and the parabola $y = x^2$ (Fig. 9).

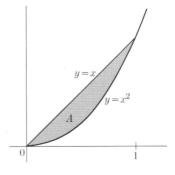

Figure 9

In this case, we have $g_1(x) = x^2$ and $g_2(x) = x$. Thus our integral is equal to

$$\int_0^1 \left[\int_{x^2}^x (x^2 + y^2)\, dy \right] dx.$$

Now the inner integral is given by

$$\int_{x^2}^x (x^2 + y^2)\, dy = x^2 y + \frac{y^3}{3}\Big|_{x^2}^x$$

$$= x^3 + \frac{x^3}{3} - x^4 - \frac{x^6}{3}.$$

Hence the repeated integral is equal to

$$\int_A f = \int_0^1 \left(x^3 + \frac{x^3}{3} - x^4 - \frac{x^6}{3} \right) dx = \frac{x^4}{4} + \frac{x^4}{12} - \frac{x^5}{5} - \frac{x^7}{21}\Big|_0^1$$

$$= \frac{1}{4} + \frac{1}{12} - \frac{1}{5} - \frac{1}{21}.$$

(We don't need to simplify the number on the right.)

Given a region A, it is frequently possible to break it up into smaller regions having only boundary points in common, and such that each smaller region is of the type we have just described. In that case, to compute the integral of a function over S, we can apply Property 3.

Example 3. Let $f(x, y) = 2xy$. Find the integral of f over the triangle bounded by the lines $y = 0$, $y = x$, and the line $x + y = 2$.

The region is as shown in Fig. 10.

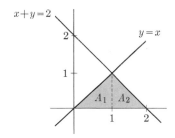

Figure 10

We break up our region into the portion from 0 to 1 and the portion from 1 to 2. These correspond to the small triangles A_1, A_2, as indicated in the picture. Then

$$\int_{A_1} f = \int_0^1 \left[\int_0^x 2xy\, dy \right] dx \qquad \text{and} \qquad \int_{A_2} f = \int_1^2 \left[\int_0^{2-x} 2xy\, dy \right] dx.$$

There is no difficulty in evaluating these integrals, and we leave them to you.

Finally, we define the *area* of a region A to be the integral of the function 1 over A, i.e.

$$\text{Vol}(A) = \iint_A 1 \, dy \, dx.$$

Example 4. Find the area of the region bounded by the straight line $y = x$ and the curve $y = x^2$.

The region has been sketched in Example 2. By definition,

$$\text{Vol}(A) = \int_0^1 \int_{x^2}^x dy \, dx = \int_0^1 (x - x^2) \, dx$$

$$= \frac{x^2}{2} - \frac{x^3}{3}\Big|_0^1 = \frac{1}{2} - \frac{1}{3} = \frac{1}{6}.$$

We also observe that the same arguments as before apply if we interchange the role of x and y. Thus for the rectangle R we also have

$$\int_R f(x, y) \, dy \, dx = \int_R f(x, y) \, dx \, dy = \int_c^d \left[\int_a^b f(x, y) \, dx \right] dy.$$

The same goes for a region described by functions

$$x = g_1(y)$$

and

$$x = g_2(y)$$

with $g_1 \leqq g_2$ between $y = c$ and $y = d$.

If A is a region in the plane bounded by a finite number of smooth curves, and f is a function on A such that $f(x) \geqq 0$ for $x \in A$, then we can interpret f as a density function, and we also call the integral $\int_A f$ the *mass* of A.

Example 5. Find the integral of the function $f(x, y) = x^2 y^2$ over the region bounded by the lines $y = 1$, $y = 2$ and $x = y$ (Fig. 11).

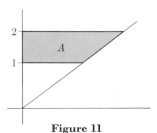

Figure 11

We have to compute the integral as prescribed, namely:

$$\int_1^2 \left[\int_0^y x^2 y^2 \, dx \right] dy = \int_1^2 y^2 \frac{x^3}{3} \Big|_0^y \, dy = \int_1^2 \frac{y^5}{3} \, dy = \frac{7}{2} \cdot$$

We can also say that the preceding integral, namely 7/2, is the mass of A corresponding to the density given by the function f. Of course the units of mass are those determined by the units of density.

We now give the proof of Theorem 5. We let R be the product of the intervals I, J so $R = I \times J$. We consider a partition $P = P_I \times P_J$ of R, where P_I, P_J are partitions of the intervals I, J respectively. Each sub-rectangle of P can then be written as

$$S = S_I \times S_J,$$

where S_I is a subinterval of I and S_J a subinterval of J. Then

$$\text{Vol}(S) = l(S_J)l(S_I),$$

where l denotes the length of an interval.

We denote the function

$$x \mapsto \int_c^d f(x, y) \, dy$$

by $\int_J f$, so that the value of this function at x is

$$\int_J f_x = \int_c^d f(x, y) \, dy.$$

We have:

$$L(P_I \times P_J, f) = \sum_S (\inf_S f) \, \text{Vol}(S)$$

$$= \sum_{S_I} \sum_{S_J} (\inf_{S_I \times S_J} f) \, \text{Vol}(S_I \times S_J)$$

(*)
$$= \sum_{S_I} \left[\sum_{S_J} \left(\inf_{(x,y) \in S_I \times S_J} f(x, y) \right) l(S_J) \right] l(S_I).$$

For any x in I we have

$$\sum_{S_J} \left(\inf_{(x,y) \in S_I \times S_J} f(x, y) \right) l(S_J) \leq \sum_{S_J} \inf_{y \in S_J} f(x, y) l(S_J)$$

$$= L(P_J, f_x)$$

$$\leq \int_J f_x,$$

because each term in the expression on the left involves an inf over all (x, y) rather than only over y, and thus contributes less to the sum. Thus the expression on the left is a lower bound for the expression on the right. From this we conclude that the expression on the left is $\leq \inf_{x \in S_I} \int_J f_x$, and hence by (*)

$$L(P, f) = L(P_I \times P_J, f) \leq \sum_{S_I} \left(\inf_{x \in S_I} \int_J f_x \right) l(S_I)$$

$$= L\left(P_I, \int_J f\right)$$

$$\leq U\left(P_I, \int_J f\right).$$

By similar arguments applied to upper sums instead of lower sums, we conclude that

$$L(P, f) \leq L\left(P_I, \int_J f\right) \leq U\left(P_I, \int_J f\right) \leq U(P_I \times P_J, f) = U(P, f).$$

Since f is assumed to be integrable, it follows that for suitable partitions, $L(P,f)$ and $U(P,f)$ are arbitrarily close together. Thus the lower sums for the function $\int_J f$ and the upper sums for this function are arbitrarily close for suitable partitions P. This implies that the function $\int_J f$ is integrable, and the fact that these lower sums and upper sums are squeezed between $L(P,f)$ and $U(P,f)$ shows that the double integral is equal to the repeated integral, as desired.

EXERCISES

1. Find the value of the following repeated integrals.

   (a) $\int_0^2 \int_1^3 (x + y)\, dx\, dy$ (b) $\int_0^2 \int_1^{x^2} y\, dy\, dx$ (c) $\int_0^1 \int_{y^2}^y \sqrt{x}\, dx\, dy$

   (d) $\int_0^\pi \int_0^x x \sin y\, dy\, dx$ (e) $\int_1^2 \int_y^{y^2} dx\, dy$ (f) $\int_0^\pi \int_0^{\sin x} y\, dy\, dx$

2. Sketch the regions described by the following inequalities.

   (a) $|x| \leq 1,\ -1 \leq y \leq 2$ (b) $|x| \leq 3,\ |y| \leq 4$

   (c) $x + y \leq 1,\ x \geq 0,\ y \geq 0$ (d) $0 \leq y \leq |x|,\ 0 \leq x \leq 5$

   (e) $0 \leq x \leq y,\ 0 \leq y \leq 5$ (f) $|x| + |y| \leq 1$

3. Find the integral of the following functions.

   (a) $x \cos(x + y)$ over the triangle whose vertices are $(0, 0)$, $(\pi, 0)$, and (π, π).

   (b) e^{x+y} over the region defined by $|x| + |y| \leq 1$.

   (c) $x^2 - y^2$ over the region bounded by the curve $y = \sin x$ between 0 and π.

   (d) $x^2 + y$ over the triangle whose vertices are $(-\frac{1}{2}, \frac{1}{2})$, $(1, 2)$, $(1, -1)$.

4. Find the numerical answer in Example 2.

5. Let a be a number > 0. Show that the area of the region consisting of all points (x, y) such that $|x| + |y| \leq a$, is $(2a)^2/2!$.

6. Find the following integrals and sketch the region of integration in each case.

(a) $\displaystyle\int_1^2 \int_{x^2}^{x^3} x \, dy \, dx$

(b) $\displaystyle\int_1^{-1} \int_x^{2x} e^{x+y} \, dy \, dx$

(c) $\displaystyle\int_0^2 \int_1^3 |x - 2| \sin y \, dx \, dy$

(d) $\displaystyle\int_0^{\pi/2} \int_{-y}^y \sin x \, dx \, dy$

(e) $\displaystyle\int_{-1}^1 \int_0^{|x|} dy \, dx$

(f) $\displaystyle\int_0^{\pi/2} \int_0^{\cos y} x \sin y \, dx \, dy$

7. Sketch the region defined by $x \geq 0$, $x^2 + y^2 \leq 2$, and $x^2 + y^2 \geq 1$. Determine the integral of $f(x, y) = x^2$ over this region.

8. Integrate the function f over the indicated region.

(a) $f(x, y) = 1/(x + y)$ over the region bounded by the lines $y = x$, $x = 1$, $x = 2$, $y = 0$.

(b) $f(x, y) = x^2 - y^2$ over the region defined by the inequalities

$$0 \leq x \leq 1 \quad \text{and} \quad x^2 - y^2 \geq 0.$$

(c) $f(x, y) = x \sin xy$ over the rectangle $0 \leq x \leq \pi$ and $0 \leq y \leq 1$.

(d) $f(x, y) = x^2 - y^2$ over the triangle whose vertices are $(-1, 1)$, $(0, 0)$, $(1, 1)$.

(e) $f(x, y) = 1/(x + y + 1)$ over the square $0 \leq x \leq 1, 0 \leq y \leq 1$.

9. In the proof of Theorem 5, write out in detail the proof of the inequality

$$U\left(P_I, \int_J f\right) \leq U(P, f).$$

10. We recall that a translation $T: \mathbf{R}^2 \to \mathbf{R}^2$ is a map of the type $T(X) = X + w$ for some vector w. It is a geometric property of area that the area of a region does not change under translation. We shall now sketch a proof for the area given by an integral.

(a) Let g be a function of one variable, and t a number. Show that

$$\int_{c+s}^{d+s} g(y - s) \, dy = \int_c^d g(y) \, dy.$$

(b) If s, t are numbers, show that

$$\int_{a+t}^{b+t} \int_{c+s}^{d+s} f(x - t, y - s) \, dy \, dx = \int_a^b \int_c^d f(x, y) \, dy \, dx.$$

(Assume all functions occurring here to be integrable.)

(c) Let ψ_A be the characteristic function of a region A, that is the function such that $\psi_A(v) = 1$ if v is in A and $\psi_A(v) = 0$ if v is not in A. Let w be a vector in $\mathbf{R}^2$. Show that the characteristic function of the translation $A + w$ is the function ψ such that $\psi(v) = \psi_A(v - w)$.

(d) Conclude that

$$\int_A \psi_A = \int_{A+w} \psi_{A+w}.$$

§3. POLAR COORDINATES

It is frequently more convenient to describe a region by means of polar coordinates than with the "rectangular" coordinates of the preceding section. Such a region can then be described as the image of a simpler region as follows.

Let a, b be numbers with $0 \leq a \leq b \leq 2\pi$. Let c, d be two numbers with $0 \leq c \leq d$. Then the inequalities

$$a \leq \theta \leq b \qquad \text{and} \qquad c \leq r \leq d$$

describe a rectangle in the (r, θ)-plane. Under the map

$$G: \mathbf{R}^2 \to \mathbf{R}^2$$

given by $G(r, \theta) = (r \cos \theta, r \sin \theta)$, i.e.

$$x = r \cos \theta, \qquad y = r \sin \theta,$$

this rectangle goes into a circular region as shown in the next picture.

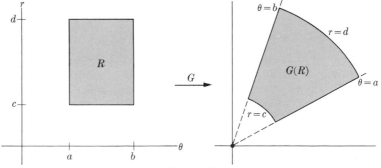

Figure 12

The preceding map G is called the *polar coordinate* map.
Consider partitions

$$a = \theta_1 \leq \theta_2 \leq \cdots \leq \theta_n = b, \qquad c = r_1 \leq r_2 \leq \cdots \leq r_m = d$$

of the two intervals $[a, b]$ and $[c, d]$. Each pair of intervals $[\theta_i, \theta_{i+1}]$ and $[r_j, r_{j+1}]$ determines a small region as shown in the following figure.

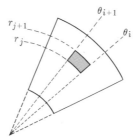

Figure 13

The area of such a region is equal to the difference between the area of the sector having angle $\theta_{i+1} - \theta_i$ and radius r_{j+1}, and the area of the sector having the same angle but radius r_j. The area of a sector having angle θ and radius r is equal to

$$\frac{\theta}{2\pi} \pi r^2 = \frac{\theta r^2}{2}.$$

Consequently the difference mentioned above is equal to

$$\frac{(\theta_{i+1} - \theta_i)r_{j+1}^2}{2} - \frac{(\theta_{i+1} - \theta_i)r_j^2}{2} = (\theta_{i+1} - \theta_i)\frac{(r_{j+1} + r_j)}{2}(r_{j+1} - r_j).$$

We note that

$$r_j \leqq \frac{r_{j+1} + r_j}{2} \leqq r_{j+1}.$$

If f is a function on the (x, y)-plane, it determines a function of (r, θ) by the formula

$$f^*(r, \theta) = f(r \cos \theta, r \sin \theta).$$

Let

$$\varphi(r, \theta) = f^*(r, \theta)r.$$

Then

$$\sum_{j=1}^{m} \sum_{i=1}^{n} f^*(r_j, \theta_i)r_j(r_{j+1} - r_j)(\theta_{i+1} - \theta_i)$$

is a Riemann sum for the function φ on the product $[a, b] \times [c, d]$. Consequently the following theorem is now very plausible.

Theorem 6. *Let $R = [a, b] \times [c, d]$ be as above, and let G be the polar coordinate map. Let f be bounded and continuous on $G(R)$, except possibly at a finite number of smooth curves. Let f^* be the corresponding function of (r, θ). Then*

$$\iint_R f^*(r, \theta)r \, dr \, d\theta = \iint_{G(R)} f(x, y) \, dy \, dx.$$

In the next section, we shall state another theorem which gives another justification for this change of variables formula. We do not prove any of these statements in this course, since the rigorous proofs depend on more developed techniques.

As with rectangular coordinates, we can deal with more general regions. Let g_1, g_2 be two smooth functions defined on the interval $[a, b]$ and assume

$$0 \leqq g_1(\theta) \leqq g_2(\theta)$$

for all θ in that interval. Let A be the region consisting of all points (θ, r) such that $a \leqq \theta \leqq b$ and $g_1(\theta) \leqq r \leqq g_2(\theta)$. We can select two numbers $c, d \geqq 0$ such that

$$c \leqq g_1(\theta) \leqq g_2(\theta) \leqq d$$

for all θ in the interval $[c, d]$. Let f be continuous on $G(A)$ and extend f to the circular sector of radius d between $\theta = a$ and $\theta = b$ by giving it the value 0 outside $G(A)$. *Then the integral of Theorem 6 taken over this sector is equal to the repeated integral*

$$\int_a^b \int_{g_1(\theta)}^{g_2(\theta)} f^*(\theta, r) r \, dr \, d\theta.$$

The following picture shows a typical region $G(A)$ under consideration. The important thing to remember about the formula of Theorem 6 is the appearance of an extra r inside the integral.

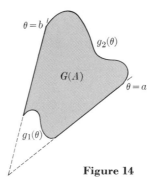

Figure 14

We also remark that a region could be described by taking θ as a function of r, and letting r vary between two constant values. In view of Theorem 5, we can evaluate the double integral of Theorem 6 by repeated integration first with respect to θ and then with respect to r.

In dealing with polar coordinates, it is useful to remember the equation of a circle. Let $a > 0$. Then

$$r = a \cos \theta, \qquad -\pi/2 \leqq \theta \leqq \pi/2,$$

is the equation of a circle of radius $a/2$ and center $(a/2, 0)$. Similarly,

$$r = a \sin \theta, \qquad 0 \leqq \theta \leqq \pi,$$

is the equation of a circle of radius $a/2$ and center $(0, a/2)$. You can easily show this, as an exercise, using the relations

$$r = \sqrt{x^2 + y^2}, \qquad x = r \cos \theta, \qquad y = r \sin \theta.$$

(*Note*. The coordinates of the center above are given in rectangular coordinates.)

   Example. Find the integral of the function $f(x, y) = x^2$ over the region enclosed by the curve given in polar coordinates by the equation

$$r = (1 - \cos \theta).$$

   The function of the polar coordinates (r, θ) corresponding to f is given by

$$f^* (r, \theta) = r^2 \cos^2 \theta.$$

The region in the polar coordinate space is described by the inequalities

$$0 \leq r \leq 1 - \cos \theta \qquad \text{and} \qquad \theta \leq \theta \leq 2\pi.$$

This region in the (x, y)-plane looks like this:

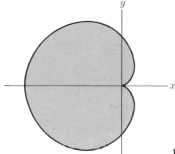

Figure 15

The desired integral is therefore the integral

$$\int_0^{2\pi} \int_0^{1-\cos\theta} r^3 \cos^2 \theta \, dr \, d\theta.$$

We integrate first with respect to r, which is easy, and see that our integral is equal to

$$\int_0^{2\pi} \tfrac{1}{4}(1 - \cos \theta)^4 \cos^2 \theta \, d\theta.$$

The evaluation of this integral is done by techniques of the first course in calculus. We expand out the expression of the fourth power, and get a sum of terms involving $\cos^k \theta$ for $k = 0, \ldots, 6$. The reader should know how to integrate powers of the cosine, using repeatedly the formula

$$\cos^2 \theta = \frac{1 + \cos 2\theta}{2},$$

or using the recursion formula in terms of lower powers. No matter what method the reader uses, he will find the final answer to be

$$\frac{49\pi}{32}.$$

EXERCISES

1. By changing to polar coordinates, find the integral of $e^{x^2+y^2}$ over the region consisting of the points (x, y) such that $x^2 + y^2 \leq 1$.

2. Find the volume of the region lying over the disc $x^2 + (y - 1)^2 \leq 1$ and bounded from above by the function $z = x^2 + y^2$.

3. Find the integral of $e^{-(x^2+y^2)}$ over the circular disc bounded by

$$x^2 + y^2 = a^2, \qquad a > 0.$$

4. What is

$$\int_{-\infty}^{\infty} \int_{-\infty}^{\infty} e^{-(x^2+y^2)} \, dx \, dy?$$

5. Find the mass of a square plate of side a if the density is proportional to the square of the distance from a vertex.

6. Find the mass of a circular disk of radius a if the density is proportional to the square of the distance from a point on the circumference.

7. Find the mass of a plate bounded by one arch of the curve $y = \sin x$, and the x-axis, if the density is proportional to the distance from the x-axis.

Evaluate the following integrals. Take $a > 0$.

8. $\displaystyle\int_{-a}^{a} \int_{-\sqrt{a^2-x^2}}^{\sqrt{a^2-x^2}} dy \, dx$ 　　　　9. $\displaystyle\int_{0}^{a} \int_{0}^{\sqrt{a^2-y^2}} (x^2 + y^2) \, dx \, dy$

10. $\displaystyle\int_{0}^{a/\sqrt{2}} \int_{y}^{\sqrt{a^2-y^2}} x \, dx \, dy$

11. Find the area inside the curve $r = a(1 + \cos \theta)$ and outside the circle $r = a$.

12. The base of a solid is the area of Exercise 11 and the top is given by the function $f(x, y) = x$. Find the volume.

13. Find the area enclosed by the curve $r^2 = 2a^2 \cos 2\theta$.

14. The base of a solid is the area of Exercise 13, and the top is bounded by the function (in terms of polar coordinates) $f(r, \theta) = \sqrt{2a^2 - r^2}$. Find the volume.

15. Find the integral of the function

$$f(x, y) = \frac{1}{(x^2 + y^2 + 1)^{3/2}}$$

over the disc of radius a centered at the origin. Letting a tend to infinity, show that

$$\int_{-\infty}^{-\infty} \int_{-\infty}^{-\infty} f(x, y)\, dy\, dx = 2\pi.$$

16. Answer the same question for the function

$$f(x, y) = \frac{1}{(x^2 + y^2 + 2)^2}.$$

17. Find the integral of the function

$$f(x, y) = \frac{1}{(x^2 + y^2)^3}$$

over the region between the two circles of radius 2 and radius 3, centered at the origin.

18. (a) Find the integral of the function $f(x, y) = x$ over the region given in polar coordinates by $x = 1 - \cos\theta$.
    (b) Let a be a number > 0. Find the ingegral of the function $f(x, y) = x^2$ over the region given in polar coordinates by $v = a(1 - \cos\theta)$.

§4. DETERMINANTS AS AREA

It is remarkable that the determinant has an interpretation as a volume. We discuss the 2-dimensional case, and thus speak of area, although we continue to write Vol for the area of a 2-dimensional figure.

Consider the parallelogram spanned by two vectors v, w.

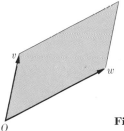

Figure 16

We view v, w as column vectors, and can thus form their determinant $D(v, w)$. This determinant may be positive or negative since

$$D(v, w) = -D(w, v).$$

Thus the determinant itself cannot be the area of this parallelogram,

558   MULTIPLE INTEGRALS   [XIV, §4]

since area is always ≥ 0. However, we shall prove:

Theorem 7. *The area of the parallelogram spanned by v, w is equal to the absolute value of the determinant, namely $|D(v, w)|$.*

To prove Theorem 7, we introduced the notion of oriented area. Let $P(v, w)$ be the parallelogram spanned by v and w. We denote by $\mathrm{Vol}_0(v, w)$ the area of $P(v, w)$ if the determinant $D(v, w)$ is ≥ 0, and minus the area of $P(v, w)$ if the determinant $D(v, w)$ is < 0. Thus at least $\mathrm{Vol}_0(v, w)$ has the same sign as the determinant, and we call $\mathrm{Vol}_0(v, w)$ the *oriented area*. We denote by $\mathrm{Vol}(v, w)$ the area of the parallelogram spanned by v, w. Hence $\mathrm{Vol}_0(v, w) = \pm\mathrm{Vol}(v, w)$.

To prove Theorem 7, it will suffice to prove:

The oriented area is equal to the determinant. In other words,

$$\mathrm{Vol}_0(v, w) = D(v, w).$$

Now to prove this, it will suffice to prove that Vol_0 satisfies the three properties characteristic of a determinant, namely:

1. Vol_0 is linear in each variable v and w.
2. $\mathrm{Vol}_0(v, v) = 0$ for all v.
3. $\mathrm{Vol}_0(e_1, e_2) = 1$ if e_1, e_2 are the standard unit vectors.

We know that these three properties characterize determinants, and this was proved in the section of uniqueness in Chapter XII. For the convenience of the reader, we repeat the argument here very briefly. We assume that we have a function g satisfying these three properties (with g replacing Vol_0). Then for any vectors

$$v = ae_1 + ce_2 \qquad \text{and} \qquad w = be_1 + de_2$$

we have

$$g(ae_1 + ce_2, be_1 + de_2) = abg(e_1, e_1) + adg(e_1, e_2)$$
$$+ cbg(e_2, e_1) + cdg(e_2, e_2).$$

The first and fourth term are equal to 0. By Exercise 1,

$$g(e_2, e_1) = -g(e_1, e_2)$$

and hence

$$g(v, w) = (ad - bc)g(e_1, e_2) = ad - bc.$$

This proves what we wanted.

Consider now Vol_0. The last two properties are obvious. Indeed, the parallelogram spanned by v, w is simply a line segment, and its 2-dimensional area is therefore equal to 0. Thus property 2 is satisfied. As for the third property, the parallelogram spanned by the unit vectors e_1, e_2 is simply the unit square, whose area is 1.   Hence in this case we have $\text{Vol}_0(e_1, e_2) = 1$.

The harder property is the first. If the reader has not already done so, he should now read the geometric applications, §5 of Chapter X, before reading the rest of this proof, which we shall base on geometric considerations concerning area.

We shall need a lemma.

Lemma 1. *If v, w are linearly dependent, then $\text{Vol}_0(v, w) = 0$.*

Proof. Suppose that we can write

$$av + bw = 0$$

with a or $b \neq 0$. Say $a \neq 0$. Then

$$v = -\frac{b}{a} w = cw$$

Figure 17

so that v, w lie on the same straight line, and the parallelogram spanned by v, w is a line segment (Fig. 17). Hence $\text{Vol}_0(v, w) = 0$, thus proving the lemma.

We also know that when v, w are linearly dependent, then $D(v, w) = 0$, so in this trivial case, our theorem is proved. In the subsequent lemmas, we assume that v, w are linearly independent.

Lemma 2. *Assume that v, w are linearly independent, and let n be a positive integer. Then*

$$\text{Vol}(nv, w) = n \, \text{Vol}(v, w).$$

Proof. The parallelogram spanned by nv and w consists of n parallelograms as shown in the following picture.

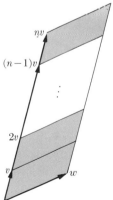

Figure 18

These n parallelograms are simply the translations of $P(v, w)$ by $v, 2v, \ldots, (n - 1)v$, and each translation of $P(v, w)$ has the same area as $P(v, w)$. These translations have only line segments in common, and hence

$$\text{Vol}(nv, w) = n\,\text{Vol}(v, w)$$

as desired.

Corollary. *Assume that v, w are linearly independent and let n be a positive integer. Then*

$$\text{Vol}\left(\frac{1}{n}v, w\right) = \frac{1}{n}\text{Vol}(v, w).$$

If m, n are positive integers, then

$$\text{Vol}\left(\frac{m}{n}v, w\right) = \frac{m}{n}\text{Vol}(v, w).$$

Proof. Let $v_1 = (1/n)v$. By the lemma, we know that

$$\text{Vol}(nv_1, w) = n\,\text{Vol}(v_1, w).$$

This is merely a reformulation of our first assertion, since $nv_1 = v$. As for the second assertion, we write $m/n = m \cdot 1/n$ and apply the proved statements successively:

$$\text{Vol}\left(m \cdot \frac{1}{n}v, w\right) = m\,\text{Vol}\left(\frac{1}{n}v, w\right)$$

$$= m \cdot \frac{1}{n}\text{Vol}(v, w)$$

$$= \frac{m}{n}\text{Vol}(v, w).$$

Lemma 3. $\text{Vol}(-v, w) = \text{Vol}(v, w).$

Proof. The parallelogram spanned by $-v$ and w is a translation by $-v$ of the parallelogram $P(v, w)$. Hence $P(v, w)$ and $P(-v, w)$ have the same area. (Cf. Fig. 19.)

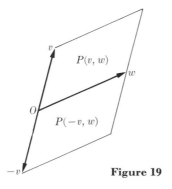

Figure 19

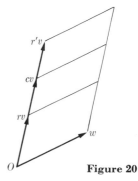

Figure 20

Lemma 4. *If c is any real number > 0, then*

$$\mathrm{Vol}(cv, w) = c\,\mathrm{Vol}(v, w).$$

Proof. Let r, r' be rational numbers such that $0 < r < c < r'$ (Fig. 20). Then

$$P(rv, w) \subset P(cv, w) \subset P(r'v, w).$$

Hence by Lemma 2,

$$
\begin{aligned}
r\,\mathrm{Vol}(v, w) &= \mathrm{Vol}(rv, w) \\
&\leq \mathrm{Vol}(cv, w) \\
&\leq \mathrm{Vol}(r'v, w) \\
&= r'\,\mathrm{Vol}(v, w).
\end{aligned}
$$

Letting r and r' approach c as a limit, we find that

$$\mathrm{Vol}(cv, w) = c\,\mathrm{Vol}(v, w),$$

as was to be shown.

From Lemmas 3 and 4 we can now prove that

$$\boxed{\mathrm{Vol}_0(cv, w) = c\,\mathrm{Vol}_0(v, w)}$$

for any real number c, and any vectors v, w. Indeed, if v, w are linearly dependent, then both sides are equal to 0. If v, w are linearly independent, we use the definition of Vol_0 and Lemmas 3, 4. Say $D(v, w) > 0$ and c is negative, $c = -d$. Then $D(cv, w) \leq 0$ and consequently

$$
\begin{aligned}
\mathrm{Vol}_0(cv, w) = -\mathrm{Vol}(cv, w) &= -\mathrm{Vol}(-dv, w) \\
&= \mathrm{Vol}(dv, w) \\
&= -d\,\mathrm{Vol}(v, w) \\
&= c\,\mathrm{Vol}(v, w) = c\,\mathrm{Vol}_0(v, w).
\end{aligned}
$$

A similar argument works when $D(v, w) \leq 0$. We have therefore proved one of the conditions of linearity of the function Vol_0. The analogous property of course works on the other side, namely

$$\boxed{\mathrm{Vol}_0(v, cw) = c\,\mathrm{Vol}_0(v, w).}$$

For the other condition, we again have a lemma.

Lemma 5. *Assume that v, w are linearly independent. Then*

$$\mathrm{Vol}(v + w, w) = \mathrm{Vol}(v, w).$$

Proof. We have to prove that the parallelogram spanned by v, w has the same area as the parallelogram spanned by $v + w$, w.

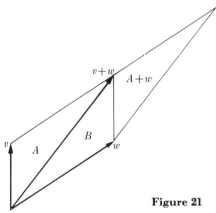

Figure 21

The parallelogram spanned by v, w consists of two triangles A and B as shown in the picture. The parallelogram spanned by $v + w$ and w consists of the triangles B and the translation of A by w. Since A and $A + w$ have the same area, we get:

$$\text{Vol}(v, w) = \text{Vol}(A) + \text{Vol}(B) = \text{Vol}(A + w) + \text{Vol}(B) = \text{Vol}(v + w, w),$$

as was to be shown.

We are now in a position to deal with the second property of linearity. Let w be a fixed non-zero vector in the plane, and let v be a vector such that $\{v, w\}$ is a basis of the plane. We shall prove that for any numbers c, d we have

$$(1) \qquad \text{Vol}_0(cv + dw, w) = c \, \text{Vol}_0(v, w).$$

Indeed, if $d = 0$, this is nothing but what we have shown previously. If $d \neq 0$, then again by what has been shown previously,

$$d \, \text{Vol}_0(cv + dw, w) = \text{Vol}_0(cv + dw, dw) = c \, \text{Vol}_0(v, dw) = cd \, \text{Vol}_0(v, w).$$

Canceling d yields relation (1).

From this last formula, the linearity now follows. Indeed, if

$$v_1 = c_1 v + d_1 w \qquad \text{and} \qquad v_2 = c_2 v + d_2 w,$$

then

$$
\begin{aligned}
\text{Vol}_0(v_1 + v_2, w) &= \text{Vol}_0((c_1 + c_2)v + (d_1 + d_2)w, w) \\
&= (c_1 + c_2) \, \text{Vol}_0(v, w) \\
&= c_1 \, \text{Vol}_0(v, w) + c_2 \, \text{Vol}_0(v, w) \\
&= \text{Vol}_0(v_1, w) + \text{Vol}_0(v_2, w).
\end{aligned}
$$

This concludes the proof of the fact that

$$\text{Vol}_0(v, w) = D(v, w),$$

and hence of Theorem 7.

Remark 1. The proof given above is slightly long, but each step is quite simple. Furthermore, when one wishes to generalize the proof to higher dimensional space (even 3-space), one can give an entirely similar proof. The reason for this is that the conditions characterizing a determinant involve only two coordinates at a time and thus always take place in some two dimensional plane. Keeping all but two coordinates fixed, the above proof then can be extended at once. Thus for instance in 3-space, let us denote by $P(u, v, w)$ the box spanned by vectors u, v, w (Fig. 22), namely all combinations

$$t_1 u + t_2 v + t_3 w \qquad \text{with} \qquad 0 \leqq t_i \leqq 1.$$

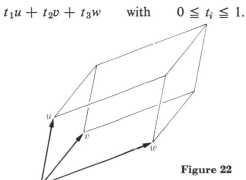

Figure 22

Let $\text{Vol}(u, v, w)$ be the volume of this box. Then

$$\text{Vol}(u, v, w) = |D(u, v, w)|$$

is again the absolute value of the determinant.

Remark 2. We have used geometric properties of area to carry out the above proof. One can lay foundations for all this purely analytically. If the reader is interested, cf. my book *Analysis I.*

We interpret Theorem 7 in terms of linear maps. Given vectors v, w in the plane, we know that there exists a unique linear map

$$L: \mathbf{R}^2 \to \mathbf{R}^2$$

such that $L(e_1) = v$ and $L(e_2) = w$. In fact, if

$$v = ae_1 + ce_2, \qquad w = be_1 + de_2,$$

then the matrix associated with the linear map is

$$\begin{pmatrix} a & b \\ c & d \end{pmatrix}.$$

Furthermore, if we denote by C the unit cube spanned by e_1, e_2, and by P the parallelogram spanned by v, w, then P is the image under L of C, that is $L(C) = P$. Indeed, as we have seen, for $0 \leq t_i \leq 1$ we have

$$L(t_1 e_1 + t_2 e_2) = t_1 L(e_1) + t_2 L(e_2) = t_1 v + t_2 w.$$

If we define the determinant of a linear map to be the determinant of its associated matrix, we conclude that

(*)   (Area of P) $= |\text{Det}(L)|$.

To take a numerical example, the area of the parallelogram spanned by the vectors $(2, 1)$ and $(3, -1)$ (Fig. 23) is equal to the absolute value of

$$\begin{vmatrix} 2 & 1 \\ 3 & -1 \end{vmatrix} = -5$$

and hence is equal to 5.

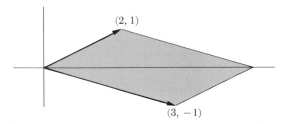

(2, 1)

(3, -1)   **Figure 23**

Theorem 8. *Let P be a parallelogram spanned by two vectors. Let $L: \mathbf{R}^2 \rightarrow \mathbf{R}^2$ be a linear map. Then*

Area of $L(P) = |\text{Det } L|$ (Area of P).

Proof. Suppose that P is spanned by two vectors v, w. Then $L(P)$ is spanned by $L(v)$ and $L(w)$. (Cf. Fig. 24.) There is a linear map $L_1: \mathbf{R}^2 \rightarrow \mathbf{R}^2$ such that

$$L_1(e_1) = v \qquad \text{and} \qquad L_1(e_2) = w.$$

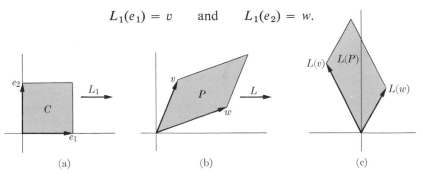

Figure 24

Then $P = L_1(C)$, where C is the unit cube, and

$$L(P) = L(L_1(C)) = (L \circ L_1)(C).$$

By what we proved above in (*), we obtain

$$\text{Vol } L(P) = |\text{Det}(L \circ L_1)| = |\text{Det}(L) \, \text{Det}(L_1)| = |\text{Det}(L)| \, \text{Vol}(P),$$

thus proving our assertion.

Corollary. *For any rectangle R and any linear map $L \colon \mathbf{R}^2 \to \mathbf{R}^2$ we have*

$$\text{Vol } L(R) = |\text{Det}(L)| \, \text{Vol}(R).$$

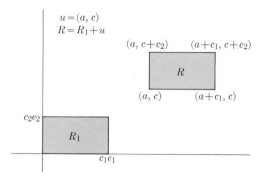

Figure 25

Proof. Let c_1, c_2 be the lengths of the sides of R. Let R_1 be the rectangle spanned by $c_1 e_1$ and $c_2 e_2$. Then R is the translation of R_1 by some vector, say $R = R_1 + u$. Then

$$L(R) = L(R_1 + u) = L(R_1) + L(u)$$

is the translation of $L(R_1)$ by $L(u)$. (Cf. Fig. 25.) Since area does not change under translation, we need only apply Theorem 8 to conclude the proof.

EXERCISE

1. If g satisfies the first two axioms of a determinant, prove that

$$g(v, w) = -g(w, v)$$

for all vectors v, w. This fact was used in the uniqueness proof. [*Hint:* Expand $g(v + w, v + w) = 0$.]

§5. CHANGE OF VARIABLES FORMULA

Let R be a rectangle in $\mathbf{R}^2$ and suppose that R is contained in some open set U. Let

$$G \colon U \to \mathbf{R}^2$$

be a C^1-map. If G has two coordinate functions,

$$G(u, v) = (g_1(u, v), g_2(u, v)),$$

this means that the partial derivatives of g_1, g_2 exist and are continuous. We let $G(u, v) = (x, y)$, so that

$$x = g_1(u, v) \qquad \text{and} \qquad y = g_2(u, v).$$

Then the Jacobian determinant of the map G is by definition

$$\Delta_G(u, v) = \begin{vmatrix} \dfrac{\partial g_1}{\partial u} & \dfrac{\partial g_1}{\partial v} \\[2mm] \dfrac{\partial g_2}{\partial u} & \dfrac{\partial g_2}{\partial v} \end{vmatrix}.$$

This determinant is nothing but the determinant of the linear map $G'(u, v)$, which is the tangent linear map to G at (u, v).

Theorem 9. *Assume that G is C^1-invertible on the interior of the rectangle R. Let f be a function on $G(R)$ which is continuous except on a finite number of smooth curves. Then*

$$\int_R (f \circ G)|\Delta_G| = \int_{G(R)} f$$

or in terms of coordinates,

$$\iint_R f(G(u, v))|\Delta_G(u, v)| \, du \, dv = \iint_{G(R)} f(x, y) \, dy \, dx.$$

The proof of Theorem 9 is not easy to establish rigorously, depending on ϵ and δ arguments. However, we can make it plausible in view of Theorem 8.

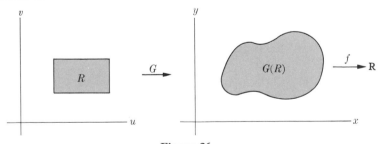

Figure 26

Indeed, suppose first that f is a constant function, say $f(x, y) = 1$ for all (x, y). Then the integral on the right, over $G(R)$, is simply the area of $G(R)$, and our formula reduces to

$$\int_R |\Delta_G| = \int_{G(R)} 1.$$

As we pointed out before, Δ_G is the determinant of the approximating linear map to G. If G is itself linear, then $G'(u, v) = G$ for all u, v and in this case, our formula reduces to Theorem 8, or rather its corollary. In the general case, one has to show that when one approximates G by its tangent linear map, which depends on (u, v), and then integrates $|\Delta_G|$ one still obtains the same result. Cf. for instance my *Analysis I* for a complete proof. A special case will be proved in the next chapter.

When f is not a constant function, one still has the problem of reducing this case to the case of constant functions. This is done by taking a partition of R into small rectangles S, and then approximating f on each $G(S)$ by a constant function. Again, the details are out of the bounds of this book.

We shall now see how we recover the integral in terms of polar coordinates from the general Theorem 9.

Example 1. Let $x = r \cos \theta$ and $y = r \sin \theta$, $r \geqq 0$. Then in this case, we have computed previously the determinant, which is

$$\Delta_G(r, \theta) = r.$$

Thus we find again the formula

$$\iint_R f(r \cos \theta, r \sin \theta) r \, dr \, d\theta = \iint_{G(R)} f(x, y) \, dy \, dx.$$

Of course, we have to take a rectangle for which the map

$$G(r, \theta) = (r \cos \theta, r \sin \theta)$$

is invertible on the interior of the rectangle. For instance, we can take

$$0 \leqq r_1 \leqq r \leqq r_2 \quad \text{and} \quad 0 \leqq \theta_1 \leqq \theta \leqq \theta_2 \leqq 2\pi.$$

The image of the rectangle R is the portion $G(R)$ of the sector as shown in Fig. 27.

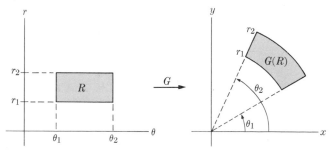

Figure 27

The analogue of Theorem 9 also holds for arbitrary regions A instead of rectangles, provided the boundary consists of a finite number of smooth curves. Thus the general formula states that

$$\int_A (f \circ G)|\Delta_G| = \int_{G(A)} f.$$

Example 2. Let A be the triangle whose vertices are $(1, 2)$, $(3, -1)$, and $(0, 0)$. Find the area of this triangle.

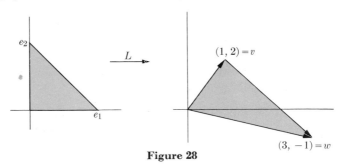

Figure 28

This triangle is the image of the triangle spanned by 0, e_1, e_2 under a linear map, namely the linear map L such that

$$L(e_1) = (1, 2)$$

and

$$L(e_2) = (3, -1).$$

It is verified at once that $|\text{Det}(L)| = 7$. Since the area of the triangle spanned by 0, e_1, e_2 is $\frac{1}{2}$, it follows that the desired area is equal to $\frac{7}{2}$.

Example 3. Let $(x, y) = G(u, v) = (e^u \cos v, e^u \sin v)$. Let R be the rectangle in the (u, v)-space defined by the inequalities $0 \leq u \leq 1$ and $0 \leq v \leq \pi$. It is not difficult to show that G satisfies the hypotheses of Theorem 9, but we shall assume this. The Jacobian matrix of G is given by

$$\begin{pmatrix} e^u \cos v & -e^u \sin v \\ e^u \sin v & e^u \cos v \end{pmatrix}$$

so that its Jacobian determinant is equal to

$$\Delta_G(u, v) = e^{2u}.$$

Let $f(x, y) = x^2$. Then $f^*(u, v) = e^{2u} \cos^2 v$. According to Theorem 9, the integral of f over $G(R)$ is given by the integral

$$\int_0^1 \int_0^\pi e^{4u} \cos^2 v \, du \, dv$$

which can be evaluated very simply by integrating e^{4u} with respect to u and $\cos^2 v$ with respect to v, and taking the product. The final answer is then equal to

$$\frac{e^4 - 1}{4} + \tfrac{1}{2}\pi.$$

EXERCISES

In the following exercises, you may assume that the map G satisfies the hypotheses of Theorem 9.

1. Let $(x, y) = G(u, v) = (u^2 - v^2, 2uv)$. Let A be the region defined by $u^2 + v^2 \leq 1$ and $0 \leq u, 0 \leq v$. Find the integral of the function

$$f(x, y) = 1/(x^2 + y^2)^{1/2}$$

   over $G(A)$.

2. (a) Let $(x, y) = G(u, v)$ be the same map as in Exercise 1. Let A be the square $0 \leq u \leq 2$ and $0 \leq v \leq 2$. Find the area of $G(A)$.
   (b) Find the integral of $f(x, y) = x$ over $G(A)$.

3. (a) Let R be the rectangle whose corners are $(1, 2)$, $(1, 5)$, $(3, 2)$, and $(3, 5)$. Let G be the linear map represented by the matrix

$$\begin{pmatrix} 2 & 1 \\ -1 & 3 \end{pmatrix}.$$

   Find the area of $G(R)$.

   (b) Same question if G is represented by the matrix $\begin{pmatrix} 3 & 2 \\ 1 & -6 \end{pmatrix}$.

4. Let $(x, y) = G(u, v) = (u + v, u^2 - v)$. Let A be the region in the first quadrant bounded by the axes and the line $u + v = 2$. Find the integral of the function $f(x, y) = 1/\sqrt{1 + 4x + 4y}$ over $G(A)$.

5. Let $(x, y) = G(u, v) = (au, bv)$ where a, b are numbers > 0. For any region A, show that $\operatorname{Vol} G(A) = ab \operatorname{Vol}(A)$.

6. Compute the area enclosed by the ellipse, defined by

$$\frac{x^2}{a^2} + \frac{y^2}{b^2} \leq 1.$$

   Take $a, b > 0$.

7. Let $(x, y) = G(u, v) = (u, v(1 + u^2))$. Let R be the rectangle $0 \leq u \leq 3$ and $0 \leq v \leq 2$. Find the integral of $f(x, y) = x$ over $G(R)$.

8. Let G be the linear map represented by the matrix

$$\begin{pmatrix} 3 & 0 \\ 1 & 5 \end{pmatrix}.$$

   If A is the interior of a circle of radius 10, what is the area of $G(A)$?

9. Let G be the linear map of Exercise 8, and let A be the ellipse defined as in Exercise 6. What is the area of $G(A)$?

10. Let T be the triangle bounded by the x-axis, the y-axis, and the line $x + y = 1$. Let φ be a continuous function of one variable on the interval $[0, 1]$. Let m, n be positive integers. Show that

$$\iint_T \varphi(x + y)x^m y^n \, dy \, dx = c_{m,n} \int_0^1 \varphi(t)t^{m+n+1} \, dt,$$

where $c_{m,n}$ is the constant given by the integral $\int_0^1 (1 - t)^m t^n \, dt$. [*Hint:* Let $x = u - v$ and $y = v$.]

11. Let B be the region bounded by the ellipse $x^2/a^2 + y^2/b^2 = 1$. Find the integral

$$\iint_B y \, dy \, dx.$$

§6. TRIPLE INTEGRALS

The entire discussion concerning 2-dimensional integrals generalizes to higher dimensions. We discuss briefly the 3-dimensional case.

A 3-dimensional rectangle (rectangular parallelepiped) can be written as a product of three intervals:

$$R = [a_1, b_1] \times [a_2, b_2] \times [a_3, b_3].$$

A partition P of R is then determined by partitions P_1, P_2, P_3 of the three intervals respectively, and partitions R into 3-dimensional subrectangles, which we denote again by S.

If f is a bounded function on R, we may then form upper and lower sums. Indeed, we define the volume of the rectangle R above to be the 3-dimensional volume

$$\text{Vol}(R) = (b_3 - a_3)(b_2 - a_2)(b_1 - a_1)$$

and similarly for the subrectangles of the partition. Then we have

$$L(P, f) = \sum_S (\inf_S f) \, \text{Vol}(S),$$

$$U(P, f) = \sum_S (\sup_S f) \, \text{Vol}(S).$$

A refinement P' of P is determined by refinements P'_1, P'_2, P'_3 of P_1, P_2, P_3 respectively, and the Lemma of §1 extends to this case.

Again, we say that f is integrable if the least upper bound of the lower sums is equal to the greatest lower bound of the upper sums, and if this is the case, we define it to be the integral of f over R, written

$$\int_R f = \iiint_R f(x, y, z) \, dz \, dy \, dx$$

if the variables are x, y, z.

If $f \geqq 0$, then we interpret this integral as the 4-dimensional volume of the 4-dimensional region lying in 4-space, bounded from below by R, and from above by the graph of f. Of course, we cannot draw this figure because it is in 4-space, but the terminology goes right over.

Theorem 1 and Theorem 2 are again valid, that is the integral is linear, and satisfies the usual inequality.

The criterion of Theorem 3 for a function to be integrable also has an analogue. In this case, however, we have to parametrize the boundary of a 3-dimensional region by 2-dimensional smooth pieces of surfaces. Thus let T be a 2-dimensional rectangle, and let

$$F: \mathbf{T} \to \mathbf{R}^3$$

be a map. If F is of class C^1 we shall say that F is smooth, and we call the image of F a smooth surface (Fig. 29).

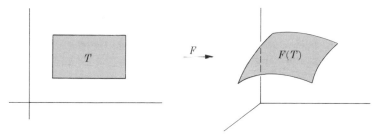

Figure 29

The analogue of Theorem 3 is then: *Let R be a 3-dimensional rectangle, and let f be a function defined on R, bounded and continuous except possibly at the points lying on a finite number of smooth surfaces. Then f is integrable on R.*

Again we can integrate over a more general region than a rectangle, provided such a region A has a boundary which is contained in a finite number of smooth surfaces. Then Theorem 4 holds. If A denotes a 3-dimensional region and f is a function on A, we denote the integral of f over A by

$$\int_A f \quad \text{or} \quad \iiint_A f(x, y, z) \, dz \, dy \, dx.$$

If we view A as a solid piece of material, and f is interpreted as a density distribution over A, then the integral of f over A may be interpreted as the *mass* of A.

To compute multiple integrals in the 3-dimensional case, we have the same situation as in the 2-dimensional case.

The theorem concerning the relation with repeated integrals holds, so that if R is the rectangle given by

$$R = [a_1, b_1] \times [a, b_{22}] \times [a_3, b_3],$$

then
$$\int_R f = \int_{a_1}^{b_1} \left[\int_{a_2}^{b_2} \left(\int_{a_3}^{b_3} f(x, y, z) \, dz \right) dy \right] dx.$$

Of course, the repeated integral can be evaluated in any order.

Example 1. Find the integral of the function $f(x, y, z) = \sin x$ over the rectangle $0 \leq x \leq \pi, 2 \leq y \leq 3$, and $-1 \leq z \leq 1$.
The integral is equal to

$$\int_0^{\pi} \int_2^3 \int_{-1}^1 \sin x \, dz \, dy \, dx.$$

If we first integrate with respect to z, we get $z|_{-1}^1 = 2$. Next with respect to y, we get $y|_2^3 = 1$. We are then reduced to the integral

$$\int_0^{\pi} 2 \sin x \, dx = -2 \cos x \Big|_0^{\pi} = -2(\cos \pi - \cos 0) = 4.$$

We also have the integral over regions determined by inequalities.

Case 1. Rectangular coordinates. Let a, b be numbers, $a \leq b$. Let g_1, g_2 be two smooth functions defined on the interval $[a, b]$ such that

$$g_1(x) \leq g_2(x),$$

and let $h_1(x, y) \leq h_2(x, y)$ be two smooth functions defined on the region consisting of all points (x, y) such that

$$a \leq x \leq b \quad \text{and} \quad g_1(x) \leq y \leq g_2(x).$$

Let A be the set of points (x, y, z) such that

$$a \leq x \leq b, \quad g_1(x) \leq y \leq g_2(x), \quad \text{and} \quad h_1(x, y) \leq z \leq h_2(x, y).$$

Let f be continuous on A. Then

$$\int_A f = \int_a^b \left[\int_{g_1(x)}^{g_2(x)} \left(\int_{h_1(x,y)}^{h_2(x,y)} f(x, y, z) \, dz \right) dy \right] dx.$$

For simplicity, the integral on the right will also be written without the brackets.

For example, consider the tetrahedron T spanned by 0 and the three unit vectors (Fig. 30).

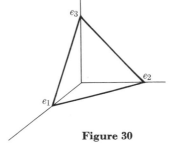

Figure 30

This tetrahedron is described by the inequalities:

$$0 \leqq x \leqq 1, \qquad 0 \leqq y \leqq 1 - x, \qquad 0 \leqq z \leqq 1 - x - y.$$

Hence if f is a function on the tetrahedron, its integral over T is given by

$$\int_T f = \int_0^1 \int_0^{1-x} \int_0^{1-x-y} f(x, y, z)\, dz\, dy\, dx.$$

There is no difficulty in evaluating these integrals, which we leave to the reader [Exercise 17(a)].

Before discussing the other two cases, namely cylindrical and spherical coordinates, we point out that the change of variables formula is valid in three dimensions. We can state it as follows.

Change of variables formula. Let A be a bounded region in $\mathbf{R}^3$ whose boundary consists of a finite number of smooth surfaces. Let A be contained in some open set U, and let

$$G: U \to \mathbf{R}^3$$

be a C^1-map, which we assume to be C^1-invertible on the interior of A. Let f be a function on $G(A)$, continuous except on a finite number of smooth surfaces. Then

$$\int_A (f \circ G)|\Delta_G| = \int_{G(A)} f.$$

In the 3-dimensional case, the Jacobian matrix of G at every point is then a 3×3 matrix.

Example 2. Let R be the 3-dimensional rectangle spanned by the three unit vectors e_1, e_2, e_3. Let v_1, v_2, v_3 be three vectors in 3-space, and let

$$G: \mathbf{R}^3 \to \mathbf{R}^3$$

be the linear map such that $G(e_i) = v_i$. Then $G(R)$ is a parallelotope (not necessarily rectangular). (Cf. Fig. 31.)

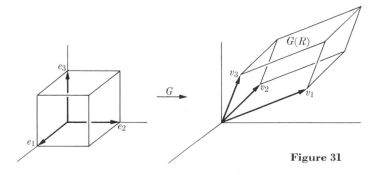

Figure 31

The volume of the unit cube is equal to 1. Hence the volume of $G(R)$ is equal to $|\text{Det}(G)|$.

For instance, if

$$v_1 = (3, 1, 2),$$
$$v_2 = (1, -1, 4),$$
$$v_3 = (2, 1, 0),$$

then

$$\text{Det}(G) = \begin{vmatrix} 3 & 1 & 2 \\ 1 & -1 & 4 \\ 2 & 1 & 0 \end{vmatrix} = -4$$

so the volume of $G(R)$ is equal to 4.

Case 2. Cylindrical coordinates. We consider the map given by

$$G(r, \theta, z) = (r \cos \theta, r \sin \theta, z).$$

Then the Jacobian determinant of G is equal to r, so that if a region is described by cylindrical coordinates in 3-space, the integral is given by

$$\iiint_A f(r \cos \theta, r \sin \theta, z)r \, dz \, dr \, d\theta = \iiint_{G(A)} f(x, y, z) \, dz \, dy \, dx.$$

Example 3. The image of a box B defined by the inequalities:

$$0 \leqq \theta_1 \leqq \theta \leqq \theta_2 \leqq 2\pi, \quad 0 \leqq r_1 \leqq r \leqq r_2, \quad \text{and} \quad z_1 \leqq z \leqq z_2,$$

under the map G is shown in the following picture.

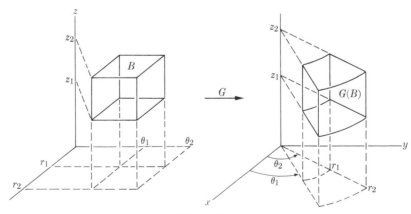

Figure 32

Hence the volume of $G(B)$ is equal to

$$\int_{\theta_1}^{\theta_2} \int_{r_1}^{r_2} \int_{z_1}^{z_2} r \, dz \, dr \, d\theta = (z_2 - z_1)\left(\frac{r_2^2 - r_1^2}{2}\right)(\theta_2 - \theta_1).$$

A region may be described by inequalities given by functions. For instance, *let A be the region in the (θ, r, z)-space consisting of all points (θ, r, z) satisfying conditions:*

$$a \leqq \theta \leqq b, \qquad (b \leqq a + 2\pi),$$
$$0 \leqq g_1(\theta) \leqq r \leqq g_2(\theta),$$

with smooth functions g_1, g_2 defined on the interval $[a, b]$, and

$$h_1(\theta, r) \leqq z \leqq h_2(\theta, r),$$

with smooth functions h_1, h_2 defined on the 2-dimensional region bounded by $\theta = a$, $\theta = b$, and g_1, g_2, i.e. the region consisting of all points (θ, r) satisfying the above inequalities. Let G be the map of cylindrical coordinates given above. Let f be a continuous function on the region $G(A)$ in the (x, y, z)-space. Let

$$f^*(\theta, r, z) = f(r \cos \theta, r \sin \theta, z).$$

Then

$$\int_{G(A)} f = \int_a^b \int_{g_1(\theta)}^{g_2(\theta)} \int_{h_1(\theta, r)}^{h_2(\theta, r)} f^*(\theta, r, z) r \, dz \, dr \, d\theta.$$

The function which we denote by f^* may be viewed as the function f in terms of the cylindrical coordinates.

Example 4. Find the mass of a solid bounded by the polar coordinates $\pi/3 \leqq \theta \leqq 2\pi/3$ and $r = \cos \theta$ and by $z = 0$, $z = r$, if the density is given by the function

$$f^*(r, \theta, z) = 3r.$$

The mass is given by the integral

$$\int_{\pi/3}^{2\pi/3} \int_0^{\cos \theta} \int_0^r 3r \cdot r \, dz \, dr \, d\theta.$$

integrating the inner integral with respect to z yields $3r^2 r = 3r^3$. Integrating with respect to r between 0 and $\cos \theta$ yields

$$\left. \frac{3r^4}{4} \right|_0^{\cos \theta} = \frac{3 \cos^4 \theta}{4}.$$

Finally we integrate with respect to θ, using elementary techniques of integration: $\cos^2 \theta = (1 + \cos 2\theta)/2$ so that

$$\cos^4 \theta = \tfrac{1}{4}(1 + 2 \cos 2\theta + \cos^2 2\theta)$$
$$= \frac{1}{4}\left(1 + 2 \cos 2\theta + \frac{1 + \cos 4\theta}{2}\right).$$

We can now integrate this between the given limits, and we find

$$\frac{3}{4} \int_{\pi/3}^{2\pi/3} \cos^4 \theta \, d\theta = \frac{3}{16} \left(\frac{\pi}{3} - \sqrt{3} + \frac{\pi}{6} + \frac{\sqrt{3}}{8} \right).$$

Note. In Example 4, the function is already given in terms of (r, θ, z). It corresponds to the function $f(x, y, z) = 3\sqrt{x^2 + y^2}$. Indeed, taking $f(r \cos \theta, r \sin \theta, z)$ yields $3r$.

Case 3. Spherical coordinates. We consider the mapping $G: \mathbf{R}^3 \to \mathbf{R}^3$ given by $G(\rho, \theta, \varphi) = (\rho \sin \varphi \cos \theta, \rho \sin \varphi \sin \theta, \cos \varphi)$, so that we let

$$x = \rho \sin \varphi \cos \theta, \qquad y = \rho \sin \varphi \sin \theta, \qquad z = \rho \cos \varphi.$$

Then the Jacobian determinant is given by

$$\Delta_G(\rho, \theta, \varphi) = \rho^2 \sin \varphi.$$

We consider the region in the (ρ, θ, φ)-coordinates described by

$$0 \leq \rho, \qquad 0 \leq \varphi \leq \pi, \qquad 0 \leq \theta \leq 2\pi.$$

Then G is invertible in the interior of this region. Indeed, G gives us the spherical coordinates of a point (x, y, z) as shown in the following picture.

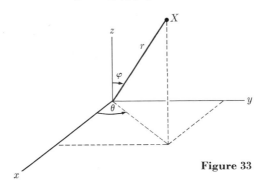

Figure 33

In fact, we have

$$\rho = \sqrt{x^2 + y^2 + z^2}.$$

We denote this by ρ to distinguish it from the polar coordinate r in the (x, y)-plane. We see that

$$x^2 + y^2 = \rho^2 - z^2 = \rho^2 \sin^2 \varphi$$

so that the polar r is given by

$$r = \sqrt{x^2 + y^2} = \rho \sin \varphi.$$

In taking the square root, we do not need to use the absolute value $|\sin \varphi|$ because we take $0 \leq \varphi \leq \pi$ so that $\sin \varphi \geq 0$ for our values of φ.

In the present case, the change of variables formula yields:

$$\iiint_{A} f(G(\rho, \theta, \varphi))\rho^2 \sin \varphi \, d\rho \, d\varphi \, d\theta = \iiint_{G(A)} f(x, y, z) \, dz \, dy \, dx.$$

For instance, let R be the 3-dimensional rectangle in the (ρ, θ, φ)-space described by the inequalities:

$$\theta_1 \leqq \theta \leqq \theta_2, \qquad (\theta_2 \leqq \theta_1 + 2\pi),$$
$$0 \leqq \rho_1 \leqq \rho \leqq \rho_2,$$
$$0 \leqq \varphi_1 \leqq \varphi \leqq \varphi_2 \leqq \pi.$$

The image of R under the map G is then an elementary spherical region as shown in the next picture.

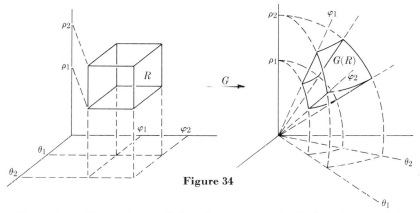

Figure 34

Example 5. The volume of the elementary spherical region $G(R)$ just described is equal to the integral

$$\int_{\theta_1}^{\theta_2} \int_{\varphi_1}^{\varphi_2} \int_{\rho_1}^{\rho_2} \rho^2 \sin \varphi \, d\rho \, d\varphi \, d\theta = \left(\frac{\rho_2^3}{3} - \frac{\rho_1^3}{3} \right) (\cos \varphi_1 - \cos \varphi_2)(\theta_2 - \theta_1).$$

In this case, the repeated 3-fold integral splits into separate integrals with respect to ρ, φ, θ independently. These integrals are of course very simple to evaluate, as we have done above. In this case, the limits of integration are constant.

Example 6. Find the mass of a solid body S determined by the inequalities of spherical coordinates:

$$0 \leqq \theta \leqq \frac{\pi}{2}, \qquad \frac{\pi}{4} \leqq \varphi \leqq \arctan 2, \qquad 0 \leqq \rho \leqq \sqrt{6},$$

if the density, given as a function of the spherical coordinates (θ, φ, ρ), is equal to $1/\rho$.

To find the mass, we have to integrate the given function over the region. The integral is given by

$$\int_0^{\pi/2} \int_{\pi/4}^{\arctan 2} \int_0^{\sqrt{6}} \frac{1}{\rho} \rho^2 \sin \varphi \, d\rho \, d\varphi \, d\theta.$$

Performing the repeated integral, we obtain

$$\frac{3\pi}{2}\left(\frac{1}{\sqrt{2}} - \frac{1}{\sqrt{5}}\right).$$

We note that in the present example, the limits of integration are constants, and hence the repeated integral is equal to a product of the integrals

$$\int_0^{\pi/2} d\theta \cdot \int_{\pi/4}^{\arctan 2} \sin \varphi \, d\varphi \cdot \int_0^{\sqrt{6}} \rho \, d\rho.$$

Each integration can be performed separately. Of course, this does not hold when the limits of integration are non-constant functions.

As before, we have a similar integral when the boundaries of integration are not constant. We state the result:

Let a, b be numbers such that $0 \leq b - a \leq 2\pi$. Let $g_1(\theta)$, $g_2(\theta)$ be smooth functions of θ, defined on the interval $a \leq \theta \leq b$ such that

$$0 \leq g_1(\theta) \leq g_2(\theta) \leq \pi.$$

Let h_1, h_2 be functions of two variables, defined and smooth on the region consisting of all points (θ, φ) such that

$$a \leq \theta \leq b,$$
$$g_1(\theta) \leq \varphi \leq g_2(\theta)$$

and such that $0 \leq h_1(\theta, \varphi) \leq h_2(\theta, \varphi)$ for all (θ, φ) in this region. Let A be the 3-dimensional region in the (θ, φ, ρ)-space consisting of all points such that

$$a \leq \theta \leq b,$$
$$g_1(\theta) \leq \varphi \leq g_2(\theta),$$
$$h_1(\theta, \varphi) \leq \rho \leq h_2(\theta, \varphi).$$

Let G be the spherical coordinate map, and let f be a continuous function on $G(A)$. Let $f^*(\theta, \varphi, \rho) = f(G(\theta, \varphi, \rho))$. Then

$$\int_{G(A)} f = \int_a^b \int_{g_1(\theta)}^{g_2(\theta)} \int_{h_1(\theta,\varphi)}^{h_2(\theta,\varphi)} f^*(\theta, \varphi, \rho)\rho^2 \sin \varphi \, d\rho \, d\varphi \, d\theta.$$

Example 7. Find the volume above the cone $z^2 = x^2 + y^2$ and inside the sphere $x^2 + y^2 + z^2 = z$ (Fig. 35).

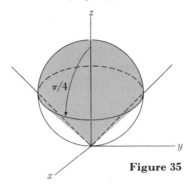

Figure 35

The equation for the sphere in spherical coordinates is obtained by the values

$$\rho^2 = x^2 + y^2 + z^2$$

and

$$z = \rho \cos \varphi.$$

Thus the sphere is given by the equation

$$\rho = \cos \varphi.$$

The cone is given by $\cos^2 \varphi = \sin^2 \varphi$, and since $0 \leq \varphi \leq \pi$ this is the same as $\varphi = \pi/4$. Thus the region of integration is the image under the spherical coordinate map of the region A described by the inequalities:

$$0 \leq \theta \leq 2\pi, \qquad 0 \leq \varphi \leq \pi/4, \qquad 0 \leq \rho \leq \cos \varphi.$$

Hence our volume is equal to the integral

$$\int_{G(A)} 1 = \int_0^{2\pi} \int_0^{\pi/4} \int_0^{\cos \varphi} \rho^2 \sin \varphi \, d\rho \, d\varphi \, d\theta.$$

The inside integral with respect to ρ is equal to

$$(\sin \varphi) \left. \frac{\rho^3}{3} \right|_0^{\cos \varphi} = \frac{1}{3} \cos^3 \varphi \sin \varphi.$$

This is now easily integrated with respect to φ, and yields

$$\frac{1}{3} \left. \frac{-\cos^4 \varphi}{4} \right|_0^{\pi/4} = \frac{1}{12} \left(-\frac{1}{4} + 1 \right) = \frac{3}{48}.$$

Finally, we integrate with respect to θ, and the final answer is therefore equal to

$$\tfrac{3}{48} \cdot 2\pi = \tfrac{1}{8}\pi.$$

EXERCISES

1. (a) Let $G: \mathbf{R}^3 \to \mathbf{R}^3$ be the map which sends spherical coordinates (θ, φ, ρ)
   into cylindrical coordinates (θ, r, z). Write down the Jacobian matrix
   for this map, and its Jacobian determinant.
   (b) Write down the change of variables formula for this case.
   (c) Evaluate the volume of the region given in cylindrical coordinates by

$$0 \leq \theta_1 \leq \theta \leq \theta_2 \leq 2\pi,$$

$$0 \leq r \leq \rho_1 \sin \varphi_1, \qquad r \cot \varphi_1 \leq z \leq \sqrt{\rho_1^2 - r^2}$$

   by an integral taken directly in terms of cylindrical coordinates, and
   then by using the change of variables formula and integrating in terms
   of the spherical coordinates. By what inequalities is the region described in terms of the spherical coordinates?

2. Find the integral

$$\int_0^\pi \int_0^{\sin \theta} \int_0^{\rho \cos \theta} \rho^2 \, dz \, d\rho \, d\theta.$$

3. Find the mass of a spherical ball of radius $a > 0$ if the density at any point
   is equal to a constant k times the distance of that point to the center.

4. Find the mass of a spherical shell of inside radius a and outside radius b if
   the density at any point is inversely proportional to the distance from the
   center.

5. Find the integral of the function

$$f(x, y, z) = x^2$$

   over that portion of the cylinder

$$x^2 + y^2 = a^2$$

   lying between the planes

$$z = 0 \qquad \text{and} \qquad z = b > 0.$$

6. Find the mass of a sphere of radius a if the density at any point is proportional to the distance from a fixed plane passing through a diameter.

7. Find the volume of the region bounded by the cylinder $y = \cos x$, and the
   planes

$$z = y, \qquad x = 0, \qquad x = \pi/2, \qquad \text{and} \qquad z = 0.$$

8. Find the volume of the region bounded above by the sphere

$$x^2 + y^2 + z^2 = 1$$

   and below by the surface

$$z = x^2 + y^2.$$

9. Find the volume of that portion of the sphere $x^2 + y^2 + z^2 = a^2$, which
   is inside the cylinder $r = a \sin \theta$, using cylindrical coordinates.

10. Find the volume above the cone $z^2 = x^2 + y^2$ and inside the sphere $\rho = 2a \cos \varphi$ (spherical coordinates). [Draw a picture. What is the center of the sphere? What is the equation of the cone in spherical coordinates?]

11. Find the volumes of the following regions, in 3-space.

   (a) Bounded above by the plane $z = 1$, and below by the top half of $z^2 = x^2 + y^2$.
   (b) Bounded above and below by $z^2 = x^2 + y^2$, and on the sides by $x^2 + y^2 + z^2 = 1$.
   (c) Bounded above by $z = x^2 + y^2$, below by $z = 0$, and on the sides by $x^2 + y^2 = 1$.
   (d) Bounded above by $z = x$, and below by $z = x^2 + y^2$.

12. Find the integral of the following functions over the indicated region, in 3-space.

   (a) $f(x, y, z) = x^2$ over the tetrahedron bounded by the plane

$$12x + 20y + 15z = 60,$$

   and the coordinate planes.
   (b) $f(x, y, z) = y$ over the tetrahedron as in (a).
   (c) $f(x, y, z) = 7yz$ over the region on the positive side of the (x, z)-plane, bounded by the planes $y = 0$, $z = 0$, and $z = a$ (for some positive number a), and the cylinder $x^2 + y^2 = b^2$ ($b > 0$).

13. Find the volume inside the sphere

$$x^2 + y^2 + z^2 = 1.$$

14. Let A be a region in $\mathbf{R}^3$ and assume that its volume is equal to k. Let $G: \mathbf{R}^3 \to \mathbf{R}^3$ be the map such that $G(x, y, z) = (ax, by, cz)$, where a, b, c are positive numbers. What is the volume of $G(A)$?

15. What is the volume of the ellipsoid

$$\frac{x^2}{a^2} + \frac{y^2}{b^2} + \frac{z^2}{c^2} \leq 1.$$

16. Find the volume of the image of the solid which is the image of a ball of radius a under the linear map represented by the matrix

$$\begin{pmatrix} 1 & -1 & 1 \\ 0 & 2 & 5 \\ 0 & 0 & 7 \end{pmatrix}.$$

17. (a) Find the volume of the tetrahedron A determined by the inequalities

$$0 \leq x, \quad 0 \leq y, \quad 0 \leq z \quad \text{and} \quad x + y + z \leq 1.$$

   (b) This tetrahedron can also be written in the form

$$t_1 e_1 + t_2 e_2 + t_3 e_3 \quad \text{with} \quad t_1 + t_2 + t_3 \leq 1, \quad 0 \leq t_i.$$

If w_1, w_2, w_3 are linearly independent vectors in 3-space, and L is the linear map such that $L(e_i) = w_i$, show that $L(A)$ is described by similar inequalities. We call it the tetrahedron spanned by 0, w_1, w_2, w_3.

(c) Determine the volume of the tetrahedron spanned by the origin and the three vectors $(1, 1, 2)$, $(2, 0, -1)$, $(3, 1, 2)$.

(d) Using the fact that the volume of a region does not change under translation, determine the volume of the tetrahedron spanned by the four points $(1, 1, 1)$, $(2, 2, 3)$, $(3, 1, 0)$, and $(4, 2, 3)$.

18. (a) Determine the volume of the tetrahedron spanned by the four points $(2, 1, 0)$, $(3, -1, 1)$, $(-1, 1, 2)$, $(0, 0, 1)$.

(b) Same question for the four points $(3, 1, 2)$, $(2, 0, 0)$, $(4, 1, 5)$, $(5, -1, 1)$.

Chapter XV

Green's Theorem

§1. STATEMENT OF THE THEOREM

In this chapter, we shall change slightly our notation concerning curve integrals.

Suppose we are given a vector field on some open set U in the plane. Then this vector field has two components, i.e. we can write

$$F(x, y) = (P(x, y), Q(x, y)),$$

where P, Q are functions of two variables (x, y). In everything that follows, we assume that all functions we deal with are C^1, i.e. that these functions have continuous partial derivatives.

Let $C: [a, b] \to U$ be a curve. We shall use a new notation for the integral of F over C, namely we write

$$\int_C F = \int_a^b F(C(t)) \cdot C'(t) \, dt = \int_C P(x, y) \, dx + Q(x, y) \, dy$$

or abbreviate this as

$$\int_C P \, dx + Q \, dy.$$

This is reasonable since the curve gives

$$x = x(t)$$

and

$$y = y(t)$$

as functions of t, and

$$F(C(t)) \cdot \frac{dC}{dt} = P(x, y) \frac{dx}{dt} + Q(x, y) \frac{dy}{dt}.$$

Green's theorem. *Let P, Q be C^1-functions on a region A, which is the interior of a closed piecewise C^1-path C, parametrized counterclockwise. Then*

$$\int_C P \, dx + Q \, dy = \iint_A \left(\frac{\partial Q}{\partial x} - \frac{\partial P}{\partial y} \right) dy \, dx.$$

583

The region and its boundary may look as follows:

Figure 1

It is difficult to prove Green's theorem in general, partly because it is difficult to make rigorous the notion of "interior" of a path, and also the notion of counterclockwise. In practice, for any specifically given region, it is always easy, however. That it may be difficult in general is already suggested by drawing a somewhat less simple region as follows:

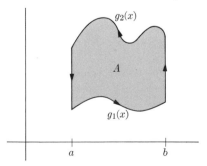

Figure 2

We shall therefore prove Green's theorem only in special cases, where we can give the region and the parametrization of its boundary explicitly.

Case 1. Suppose that the region A is given by the inequalities

$$a \leqq x \leqq b \quad \text{and} \quad g_1(x) \leqq y \leqq g_2(x)$$

in the same manner as we studied before in Chapter XIV, §2.

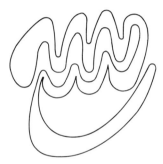

Figure 3

The boundary of A then consists of four pieces, the two vertical segments, and the pieces parametrized by the maps:

$$\gamma_1: t \mapsto (t, g_1(t)), \qquad\qquad a \leq t \leq b,$$
$$\gamma_2: t \mapsto (t, g_2(t)), \qquad\qquad a \leq t \leq b.$$

Then we can prove one-half of Green's theorem, namely

$$\int_C P \, dx = \iint_A -\frac{\partial P}{\partial y} \, dy \, dx.$$

Proof. We have

$$\iint_A \frac{\partial P}{\partial y} \, dy \, dx = \int_a^b \int_{g_1(x)}^{g_2(x)} D_2 P(x, y) \, dy \, dx$$

$$= \int_a^b \left(P(x, y) \Big|_{g_1(x)}^{g_2(x)} \right) dx$$

$$= \int_a^b [P(x, g_2(x)) - P(x, g_1(x))] \, dx$$

$$= \int_{\gamma_2} P \, dx - \int_{\gamma_1} P \, dx.$$

However, the boundary of A, oriented counterclockwise, consists of four pieces,

$$\gamma_1, \gamma_2^-, \gamma_3, \gamma_4,$$

where γ_2^- is the opposite curve to γ_2, and γ_3, γ_4 are the vertical segments. One sees at once that the integrals

$$\int_{\gamma_3} P \, dx \qquad \text{and} \qquad \int_{\gamma_4} P \, dx$$

are equal to 0, and thus we obtain the formula in this case.

Case 2. Suppose that the region is given by similar inequalities as in Case 1, but with respect to the y-axis. In other words, the region A is defined by inequalities

$$c \leq y \leq d \qquad \text{and} \qquad g_1(y) \leq x \leq g_2(y).$$

Then we prove the other half of Green's theorem, namely

$$\iint_A \frac{\partial Q}{\partial x} \, dy \, dx = \int_C Q \, dy.$$

Proof. We take the integral with respect to x first:

$$\iint\limits_{A} \frac{\partial Q}{\partial x}\, dx\, dy = \int_{c}^{d}\left[\int_{g_1(y)}^{g_2(y)} D_1 Q(x, y)\, dx\right] dy$$

$$= \int_{c}^{d} [Q(g_2(y), y) - Q(g_1(y), y)]\, dy.$$

In this case, the integral of $Q\, dy$ over the horizontal segments is equal to 0, and hence our formula is proved.

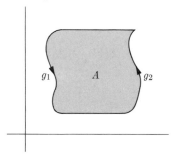

Figure 4

In particular, if a region is of a type satisfying both the preceding conditions, then the full theorem follows. Examples of such regions are rectangles and triangles and interiors of circles:

Figure 5

We have therefore proved Green's theorem in these cases.

Frequently, a region can be decomposed into regions of the preceding types. We draw a picture to illustrate this, namely the annulus lying between two circles.

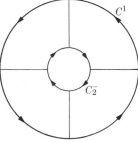

Figure 6

By drawing four line segments as shown, we decompose this annulus into four regions, and it would thus suffice to prove Green's theorem for each one of these four regions. None of them yet satisfies the desired hypotheses, but one more decomposition will do for each region, as shown in the next picture.

Figure 7

Consequently if we denote by C_1 the outside circle taken counterclockwise, and by C_2 the inside circle taken counterclockwise, if we let $C = \{C_1, C_2^-\}$, and if A is the region between C_1 and C_2, then

$$\iint_A \left(\frac{\partial Q}{\partial x} - \frac{\partial P}{\partial y}\right) dy\, dx = \int_C P\, dx + Q\, dy$$

$$= \int_{C_1} P\, dx + Q\, dy - \int_{C_2} P\, dx + Q\, dy.$$

Example 1. Let A be the region between two concentric circles C_1, C_2 as shown, both with counterclockwise orientation (Fig. 8).

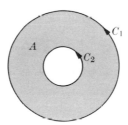

Figure 8

Let F be a vector field on A, $F = \text{grad } \varphi$ for some function φ. Show that the integral of F over C_1 is equal to the integral of F over C_2. (As usual, assume all functions to be differentiable as needed.)

We can write

$$F(x, y) = \left(\frac{\partial \varphi}{\partial x}, \frac{\partial \varphi}{\partial y}\right)$$

so that $P = \partial\varphi/\partial x$ and $Q = \partial\varphi/\partial y$. Then $\partial Q/\partial x = \partial P/\partial y$ so that in Green's theorem we have

$$\iint_A \left(\frac{\partial Q}{\partial x} - \frac{\partial P}{\partial y}\right) dy\, dx = 0.$$

By the remark made previously, this implies that

$$\int_{C_1} P\, dx + Q\, dy = \int_{C_2} P\, dx + Q\, dy,$$

as was to be shown.

Example 2. Find the integral of the vector field

$$F(x, y) = (y + 3x, 2y - x)$$

counterclockwise around the ellipse $4x^2 + y^2 = 4$.

Let $P(x, y) = y + 3x$ and $Q(x, y) = 2y - x$. Then $\partial Q/\partial x = -1$ and $\partial P/\partial y = -1$. By Green's theorem, we get

$$\int_C P\, dx + Q\, dy = \iint_A (-2)\, dy\, dx = -2\, \mathrm{Vol}(A),$$

where $\mathrm{Vol}(A)$ is the area of the ellipse, which is known to be 2π ($= \pi ab$ when the ellipse is in the form $x^2/a^2 + y^2/b^2 = 1$).

EXERCISES

1. Use Green's theorem to find the integral $\int_C y^2\, dx + x\, dy$ when C is the following curve (taken counterclockwise).

   (a) The square with vertices $(0, 0)$, $(2, 0)$, $(2, 2)$, $(0, 2)$.
   (b) The square with vertices $(\pm 1, \pm 1)$.
   (c) The circle of radius 2 centered at the origin.
   (d) The circle of radius 1 centered at the origin.
   (e) The square with vertices $(\pm 2, 0)$, $(0, \pm 2)$.
   (f) The ellipse $x^2/a^2 + y^2/b^2 = 1$.

2. Let A be a region, which is the interior of a closed curve C oriented counterclockwise. Show that the area of A is given by

$$\mathrm{Vol}(A) = \tfrac{1}{2}\int_C - y\, dx + x\, dy = \int_C x\, dy.$$

3. Let C_1 be the curve bounded by the parabola

$$y^2 = 2(x + 2)$$

and the line

$$x = 2$$

as shown in Fig. 9. Find the integral

$$\int_{C_1} \frac{-y}{x^2 + y^2}\, dx + \frac{x}{x^2 + y^2}\, dy.$$

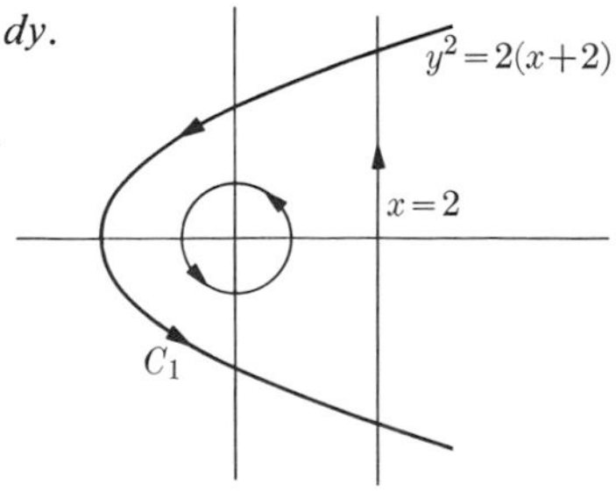

Figure 9

[*Hint:* Reduce this to an integral over the circle of radius 1.]

4. Assume that the function f satisfies Laplace's equation,

$$\frac{\partial^2 f}{\partial x^2} + \frac{\partial^2 f}{\partial y^2} = 0,$$

on a region A which is the interior of a curve C, oriented counterclockwise. Show that

$$\int_C \frac{\partial f}{\partial y}\, dx - \frac{\partial f}{\partial x}\, dy = 0.$$

5. If $F = (Q, P)$ is a vector field, we recall that its divergence is defined to be $\operatorname{div} F = \partial Q/\partial x + \partial P/\partial y$. If C is a curve, we say that C is parametrized by arc length if $\|C'(s)\| = 1$ (we then use s as the parameter). Let

$$C(s) = (g_1(s), g_2(s))$$

be parametrized by arc length. Define the unit normal vector at s to be the vector

$$N(s) = (g_2'(s), -g_1'(s)).$$

Verify that this is a unit vector. Show that if F is a vector field on a region A, which is the interior of the closed curve C, oriented counterclockwise, and parametrized by arc length, then

$$\iint_A (\operatorname{div} F)\, dy\, dx = \int_C F \cdot N\, ds.$$

6. Let $C : [a, b] \rangle U$ be a C^1-curve in an open set U of the plane. If f is a function on U (assumed to be differentiable as needed), we define

$$\int_C f = \int_a^b f(C(t)) \|C'(t)\|\, dt$$

$$= \int_a^b f(C(t)) \sqrt{\left(\frac{dx}{dt}\right)^2 + \left(\frac{dy}{dt}\right)^2}\, dt.$$

For $r > 0$, let $x = r \cos \theta$ and $y = r \sin \theta$. Let φ be the function of r defined by

$$\varphi(r) = \frac{1}{2\pi r} \int_{C_r} f = \frac{1}{2\pi r} \int_0^{2\pi} f(r \cos \theta, r \sin \theta) r\, d\theta.$$

where C_r is the circle of radius r, parametrized as above. Assume that f satisfies Laplace's equation

$$\frac{\partial^2 f}{\partial x^2} + \frac{\partial^2 f}{\partial y^2} = 0.$$

Show that $\varphi(r)$ does not depend on r and in fact

$$f(0, 0) = \frac{1}{2\pi r} \int_{C_r} f.$$

[*Hint:* First take $\varphi'(r)$ and differentiate under the integral, with respect to r. Let D_r be the disc of radius r which is the interior of C_r. Using Exercise 5, you will find that

$$\varphi'(r) = \frac{1}{2\pi r} \iint_{D_r} \text{div grad } f(x, y) \, dy \, dx$$

$$= \frac{1}{2\pi r} \iint_{D_r} \left(\frac{\partial^2 f}{\partial x^2} + \frac{\partial^2 f}{\partial y^2} \right) dy \, dx$$

$$= 0.$$

Taking the limit as $r \to 0$, prove the desired assertion.]

§2. APPLICATION TO THE CHANGE OF VARIABLES FORMULA

When a region A is the interior of a closed path, then we can use Green's theorem to prove the change of variables formula in special cases. Indeed, Green's theorem reduces a double integral to an integral over a curve, and change of variables formulas for curves are easier to establish than for 2-dimensional areas. Thus we begin by looking at a special case of a change of variables formula for curves.

Let $C: [a, b] \to U$ be a C^1-curve in an open set of $\mathbf{R}^2$. Let $G: U \to \mathbf{R}^2$ be a C^2-map, given by coordinate functions,

$$G(u, v) = (x, y) = (f(u, v), g(u, v)).$$

Then the composite $G \circ C$ is a curve. If $C(t) = (\alpha(t), \beta(t))$, then

$$G \circ C(t) = G(C(t)) = (f(\alpha(t), \beta(t)), g(\alpha(t), \beta(t))).$$

Example 1. Let $G(u, v) = (u, -v)$ be the reflection along the horizontal axis. If $C(t) = (\cos t, \sin t)$, then

$$G \circ C(t) = (\cos t, -\sin t).$$

Thus $G \circ C$ again parametrizes the circle, but observe that the orientation of $G \circ C$ is opposite to that of C, i.e. it is clockwise!

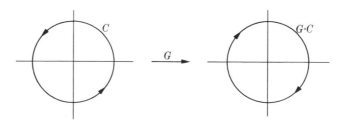

Figure 10

The reason for this reversal of orientation is that the Jacobian determinant of G is negative, namely it is the determinant of

$$\begin{pmatrix} 1 & 0 \\ 0 & -1 \end{pmatrix}.$$

Thus a map G is said to *preserve orientation* if $\Delta_G(u, v) > 0$ for all (u, v) in the domain of definition of G. For simplicity, we only consider such maps G.

Green's theorem leads us to consider the integral

$$\int_{G \circ C} x \, dy.$$

By definition and the chain rule, we have

$$\int_{G \circ C} x \, dy = \int_a^b f(C(t)) \left(\frac{\partial y}{\partial u} \frac{du}{dt} + \frac{\partial y}{\partial v} \frac{dv}{dt} \right) dt$$

$$= \int_C f(u, v) \frac{\partial y}{\partial u} \, du + g(u, v) \frac{\partial y}{\partial v} \, dv.$$

This is true for any C^1-curve as above. Hence it remains true for any piecewise C^1-path, consisting of a finite number of curves.

We are now ready to state and prove the change of variables formula in the case to which Green's theorem applies.

Let U be open in $\mathbf{R}^2$, and let A be a region which is the interior of a closed path C (piecewise C^1 as usual) contained in U. Let

$$G: U \to \mathbf{R}^2$$

be a C^2-map, which is C^1-invertible on U and such that $\Delta_G > 0$. Then $G(A)$ is a region which is the interior of the path $G \circ C$. We then have

$$\boxed{\iint_{G(A)} dy \, dx = \iint_A \Delta_G(u, v) \, du \, dv.}$$

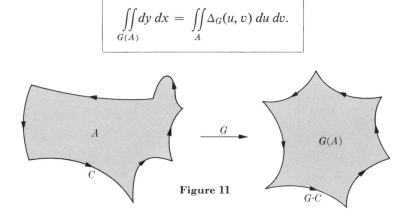

Figure 11

Proof. Let $G(u, v) = (f(u, v), g(u, v))$ be expressed by its coordinates. We have, using Green's theorem:

$$\iint\limits_{G(A)} dy\,dx = \int_{G \circ C} x\,dy = \int_C f \frac{\partial g}{\partial u}\,du + f \frac{\partial g}{\partial v}\,dv$$

$$= \iint\limits_A \left[\frac{\partial}{\partial u}\left(f \frac{\partial g}{\partial v}\right) - \frac{\partial}{\partial v}\left(f \frac{\partial g}{\partial u}\right) \right] du\,dv$$

$$= \iint\limits_A \left[\frac{\partial f}{\partial u} \frac{\partial g}{\partial v} + f \frac{\partial g}{\partial u\,\partial v} - f \frac{\partial g}{\partial u\,\partial v} - \frac{\partial f}{\partial v} \frac{\partial g}{\partial u} \right] du\,dv$$

$$= \iint\limits_A \left[\frac{\partial f}{\partial u} \frac{\partial g}{\partial v} - \frac{\partial g}{\partial u} \frac{\partial f}{\partial v} \right] du\,dv$$

$$= \iint\limits_A \Delta_G(u, v)\,du\,dv,$$

thus proving what we wanted.

EXERCISES

1. Under the same assumptions as the theorem in this section, assume that $\varphi = \varphi(x, y)$ is a continuous function on $G(A)$, and that we can write $\varphi(x, y) = \partial Q / \partial x$ for some continuous function Q. Prove the more general formula

$$\iint\limits_{G(A)} \varphi(x, y)\,dy\,dx = \iint\limits_A \varphi(G(u, v))\,\Delta_G(u, v)\,du\,dv.$$

[*Hint:* Let $P = 0$ and follow the same pattern of proof as in the text.]

2. Let $(x, y) = G(u, v)$ as in the text. We suppose that $G: U \to \mathbf{R}^2$, and that F is a vector field on $G(U)$. Then $F \circ G$ is a vector field on U. Let C be a C^1-curve in U. Show that

$$\int_{G \circ C} F = \int_C (F \circ G) \cdot \frac{\partial G}{\partial u}\,du + (F \circ G) \cdot \frac{\partial G}{\partial v}\,dv.$$

[Let $F(x, y) = (P(x, y), Q(x, y))$ and apply the definitions.]

Chapter XVI

Orthogonality and Fourier Series

This chapter can be read immediately after Chapter XII.

§1. SCALAR PRODUCTS

Let V be a vector space. A *scalar product* on V is an association which to any pair of elements (v, w) of V associates a number, denoted by $\langle v, w \rangle$, satisfying the following properties:

SP 1. *We have* $\langle v, w \rangle = \langle w, v \rangle$ *for all* v, w *in* V.

SP 2. *If* u, v, w *are elements of* V, *then*

$$\langle u, v + w \rangle = \langle u, v \rangle + \langle u, w \rangle.$$

SP 3. *If* x *is a number, then*

$$\langle xu, v \rangle = x\langle u, v \rangle = \langle u, xv \rangle.$$

We shall also assume that the scalar product satisfies the condition:

SP 4. *For all* v *in* V *we have* $\langle v, v \rangle \geqq 0$.

This is slightly weaker than the corresponding condition for the dot product. If in addition to this we have $\langle v, v \rangle > 0$ whenever $v \neq O$, then we say that the scalar product is *positive definite*. The reason for considering the slightly more general case is that we need it for later application to Fourier series. Cf. §4.

Example 1. Let $V = \mathbf{R}^n$, and define

$$\langle X, Y \rangle = X \cdot Y$$

for elements X, Y of $\mathbf{R}^n$. Then this is a positive definite scalar product.

Example 2. Let V be the space of continuous real-valued functions on the interval $[-\pi, \pi]$. If f, g are in V, we define

$$\langle f, g \rangle = \int_{-\pi}^{\pi} f(t)g(t)\, dt.$$

Simple properties of the integral show that this is a scalar product, which is in fact positive definite.

Later in this chapter, we shall study the second example, which gives rise to the theory of Fourier series. At first, we discuss only general properties of scalar products. The notation $\langle \ , \ \rangle$ is used because in dealing with vector spaces of functions, a dot $f \cdot g$ may be confused with the ordinary product of functions.

As in the case of the dot product, we define elements v, w of V to be *orthogonal*, or *perpendicular*, and write $v \perp w$, if $\langle v, w \rangle = 0$. If S is a subset of V, we denote by $S^\perp$ the set of all elements w in V which are perpendicular to all elements of S, i.e. such that $\langle w, v \rangle = 0$ for all v in S. Then using SP 1, SP 2, and SP 3, one verifies at once that S is a subspace of V, called the *orthogonal space* of S. If w is perpendicular to S, we also write $w \perp S$. Let U be the subspace of V generated by the elements of S. If w is perpendicular to S, and if v_1, v_2 are in S, then

$$\langle w, v_1 + v_2 \rangle = \langle w, v_1 \rangle + \langle w, v_2 \rangle = 0.$$

If c is a number, then

$$\langle w, cv_1 \rangle = c\langle w, v_1 \rangle = 0.$$

Hence w is perpendicular to linear combinations of elements of S, and hence w is perpendicular to U.

Example 3. Let (a_{ij}) be an $m \times n$ matrix, and let $A_1, \ldots, A_m$ be its row vectors. Let $X = (x_1, \ldots, x_n)$ as usual. The system of homogeneous linear equations

$$(**) \qquad \begin{aligned} a_{11}x_1 + \cdots + a_{1n}x_n &= 0 \\ &\vdots \\ a_{m1}x_1 + \cdots + a_{mn}x_n &= 0 \end{aligned}$$

can also be written in abbreviated form using the dot product, as

$$A_1 \cdot X = 0, \quad \ldots, \quad A_m \cdot X = 0.$$

The set of solutions X of this homogeneous system is therefore the set of all vectors perpendicular to $A_1, \ldots, A_m$. It is therefore the subspace of $\mathbf{R}^n$ which is the orthogonal subspace to the space generated by $A_1, \ldots, A_m$. If U is the space of solutions, and if W denotes the space generated by $A_1, \ldots, A_m$, we have

$$U = W^\perp.$$

We call dim U the *dimension of the space of solutions of the system of linear equations*.

We return to the general case. Since we do not yet assume positive definiteness, it may happen that there is some element w in V such that $w \neq O$ but $\langle w, w \rangle = 0$. If such an element exists, then it must satisfy a much stronger orthogonality property:

Theorem 1. *Let w be such that $\langle w, w \rangle = 0$. Then $\langle w, v \rangle = 0$ for all elements v in V.*

Proof. Let t be a number $\neq 0$. Then:

$$0 \leq \langle v + tw, v + tw \rangle = \langle v, v \rangle + 2t\langle v, w \rangle + t^2\langle w, w \rangle$$
$$= \langle v, v \rangle + 2t\langle v, w \rangle.$$

If $\langle v, w \rangle \neq 0$ we selected t very large of opposite sign to $\langle v, w \rangle$. Then $\langle v, v \rangle + 2t\langle v, w \rangle$ is negative, a contradiction. Hence $\langle v, w \rangle = 0$, as was to be shown.

Let V_0 be the set of all elements w in V which are perpendicular to all of V. Then V_0 is a subspace, and from Theorem 1, we conclude that if w is an element of V such that $\langle w, w \rangle = 0$, then w lies in V_0.

As in Chapter I, we can now define what we call the *length* or *norm* by

$$\|v\| = \sqrt{\langle v, v \rangle}.$$

We can take the square root because of our assumption that $\langle v, v \rangle \geq 0$. We have $\|v\| = 0$ if and only if v is an element of V_0. We can prove the *Schwarz inequality* as in Chapter I.

Theorem 2. *For all v, w in V we have*

$$|\langle v, w \rangle| \leq \|v\| \, \|w\|.$$

Proof. The proof given in Chapter I is valid now because it was given without coordinates. However, we repeat it in full. Let $a = \langle w, w \rangle$ and $b = -\langle v, w \rangle$. Then:

$$0 \leq \langle av + bw, av + bw \rangle$$
$$= a^2\langle v, v \rangle + 2ab\langle v, w \rangle + b^2\langle w, w \rangle$$
$$= \|w\|^4\|v\|^2 - 2\|w\|^2\langle v, w \rangle^2 + \|w\|^2\langle v, w \rangle^2$$
$$= \|w\|^4\|v\|^2 - \|w\|^2\langle v, w \rangle^2.$$

If $\|w\| = 0$, then our inequality is obvious. If $\|w\| \neq 0$, then we can divide by $\|w\|^2$ and transposing one term we find that

$$\langle v, w \rangle^2 \leq \|v\|^2\|w\|^2.$$

Taking the square root proves our theorem.

Theorem 3. *The function* $v \mapsto \|v\|$ *satisfies the properties:*

SN 1. *We have* $\|v\| \geq 0$, *and* $\|v\| = 0$ *if and only if v is in V_0.*

SN 2. *For every number c, we have* $\|cv\| = |c|\,\|v\|$.

SN 3. *For v, w in V we have* $\|v + w\| \leq \|v\| + \|w\|$.

Proof. The first assertion follows from Theorem 1. The second is left to the reader. The third is proved with the Schwarz inequality. It suffices to prove that

$$\|v + w\|^2 \leq (\|v\| + \|w\|)^2.$$

To do this, we have

$$\|v + w\|^2 = \langle v + w, v + w \rangle = \langle v, v \rangle + 2\langle v, w \rangle + \langle w, w \rangle$$
$$\leq \|v\|^2 + 2\|v\|\,\|w\| + \|w\|^2$$
$$= (\|v\| + \|w\|)^2,$$

as was to be shown.

An element of V is said to be a *unit vector* if $\|v\| = 1$. If $\|v\| \neq 0$, then $v/\|v\|$ is a unit vector.

The three properties of Theorem 3 are those of a norm, except for the weakened version SN 1 where we use V_0. When this weak version holds, we then call a function $v \mapsto \|v\|$ satisfying these three properties a *seminorm*.

The following two identities follow directly from the definition of the length.

The Pythagoras theorem. *If v, w are perpendicular, then*

$$\|v + w\|^2 = \|v\|^2 + \|w\|^2.$$

The parallelogram law. *For any v, w we have*

$$\|v + w\|^2 + \|v - w\|^2 = 2\|v\|^2 + 2\|w\|^2.$$

The proofs are trivial. We give the first, and leave the second as an exercise. For the first, we have

$$\|v + w\|^2 = \langle v + w, v + w \rangle = \langle v, v \rangle + 2\langle v, w \rangle + \langle w, w \rangle$$
$$= \|v\|^2 + \|w\|^2.$$

Let w be an element of V such that $\|w\| \neq 0$. For any v there exists a unique number c such that $v - cw$ is perpendicular to w. Indeed, for $v - cw$ to be perpendicular to w we must have

$$\langle v - cw, w \rangle = 0,$$

whence $\langle v, w \rangle - \langle cw, w \rangle = 0$ and $\langle v, w \rangle = c\langle w, w \rangle$. Thus

$$c = \frac{\langle v, w \rangle}{\langle w, w \rangle}.$$

Conversely, letting c have this value shows that $v - cw$ is perpendicular to w. We call c the *Fourier coefficient* of v with respect to w.

Example 4. Let V be the space of continuous functions on $[-\pi, \pi]$. Let f be the function given by $f(x) = \sin kx$, where k is some integer $\neq 0$. Then

$$\|f\| = \sqrt{\langle f, f \rangle} = \left(\int_{-\pi}^{\pi} \sin^2 kx \, dx \right)^{1/2}$$

$$= \sqrt{\pi}.$$

If g is any continuous function on $[-\pi, \pi]$, then the Fourier coefficient of g with respect to f is

$$\frac{\langle g, f \rangle}{\langle f, f \rangle} = \frac{1}{\pi} \int_{-\pi}^{\pi} g(x) \sin kx \, dx.$$

As with the case of n-space, we define the projection of v along w to be the vector cw, because of our usual picture:

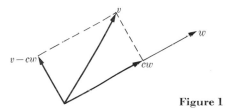

Figure 1

Let $v_1, \ldots, v_n$ be elements of V which are not in V_0, and which are mutually perpendicular, that is $\langle v_i, v_j \rangle = 0$ if $i \neq j$. Let c_i be the Fourier coefficient of v with respect to v_i. Then

$$v - c_1 v_1 - \cdots - c_n v_n$$

is perpendicular to $v_1, \ldots, v_n$. To see this, all we have to do is to take the product with v_j for any j. All the terms involving $\langle v_i, v_j \rangle$ will give 0 if $i \neq j$, and we shall have two remaining terms

$$\langle v, v_j \rangle - c_j \langle v_j, v_j \rangle$$

which cancel. Thus subtracting linear combinations as above orthogonalizes v with respect to $v_1, \ldots, v_n$. The next theorem shows that $c_1 v_1 + \cdots + c_n v_n$ gives the closest approximation to v as a linear combination of $v_1, \ldots, v_n$.

Theorem 4. *Let $v_1, \ldots, v_n$ be vectors which are mutually perpendicular, and such that $\|v_i\| \neq 0$ for all i. Let v be an element of V, and let c_i be the Fourier coefficient of v with respect to v_i. Let $a_1, \ldots, a_n$ be numbers. Then*

$$\left\| v - \sum_{k=1}^{n} c_k v_k \right\| \leq \left\| v - \sum_{k=1}^{n} a_k v_k \right\|.$$

Proof. We know that

$$v - \sum_{k=1}^{n} c_k v_k$$

is perpendicular to each v_i, $i = 1, \ldots, n$. Hence it is perpendicular to any linear combination of $v_1, \ldots, v_n$. Now we have:

$$\left\| v - \sum a_k v_k \right\|^2 = \left\| v - \sum c_k v_k + \sum (c_k - a_k) v_k \right\|^2$$

$$= \left\| v - \sum c_k v_k \right\|^2 + \left\| \sum (c_k - a_k) v_k \right\|^2$$

by the Pythagoras theorem. This proves that

$$\left\| v - \sum c_k v_k \right\|^2 \leq \left\| v - \sum a_k v_k \right\|^2,$$

and thus our theorem is proved.

The next theorem is known as the *Bessel inequality*.

Theorem 5. *If $v_1, \ldots, v_n$ are mutually perpendicular unit vectors, and if c_i is the Fourier coefficient of v with respect to v_i, then*

$$\sum_{i=1}^{n} c_i^2 \leq \|v\|^2.$$

Proof. We have

$$0 \leq \left\langle v - \sum c_i v_i, v - \sum c_i v_i \right\rangle$$

$$= \langle v, v \rangle - \sum 2 c_i \langle v, v_i \rangle + \sum c_i^2$$

$$= \langle v, v \rangle - \sum c_i^2.$$

From this our inequality follows.

EXERCISES

1. Let V be a vector space with a scalar product. Show that $\langle O, v \rangle = 0$ for all v in V.

2. Assume that the scalar product is positive definite. If $v_1, \ldots, v_n$ are non-zero elements which are mutually perpendicular, show that they are linearly independent.

3. Let M be a square $n \times n$ matrix which is equal to its transpose. If X, Y are column n-vectors, then

$$^t XMY$$

is a 1×1 matrix, which we identify with a number. Show that the map

$$(X, Y) \mapsto {}^t XMY$$

satisfies the three properties SP 1, SP 2, SP 3. Give an example of a 2×2 matrix M such that the fourth property is not satisfied.

§2. ORTHOGONAL BASES

Let V be a vector space with a positive definite scalar product throughout this section. A basis $\{v_1, \ldots, v_n\}$ of V is said to be *orthogonal* if its elements are mutually perpendicular, i.e. if $\langle v_i, v_j \rangle = 0$ whenever $i \neq j$. If in addition each element of the basis has length 1, then the basis is called *orthonormal*.

The standard unit vectors of $\mathbf{R}^n$ form an orthonormal basis of $\mathbf{R}^n$, with respect to the ordinary dot product.

Theorem 6. *Let V be a finite dimensional vector space, with a positive definite scalar product. Let W be a subspace of V, and let $\{w_1, \ldots, w_m\}$ be an orthogonal basis of W. If $W \neq V$, then there exist elements $w_{m+1}, \ldots, w_n$ of V such that $\{w_1, \ldots, w_n\}$ is an orthogonal basis of V.*

Proof. The method of proof is as important as the theorem, and is called the Gram-Schmidt orthogonalization process. We know from Chapter IX that we can find elements $v_{m+1}, \ldots, v_n$ of V such that

$$\{w_1, \ldots, w_m, v_{m+1}, \ldots, v_n\}$$

is a basis of V. Of course, it is not an orthogonal basis. Let W_{m+1} be the space generated by $w_1, \ldots, w_m, w_{m+1}$. We shall first obtain an orthogonal basis of W_{m+1}. The idea is to take v_{m+1} and subtract from it its projection along $w_1, \ldots, w_m$. Thus we let

$$c_1 = \frac{\langle v_{m+1}, w_1 \rangle}{\langle w_1, w_1 \rangle}, \quad \ldots, \quad c_m = \frac{\langle v_{m+1}, w_m \rangle}{\langle w_m, w_m \rangle}.$$

Let

$$w_{m+1} = v_{m+1} - c_1 w_1 - \cdots - c_m w_m.$$

Then w_{m+1} is perpendicular to $w_1, \ldots, w_m$. Furthermore, $w_{m+1} \neq O$ (otherwise v_{m+1} would be linearly dependent on $w_1, \ldots, w_m$), and v_{m+1} lies in the space generated by $w_1, \ldots, w_{m+1}$ because

$$v_{m+1} = w_{m+1} + c_1 w_1 + \cdots + c_m w_m.$$

Hence $\{w_1, \ldots, w_{m+1}\}$ is an orthogonal basis of W_{m+1}. We can now proceed by induction, showing that the space W_{m+s} generated by

$$w_1, \ldots, w_m, v_{m+1}, \ldots, v_{m+s}$$

has an orthogonal basis

$$\{w_1, \ldots, w_{m+1}, \ldots, w_s\}$$

with $s = 1, \ldots, n - m$. This concludes the proof.

Corollary. *Let V be a finite dimensional vector space with a positive definite scalar product. Assume that $V \neq \{O\}$. Then V has an orthogonal basis.*

Proof. By hypothesis, there exists an element v_1 of V such that $v_1 \neq O$. We let W be the subspace generated by v_1, and apply the theorem to get the desired basis.

We summarize the procedure of Theorem 6 once more. Suppose we are given an arbitrary basis $\{v_1, \ldots, v_n\}$ of V. We wish to orthogonalize it. We proceed as follows. We let:

$$v_1' = v_1$$

$$v_2' = v_2 - \frac{\langle v_2, v_1' \rangle}{\langle v_1', v_1' \rangle} v_1'$$

$$v_3' = v_3 - \frac{\langle v_3, v_2' \rangle}{\langle v_2', v_2' \rangle} v_2' - \frac{\langle v_3, v_1' \rangle}{\langle v_1', v_1' \rangle} v_1'$$

$$\vdots$$

$$v_n' = v_n - \frac{\langle v_n, v_{n-1}' \rangle}{\langle v_{n-1}', v_{n-1}' \rangle} v_{n-1}' - \cdots - \frac{\langle v_n, v_1' \rangle}{\langle v_1', v_1' \rangle} v_1'.$$

Then $\{v_1', \ldots, v_n'\}$ is an orthogonal basis.

Given an orthogonal basis, we can always obtain an orthonormal basis by dividing each vector by its length.

Example 1. Find an orthonormal basis for the vector space generated by the vectors $(1, 1, 0, 1)$, $(1, -2, 0, 0)$, and $(1, 0, -1, 2)$.

Let us denote these vectors by A, B, C. Let

$$B' = B - \frac{B \cdot A}{A \cdot A} A.$$

In other words, we subtract from B its projection along A. Then B' is perpendicular to A. We find

$$B' = \tfrac{1}{3}(4, -5, 0, 1).$$

Now we subtract from C its projection along A and B', and thus we let

$$C' = C - \frac{C \cdot A}{A \cdot A} A - \frac{C \cdot B'}{B' \cdot B'} B'.$$

Since A and B' are perpendicular, taking the scalar product of C' with A and B' shows that C' is perpendicular to both A and B'. We find:

$$C' = \tfrac{1}{7}(-4, -2, -1, 6).$$

The vectors A, B', C' are non-zero and mutually perpendicular. They lie in the space generated by A, B, C. Hence they constitute an orthogonal basis for that space. If we wish an orthonormal basis, then we divide these vectors by their length, and thus obtain

$$\frac{A}{\|A\|} = \frac{1}{\sqrt{3}}(1, 1, 0, 1), \qquad \frac{B'}{\|B'\|} = \frac{1}{\sqrt{42}}(4, -5, 0, 1),$$

$$\frac{C'}{\|C'\|} = \frac{1}{\sqrt{57}}(-4, -2, -1, 6),$$

as an orthonormal basis.

Theorem 7. *Let V be a vector space with a scalar product, of dimension n. Let W be a subspace of V of dimension r. Let U be the subspace of V consisting of all elements which are perpendicular to W. Then U has dimension $n - r$. In other words,*

$$\dim W + \dim W^\perp = \dim V.$$

Proof. If W consists of O alone, or if $W = V$, then our assertion is obvious. We therefore assume that $W \neq V$ and that $W \neq \{O\}$. Let $\{w_1, \ldots, w_r\}$ be an orthonormal basis of W. By Theorem 6, there exist elements $u_{r+1}, \ldots, u_n$ of V such that

$$\{w_1, \ldots, w_r, u_{r+1}, \ldots, u_n\}$$

is an orthonormal basis of V. We shall prove that $\{u_{r+1}, \ldots, u_n\}$ is an orthonormal basis of U.

Let u be an element of U. Then there exist numbers $x_1, \ldots, x_n$ such that

$$u = x_1 w_1 + \cdots + x_r w_r + x_{r+1} u_{r+1} + \cdots + x_n u_n.$$

Since u is perpendicular to W, taking the product with any w_i $(i = 1, \ldots, r)$, we find

$$0 = \langle u, w_i \rangle = x_i \langle w_i, w_i \rangle = x_i.$$

Hence all $x_i = 0$ $(i = 1, \ldots, r)$. Therefore u is a linear combination of $u_{r+1}, \ldots, u_n$.

Conversely, let $u = x_{r+1}u_{r+1} + \cdots + x_n u_n$ be a linear combination of $u_{r+1}, \ldots, u_n$. Taking the product with any w_i yields 0. Hence u is perpendicular to all w_i $(i = 1, \ldots, r)$, and hence is perpendicular to W. This proves that $u_{r+1}, \ldots, u_n$ generate U. Since they are mutually perpendicular, and of norm 1, they form an orthonormal basis of U, whose dimension is therefore $n - r$.

Example 2. Consider $\mathbf{R}^3$. Let A, B be two linearly independent vectors in $\mathbf{R}^3$. Then the space of vectors which are perpendicular to both A and B is a 1-dimensional space. If $\{N\}$ is a basis for this space, any other basis for this space is of type $\{tN\}$, where t is a number $\neq 0$.

Again in $\mathbf{R}^3$, let N be a non-zero vector. The space of vectors perpendicular to N is a 2-dimensional space, i.e. a plane, passing through the origin O.

EXERCISES

1. What is the dimension of the subspace of $\mathbf{R}^6$ perpendicular to the two vectors $(1, 1, -2, 3, 4, 5)$ and $(0, 0, 1, 1, 0, 7)$?

2. Find an orthonormal basis for the subspaces of $\mathbf{R}^3$ generated by the following vectors: (a) $(1, 1, -1)$ and $(1, 0, 1)$, (b) $(2, 1, 1)$ and $(1, 3, -1)$.

3. Find an orthonormal basis for the subspace of $\mathbf{R}^4$ generated by the vectors $(1, 2, 1, 0)$ and $(1, 2, 3, 1)$.

4. Find an orthonormal basis for the subspace of $\mathbf{R}^4$ generated by $(1, 1, 0, 0)$, $(1, -1, 1, 1)$, and $(-1, 0, 2, 1)$.

In the next exercises, we consider the vector space of continuous functions on the interval $[0, 1]$. We define the scalar product of two such functions f, g by the rule

$$\langle f, g \rangle = \int_0^1 f(t)g(t)\, dt.$$

5. Let V be the subspace of functions generated by the two functions $f(t) = t$ and $g(t) = t^2$. Find an orthonormal basis for V.

6. Let V be the subspace generated by the three functions 1, t, t^2 (where 1 is the constant function). Find an orthonormal basis for V.

§3. APPLICATION TO LINEAR EQUATIONS

Theorem 7 of the preceding section has an interesting application to the theory of linear equations. We consider such a system:

$$(**) \qquad \begin{array}{c} a_{11}x_1 + \cdots + a_{1n}x_n = 0 \\ \vdots \qquad\qquad \vdots \\ a_{m1}x_1 + \cdots + a_{mn}x_n = 0. \end{array}$$

We can interpret its space of solutions in three ways:

(a) *It consists of those vectors X giving linear relations*

$$x_1 A^1 + \cdots + x_n A^n = O$$

between the columns of A.

(b) *The solutions form the space orthogonal to the row vectors of the matrix A.*

(c) *The solutions form the kernel of the linear map represented by A, i.e. are the solutions of the equation $AX = O$.*

If $A = (a_{ij})$ is an $m \times n$ matrix, then the columns $A^1, \ldots, A^n$ generate a subspace, whose dimension is called the *column rank* of A. The rows $A_1, \ldots, A_m$ of A generate a subspace whose dimension is called the *row rank* of A. We may also say that the column rank of A is the maximum number of linearly independent columns, and the row rank is the maximum number of linearly independent rows of A.

Theorem 8. *Let $A = (a_{ij})$ be an $m \times n$ matrix. Then the row rank and the column rank of A are equal to the same number r. Furthermore, $n - r$ is the dimension of the space of solutions of the system of linear equations* (**).

Proof. We shall prove all our statements simultaneously. We consider the map

$$L: \mathbf{R}^n \to \mathbf{R}^m$$

given by

$$L(X) = x_1 A^1 + \cdots + x_n A^n.$$

This map is obviously linear. Its image consists of the space generated by the column vectors of A. Its kernel is by definition the space of solutions of the system of linear equations. By Theorem 3 of Chapter X, §3, we obtain

column rank + dim space of solutions = n.

On the other hand, interpreting the space of solutions as the orthogonal space to the row vectors, and using Theorem 7 of the preceding section, we obtain

row rank + dim space of solutions = n.

From this all our assertions follow at once, and Theorem 8 is proved.

Let $b_1, \ldots, b_m$ be numbers, and consider the system of inhomogeneous equations

$$
\begin{aligned}
A_1 \cdot X &= b_1 \\
&\vdots \\
A_m \cdot X &= b_m.
\end{aligned}
$$

(*)

It may happen that this system has no solution at all, i.e. that the equations are inconsistent. For instance, the system

$$2x + 3y - z = 1$$
$$2x + 3y - z = 2$$

has no solution. However, if there is at least one solution, then all solutions are obtainable from this one by adding an arbitrary solution of the associated homogeneous system (**) (cf. Exercise 7). Hence in this case again, we can speak of the dimension of the set of solutions. It is the dimension of the associated homogeneous system.

Example 1. Find the dimension of the set of solutions of the following system of equations, and determine this set in $\mathbf{R}^3$:

$$2x + y + z = 1$$
$$y - z = 0.$$

We see by inspection that there is at least one solution, namely $x = \frac{1}{2}$, $y = z = 0$. The rank of the matrix

$$\begin{pmatrix} 2 & 1 & 1 \\ 0 & 1 & -1 \end{pmatrix}$$

is 2. Hence the dimension of the set of solutions is 1. The vector space of solutions of the homogeneous system has dimension 1, and one solution is easily found to be

$$y = z = 1, \qquad x = -\tfrac{1}{2}.$$

Hence the set of solutions of the inhomogeneous system is the set of all vectors

$$(\tfrac{1}{2}, 0, 0) + t(-\tfrac{1}{2}, 1, 1),$$

where t ranges over all real numbers. We see that our set of solutions is a straight line.

Example 2. Find a basis for the space of solutions of the equation

$$3x - 2y + z = 0.$$

The space of solutions is the space orthogonal to the vector $(3, -2, 1)$ and hence has dimension 2. There are of course many bases for this space. To find one, we first extend $(3, -2, 1) = A$ to a basis of $\mathbf{R}^3$. We do this by selecting vectors B, C such that A, B, C are linearly independent. For instance, take

$$B = (0, 1, 0)$$

and

$$C = (0, 0, 1).$$

The determinant

$$\begin{vmatrix} 3 & -2 & 1 \\ 0 & 1 & 0 \\ 0 & 0 & 1 \end{vmatrix}$$

is not 0, so this choice of vectors will do. Now we must orthogonalize them. Let

$$B' = B - \frac{\langle B, A \rangle}{\langle A, A \rangle} A = (\tfrac{3}{7}, \tfrac{5}{7}, \tfrac{1}{7}),$$

$$C' = C - \frac{\langle C, A \rangle}{\langle A, A \rangle} A - \frac{\langle C, B' \rangle}{\langle B', B' \rangle} B'$$
$$= (0, 0, 1) - \tfrac{1}{14}(3, -2, 1) - \tfrac{1}{35}(3, 5, 1).$$

Then $\{B', C'\}$ is a basis for the space of solutions of the given equation.

EXERCISES

1. Find the rank of the following matrices.

(a) $\begin{pmatrix} 2 & 1 & 3 \\ 7 & 2 & 0 \end{pmatrix}$ (b) $\begin{pmatrix} -1 & 2 & -2 \\ 3 & 4 & -5 \end{pmatrix}$

(c) $\begin{pmatrix} 1 & 2 & 7 \\ 2 & 4 & -1 \end{pmatrix}$ (d) $\begin{pmatrix} 1 & 2 & -3 \\ -1 & -2 & 3 \\ 4 & 8 & -12 \\ 0 & 0 & 0 \end{pmatrix}$

2. Let A, B be two matrices which can be multiplied. Show that rank of $AB \leq$ rank of A, and also rank of $AB \leq$ rank of B.

3. Let A be a triangular matrix

$$\begin{pmatrix} a_{11} & a_{12} & \cdots & a_{1n} \\ 0 & a_{22} & \cdots & a_{2n} \\ \vdots & \vdots & \ddots & \vdots \\ 0 & 0 & \cdots & a_{nn} \end{pmatrix}.$$

Assume that none of the diagonal elements is equal to 0. What is the rank of A?

4. Find the dimension of the space of solutions of the following systems of equations. Also find a basis for this space of solutions.

(a) $2x + y - z = 0$ (b) $x - y + z = 0$
$\quad\quad y + z = 0$

(c) $4x + 7y - \pi z = 0$ (d) $x + y + z = 0$
    $2x - y + z = 0$ $x - y = 0$
                                      $y + z = 0$

5. What is the dimension of the space of solutions of the following systems of linear equations?

(a) $2x - 3y + z = 0$ (b) $2x + 7y = 0$
    $x + y - z = 0$ $x - 2y + z = 0$

(c) $2x - 3y + z = 0$ (d) $x + y + z = 0$
    $x + y - z = 0$ $2x + 2y + 2z = 0$
    $3x + 4y = 0$
    $5x + y + z = 0$

6. Let A be a non-zero vector in n-space. Let P be a point in n-space. What is the dimension of the set of solutions of the equation

$$X \cdot A = P \cdot A?$$

7. Let $AX = B$ be a system of linear equations, where A is an $m \times n$ matrix, X is an n-vector, and B is an m-vector. Assume that there is one solution $X = X_0$. Show that every solution is of the form $X_0 + Y$, where Y is a solution of the homogeneous system $AY = O$, and conversely any vector of the form $X_0 + Y$ is a solution.

8. If A is an $n \times n$ matrix whose determinant is $\neq 0$, and B is a given vector in n-space, show that the system of linear equations $AX = B$ has a unique solution. If $B = O$, this solution is $X = O$.

§4. FOURIER SERIES

In this section, we consider the special case when the scalar product is given by

$$\langle f, g \rangle = \int_{-\pi}^{\pi} f(x)g(x) \, dx.$$

We observe that the inequalities of Theorem 2, Theorem 3 (the triangle inequality), Theorem 4, and Theorem 5 give inequalities for certain integrals, which look much more complicated when written out in terms of the integral. For instance, the Schwarz inequality now reads

$$\left| \int_{-\pi}^{\pi} f(x)g(x) \, dx \right| \leq \left(\int_{-\pi}^{\pi} f(x)^2 \, dx \right)^{1/2} \left(\int_{-\pi}^{\pi} g(x)^2 \, dx \right)^{1/2}.$$

One can write out similarly the other inequalities. The advantage of the abstract notation now becomes evident, since it allows us to give a geometric interpretation for such complicated expressions, and allows us to use a simple notation which can be easily understood at once.

In our previous examples, we used continuous functions on the interval $[-\pi, \pi]$. For many applications one has to deal with somewhat more general functions. A convenient class of functions is that of piecewise continuous functions. We say that f is piecewise continuous if it is continuous except at a finite number of points, and if at each such point c the limits

$$\lim_{\substack{h \to 0 \\ h > 0}} f(c - h) \quad \text{and} \quad \lim_{\substack{h \to 0 \\ h > 0}} f(c + h)$$

both exist. The graph of a piecewise continuous function then looks like this:

Figure 2

Let V be the set of functions on the interval $[-\pi, \pi]$ which are piecewise continuous. Then V is a vector space, and furthermore, if f, g are piecewise continuous then the ordinary product fg is also piecewise continuous. We can then form the scalar product $\langle f, g \rangle$ since the integral is defined for piecewise continuous functions, and the four properties SP 1 through SP 4 are satisfied. However, the scalar product is not positive definite. A function f which is such that $f(x) = 0$ except at a finite number of points has norm 0. Such functions form precisely the subspace V_0 which we mentioned in §1. Indeed, suppose f is piecewise continuous on $[-\pi, \pi]$ and suppose we have a partition of $[-\pi, \pi]$ into intervals

$$-\pi = a_0 < a_1 < \cdots < a_r = \pi$$

such that f is continuous on each subinterval $[a_i, a_{i+1}]$ except possibly at the end points a_i, $i = 0, \ldots, r - 1$. Suppose that $\|f\| = 0$, so that also $\|f\|^2 = 0 = \langle f, f \rangle$. This means that

$$\int_{-\pi}^{\pi} f(x)^2 \, dx = 0,$$

and the integral is the sum of the integrals over the smaller intervals, so that

$$\sum_{i=0}^{r-1} \int_{a_i}^{a_{i+1}} f(x)^2 \, dx = 0.$$

Each integral satisfies

$$\int_{a_i}^{a_{i+1}} f(x)^2 \, dx \geqq 0$$

and hence each such integral is equal to 0. However, since f is continuous on an interval $[a_i, a_{i+1}]$ except possibly at the end points, we must have $f(x)^2 = 0$ for $a_i < x < a_{i+1}$, whence $f(x) = 0$ for $a_i < x < a_{i+1}$.

Hence $f(x) = 0$ except at a finite number of points. Conversely, it is clear that if $f(x) = 0$ except at a finite number of points, then $\|f\| = 0$. This gives a description of the space V_0 in the present context.

The space V of piecewise continuous functions on $[-\pi, \pi]$ is not finite dimensional. Instead of dealing with a finite number of orthogonal vectors, we must now deal with an infinite number.

For each positive integer n we consider the functions

$$\varphi_n(x) = \cos nx, \qquad \psi_n(x) = \sin nx,$$

and we also consider the function

$$\varphi_0(x) = 1.$$

It is verified by easy direct integrations that

$$\|\varphi_n\| = \|\psi_n\| = \sqrt{\pi} \qquad \text{if} \qquad n \neq 0,$$
$$\|\varphi_0\| = \sqrt{2\pi}.$$

Hence the Fourier coefficients of a function f with respect to our functions $1, \cos nx, \sin nx$ are equal to:

$$a_0 = \frac{1}{2\pi} \int_{-\pi}^{\pi} f(x)\, dx, \qquad a_n = \frac{1}{\pi} \int_{-\pi}^{\pi} f(x) \cos nx\, dx,$$

$$b_n = \frac{1}{\pi} \int_{-\pi}^{\pi} f(x) \sin nx\, dx.$$

Furthermore, the functions $1, \cos nx, \sin mx$ are easily verified to be mutually orthogonal. In other words, for any pair of distinct functions f, g among $1, \cos nx, \sin mx$ we have $\langle f, g \rangle = 0$. This means:

If $m \neq n$ and $n \geq 0$, then

$$\int_{-\pi}^{\pi} \cos nx \cos mx\, dx = 0, \qquad \int_{-\pi}^{\pi} \sin nx \sin mx = 0;$$

and for any m, n:

$$\int_{-\pi}^{\pi} \cos nx \sin mx\, dx = 0.$$

The verifications of these orthogonalities are mere exercises in elementary calculus. Cf. Exercise 6.

The Fourier series of a function f (piecewise continuous) is defined to be the series

$$a_0 + \sum_{k=1}^{\infty} (a_k \cos kx + b_k \sin kx).$$

The partial sum

$$s_n(x) = a_0 + \sum_{k=1}^{n} (a_k \cos kx + b_k \sin kx)$$

is simply the projection of the function f on the space generated by the functions 1, $\cos kx$, $\sin kx$ for $k = 1, \ldots, n$. In the finite dimensional case, when we have an orthogonal basis $\{v_1, \ldots, v_n\}$ and when c_i is the Fourier coefficient of a vector v, we have

$$v = c_1 v_1 + \cdots + c_n v_n.$$

In the present infinite dimensional case, we write

$$f \sim a_0 + \sum_{k=1}^{\infty} (a_k \cos kx + b_k \sin kx).$$

The sense in which one can replace the sign $\sim$ by an equality depends on various theorems whose proofs go beyond this course. One of these theorems is the following:

Theorem 9. *Assume that the piecewise continuous function f on $[-\pi, \pi]$ is orthogonal to every one of the functions 1, $\cos nx$, $\sin nx$. Then f belongs to V_0, that is $f(x) = 0$ except at a finite number of x. If f is continuous, then $f = 0$.*

Theorem 9 shows at least that a continuous function is entirely determined by its Fourier series. There is another sense, however, in which we would like f to be equal to its Fourier series, namely we would like the values $f(x)$ to be given by

$$f(x) = a_0 + \sum_{k=1}^{\infty} (a_k \cos kx + b_k \sin kx)$$
$$= a_0 + \lim_{n \to \infty} \sum_{k=1}^{n} (a_k \cos kx + b_k \sin kx).$$

It is false in general that if f is merely continuous then $f(x)$ is given by the series. However, it is true under some reasonable conditions, for instance:

Theorem 10. *Let $-\pi < x < \pi$ and assume that f is differentiable in some open interval containing x, and has a continuous derivative in this interval. Then $f(x)$ is equal to the value of the Fourier series.*

Example 1. Find the Fourier series of the function f such that

$$f(x) = 0 \quad \text{if} \quad -\pi < x < 0,$$
$$f(x) = 1 \quad \text{if} \quad 0 < x < \pi.$$

The graph of f is as follows.

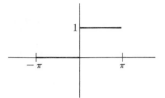

Figure 3

Since the Fourier coefficients are determined by an integral, it does not matter how we define f at $-\pi$, 0, or π. We have

$$a_0 = \frac{1}{2\pi} \int_{-\pi}^{\pi} f(x)\, dx = \frac{1}{2\pi} \int_{0}^{\pi} dx = 1,$$

$$a_n = \frac{1}{\pi} \int_{0}^{\pi} \cos nx\, dx = 0,$$

$$b_n = \frac{1}{\pi} \int_{0}^{\pi} \sin nx\, dx = \frac{1}{\pi n} (-\cos nx)\Big|_{0}^{\pi}$$

$$= \begin{cases} 0 & \text{if } n \text{ is even,} \\ \dfrac{2}{\pi n} & \text{if } n \text{ is odd.} \end{cases}$$

Hence the Fourier series of f is:

$$f(x) \sim 1 + \sum_{m=0}^{\infty} \frac{2}{(2m+1)\pi} \sin(2m+1)x.$$

By Theorem 10, we know that $f(x)$ is actually given by the series except at the points $-\pi$, 0, and π.

Example 2. Find the Fourier series of the function f such that $f(x) = -1$ if $-\pi < x < 0$ and $f(x) = x$ if $0 < x < \pi$.
The graph of f is as follows.

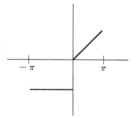

Figure 4

Again we compute the Fourier coefficients. We evaluate the integral over each of the intervals $[-\pi, 0]$ and $[0, \pi]$ since the function is given by different formulas over these intervals. We have

$$a_0 = \frac{1}{2\pi} \int_{-\pi}^{0} (-1)\, dx + \frac{1}{2\pi} \int_{0}^{\pi} x\, dx = \frac{1}{2} + \frac{\pi}{4},$$

$$a_n = \frac{1}{\pi} \int_{-\pi}^{0} (-1) \cos nx\, dx + \frac{1}{\pi} \int_{0}^{\pi} x \cos nx\, dx$$

$$= \begin{cases} 0 & \text{if } n \text{ is even,} \\ -\dfrac{2}{\pi n^2} & \text{if } n \text{ is odd,} \end{cases}$$

$$b_n = \frac{1}{\pi} \int_{-\pi}^{0} (-1) \sin nx\, dx + \frac{1}{\pi} \int_{0}^{\pi} x \sin nx\, dx$$

$$= \begin{cases} -\dfrac{1}{n} & \text{if } n \text{ is even,} \\ \dfrac{2}{\pi n} + \dfrac{1}{n} & \text{if } n \text{ is odd.} \end{cases}$$

Thus we obtain:

$$f(x) = \frac{1}{2} + \frac{\pi}{4} + \sum_{k=1}^{n} (a_k \cos kx + b_k \sin kx).$$

The equality is valid for $-\pi < x < 0$ and $0 < x < \pi$ by Theorem 10.

Example 3. Find the Fourier series of the function $\sin^2 x$.
We have

$$\sin^2 x = \frac{1 - \cos 2x}{2} = \frac{1}{2} - \frac{1}{2} \cos 2x.$$

This is already written as a Fourier series, so the expression on the right is the desired Fourier series.

A function f is said to be *periodic* of period 2π if we have $f(x + 2\pi) = f(x)$ for all x. For such a function, we then have by induction $f(x + 2\pi n) = f(x)$ for all positive integers n. Furthermore, letting $t = x + 2\pi$, we see also that

$$f(t - 2\pi) = f(t)$$

for all t, and hence $f(x - 2\pi n) = f(x)$ for all x and all positive integers n.

Given a piecewise continuous function on the interval $-\pi \leq x < \pi$, we can extend it to a piecewise continuous function which is periodic of period 2π over all of $\mathbf{R}$, simply by periodicity.

Example 4. Let $f(x) = x$ on $-\pi \leq x < \pi$. If we extend f by periodicity, then the graph of the extended function looks like this:

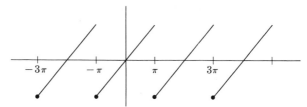

$-3\pi \qquad -\pi \qquad \pi \qquad 3\pi$

Figure 5

Example 5. Let f be the function on the interval $-\pi \leq x < \pi$ given by:

$$f(x) = 0 \quad \text{if} \quad -\pi \leq x \leq 0,$$
$$f(x) = 1 \quad \text{if} \quad 0 < x < \pi.$$

Then the graph of the function extended by periodicity looks like this:

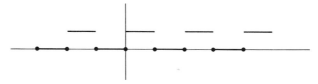

Figure 6

Example 6. Let f be the function on the interval $-\pi \leq x < \pi$ given by $f(x) = e^x$. Then the graph of the extended function looks like this:

$-5\pi \quad -4\pi \quad -3\pi \quad -2\pi \quad -\pi \qquad \pi \quad 2\pi \quad 3\pi \quad 4\pi \quad 5\pi$

Figure 7

On the other hand, we may also be given a function over the interval $[0, 2\pi]$ and then extend this function by periodicity.

Example 7. Let $f(x) = x$ on the interval $0 \leq x < 2\pi$. The graph of the function extended by periodicity to all of **R** looks like this:

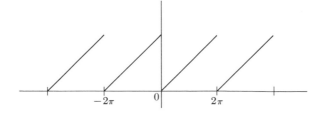

$-2\pi \qquad 0 \qquad 2\pi$

Figure 8

This is different from the function in Example 4, since in the present case, the extended function is never negative. When the function is given on an interval $[0, 2\pi]$, we compute the Fourier coefficients by taking the integral from 0 to 2π. In the present case, we therefore have:

$$a_0 = \frac{1}{2\pi} \int_0^{2\pi} x \, dx = \pi,$$

$$a_n = \frac{1}{\pi} \int_0^{2\pi} x \cos nx \, dx = 0 \qquad \text{for all } n,$$

$$b_n = \frac{1}{\pi} \int_0^{2\pi} x \sin nx \, dx = -\frac{2}{n}.$$

Hence we have, for $0 < x < 2\pi$:

$$x = \pi - 2 \left(\sin x + \frac{\sin 2x}{2} + \frac{\sin 3x}{3} + \cdots \right).$$

EXERCISES

1. Write out in full in terms of the integrals the inequality of Theorem 3 (triangle inequality).

2. If f is periodic of period 2π and a, b are numbers, show that

$$\int_a^b f(x) \, dx = \int_{a+2\pi}^{b+2\pi} f(x) \, dx = \int_{a-2\pi}^{b-2\pi} f(x) \, dx.$$

[*Hint:* Change variables, letting $u = x - 2\pi$, $du = dx$.] Also, prove:

$$\int_{-\pi}^{\pi} f(x + a) \, dx = \int_{-\pi}^{\pi} f(x) \, dx = \int_{-\pi+a}^{\pi+a} f(x) \, dx.$$

[*Hint:* Split the integral over the bounds $-\pi + a$, $-\pi$, π, $\pi + a$.]

3. Let f be an even function, that is $f(x) = f(-x)$, for all x. Assume that f is periodic of period 2π. Show that all its Fourier coefficients with respect to $\sin nx$ are 0. Let g be an odd function (that is $g(-x) = -g(x)$). Show that all its Fourier coefficients with respect to $\cos nx$ are 0.

4. Compute the Fourier series of the functions, given on the interval $-\pi < x < \pi$ by the following $f(x)$:

   (a) x (b) x^2 (c) $|x|$ (d) $\sin^2 x$
   (e) $|\sin x|$ (f) $|\cos x|$ (g) $\sin^3 x$ (h) $\cos^3 x$

5. Show that the following relations hold:

   (a) For $0 < x < 2\pi$ and $a \neq 0$,

$$\pi e^{ax} = (e^{2a\pi} - 1) \left(\frac{1}{2a} + \sum_{k=1}^{\infty} \frac{a \cos kx - k \sin kx}{k^2 + a^2} \right).$$

(b) For $0 < x < 2\pi$ and a not an integer,

$$\pi \cos ax = \frac{\sin 2a\pi}{2a} + \sum_{k=1}^{\infty} \frac{a \sin 2a\pi \cos kx + k(\cos 2a\pi - 1) \sin kx}{a^2 - k^2}.$$

(c) Letting $x = \pi$ in part (b), conclude that

$$\frac{a\pi}{\sin a\pi} = 1 + 2a^2 \sum_{k=1}^{\infty} \frac{(-1)^k}{a^2 - k^2}.$$

(d) For $0 < x < 2\pi$,

$$\frac{(\pi - x)^2}{4} = \frac{\pi^2}{12} + \sum_{k=1}^{\infty} \frac{\cos kx}{k^2}.$$

6. Prove that the functions 1, cos nx, sin mx are mutually orthogonal. *Hint:* Use formulas like

$$\sin A \cos B = \tfrac{1}{2}[\sin (A + B) + \sin (A - B)].$$

Chapter XVII

ϵ *and* δ *again*

§1. NORMED VECTOR SPACES

The natural habitat of ϵ and δ is the normed vector space. Let V be a vector space. A *norm* on V is a function, which to each element v of V associates a number, denoted by $\|v\|$, satisfying the following properties:

N 1. *If $v \neq O$, then $\|v\| > 0$, and $\|O\| = 0$.*

N 2. *If v is an element of V and c is a number, then*

$$\|cv\| = |c| \, \|v\|.$$

N 3. *If v_1, v_2 are elements of V, then*

$$\|v_1 + v_2\| \leq \|v_1\| + \|v_2\|.$$

Example 1. If $V = \mathbf{R}^n$ and $\|X\| = \sqrt{X \cdot X}$ is defined as in Chapter I, then $\| \ \|$ is a norm, called the *Euclidean norm.*

Example 2. Let $V = \mathbf{R}^n$, and define the norm of a vector

$$X = (x_1, \ldots, x_n)$$

to be the maximum of the absolute values of the coordinates, that is

$$\|X\| = \max(|x_1|, \ldots, |x_n|).$$

It is immediately verified that this is a norm, called the *sup norm.* We carry out this verification in detail. If $\|X\| = 0$, then all $|x_i| = 0$, so $X = O$. Let c be a number. Then

$$\begin{aligned}
\|cX\| &= \max(|cx_1|, \ldots, |cx_n|) \\
&= \max(|c| \, |x_1|, \ldots, |c| \, |x_n|) \\
&= |c| \max(|x_1|, \ldots, |x_n|) \\
&= |c| \, \|X\|.
\end{aligned}$$

Example 3. Let V be the space of continuous functions on the interval $[0, 1]$. If f is an element of V, we define

$$\|f\|_1 = \int_0^1 |f(x)| \, dx.$$

Elementary properties of the integral show that this is a norm on V, called the L_1-norm.

These three examples should convince the reader that norms are important in their own right, and not only the Euclidean norm which has been used mostly throughout this book.

A *normed vector space* is a vector space V, together with a prescribed norm on it.

We can define the notion of a sphere and a ball in an arbitrary normed vector space V. Indeed, let v_0 be an element of V, and let r be a number > 0. We define the open ball of center v_0 and radius r to be the set of all elements v in V such that

$$\|v - v_0\| < r.$$

Similarly, we define the closed ball by replacing the sign $<$ by $\leq$, and we define the sphere of radius r centered at v_0 to be the set of all elements v in V such that

$$\|v - v_0\| = r.$$

Example 4. Let $V = \mathbf{R}^2$ and let the norm be the sup norm. With respect to this norm, the sphere of radius 3 centered at the origin consists of all points (x, y) such that

$$\max(|x|, |y|) = 3.$$

The closed ball of radius 3 consists of all points (x, y) such that

$$\max(|x|, |y|) \leq 3.$$

We see that the sphere in this case consists of the perimeter of the square, and the ball consists of the inside and boundary of the square as shown on the following picture.

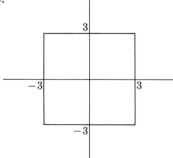

In spite of this slightly unusual interpretation, we shall find the theory of ε and δ depending only on the three properties of a norm. In fact, the sup norm in $\mathbf{R}^n$ is frequently the most convenient to deal with for purposes of analysis.

EXERCISES

1. Let $\| \ \|_1$ and $\| \ \|_2$ be norms on a vector space V. Define $\| \ \|_1$ to be equivalent to $\| \ \|_2$ if there exist numbers $C_1, C_2 > 0$ such that

$$C_1 \|v\|_1 \leqq \|v\|_2 \leqq C_2 \|v\|_1$$

   for all v in V. If $\| \ \|_1$ is equivalent to $\| \ \|_2$ and if $\| \ \|_2$ is equivalent to another norm $\| \ \|_3$, show that $\| \ \|_1$ is equivalent to $\| \ \|_3$.

2. Show that the Euclidean norm on $\mathbf{R}^n$ is equivalent to the sup norm.

3. Let V be the space of continuous functions on $[0, 1]$. If f is an element of V, define

$$\|f\| = \sup |f(x)|$$

   where $\sup |f(x)|$ means the least upper bound of all values $|f(x)|$, for x in the interval $[0, 1]$. (a) Show that this is a norm. (b) Show that this norm is not equivalent to the L_1-norm, by showing that there exist functions with arbitrarily large sup norms, but arbitrarily small L_1-norms. [*Hint:* Use a function which has a very narrow peak around 0, and has value 0 otherwise].

4. If $\| \ \|_1$ and $\| \ \|_2$ are norms on a vector space V, show that the function

$$v \mapsto \|v\|_1 + \|v\|_2$$

   is also a norm. If c is a number > 0, show that the function

$$v \mapsto c\|v\|_1$$

   is a norm.

5. Show that the complex numbers form a normed vector space over the real numbers, the norm being the ordinary absolute value.

6. Let V be a normed vector space. Prove the following inequalities:

$$\|u - v\| \geqq \|u\| - \|v\|,$$
$$\|u + v\| \geqq \|u\| - \|v\|,$$
$$\|-u\| = \|u\|.$$

   Also, if $\|v + w\| \leqq c$ for some number c, then $\|v\| \leqq c + \|w\|$.

7. If $X = (x_1, \ldots, x_n)$ is a vector in $\mathbf{R}^n$, define

$$\|X\| = |x_1| + \cdots + |x_n|.$$

   Show that this is a norm, and that this norm is equivalent to the sup norm.

§2. LIMITS

Let V, W be normed vector spaces. Let S be a subset of V, and let $f: S \rightarrow W$ be a mapping of S into W. Let v be an element of V, and w an element of W. We assume that v is *arbitrarily close* to S. By this we mean that given a number $\epsilon > 0$, there exists x in V such that $\|x - v\| < \epsilon$.

We shall say that $f(x)$ approaches the limit w as x approaches v if the following condition is satisfied.

Given $\epsilon > 0$ there exists $\delta > 0$ such that whenever x is in S and $\|x - v\| < \delta$ then $\|f(x) - w\| < \epsilon$.

We may rephrase this more geometrically by saying that given $\epsilon > 0$, there exists $\delta > 0$ such that whenever x is δ-close to v then $f(x)$ is ϵ-close to w. By δ-close to v we mean that x lies in the open ball of radius δ centered at v.

Since ϵ, δ are always > 0, we usually omit > 0 from the notation.

It is then possible to prove in exactly the same manner as for functions of one variable the various theorems concerning the formal properties of limits. We shall now do this.

Limit of a sum. *Let f, g be mappings of S into W. Assume that*

$$\lim_{x \to v} f(x) = w_1 \qquad and \qquad \lim_{x \to v} g(x) = w_2.$$

Then $\lim_{x \to v} f(x) + g(x)$ exists and is equal to $w_1 + w_2$.

Proof. Given ϵ, there exists δ_1 such that whenever x is in S and $\|x - v\| < \delta_1$ we have $\|f(x) - w_1\| < \epsilon/2$, and there exists δ_2 such that whenever x is in S and $\|x - v\| < \delta_2$ then $\|g(x) - w_2\| < \delta/2$. Let δ be the minimum of δ_1 and δ_2. When $\|x - v\| < \delta$ we have

$$\|f(x) + g(x) - (w_1 + w_2)\| = \|f(x) - w_1 + g(x) - w_2\|$$
$$\leqq \|f(x) - w_1\| + \|g(x) - w_2\|$$
$$< \epsilon/2 + \epsilon/2 = \epsilon,$$

as was to be shown.

Let U, V, W be normed vector spaces. By a product $U \times V \to W$ we mean a mapping which to each pair of elements (u, v) with u in U and v in V associates an element of W, denoted simply by uv, satisfying the following conditions:

P 1. *$(u_1 + u_2)v = u_1v + u_2v$ and $u(v_1 + v_2) = uv_1 + uv_2$.*

P 2. *If c is a number, then $(cu)v = c(uv) = u(cv)$.*

P 3. *We have $\|uv\| \leqq \|u\| \|v\|$.*

Examples. The ordinary product of numbers satisfies the preceding conditions, taking $U = V = W = \mathbf{R}$.

The dot product satisfies these conditions, the third one being nothing but the Schwarz inequality.

The cross product also satisfies the conditions, taking

$$U = V = W = \mathbf{R}^3.$$

If we view the complex numbers $\mathbf{C}$ as a vector space over the real numbers $\mathbf{R}$, then the product of complex numbers also satisfies these conditions.

Thus we see that our three conditions provide a good abstract set up for the products which we have encountered so far. They also provide the right set up for the theorem concerning limits of products, which runs as follows.

Limit of a product. Let $U \times V \to W$ be a product. Let S be a subset of a normed vector space. Let $f: S \to U$ and $g: S \to V$ be maps, and let x_0 be arbitrarily close to S. If

$$\lim_{x \to x_0} f(x) = u \qquad and \qquad \lim_{x \to x_0} g(x) = v,$$

then

$$\lim_{x \to x_0} f(x)g(x) = uv.$$

Proof. Given 1, there exists δ_1 such that if $\|x - x_0\| < \delta_1$, then

$$\|g(x) - v\| \leq 1,$$

whence

$$\|g(x)\| \leq 1 + \|v\|.$$

Given ϵ, there exists δ_2 such that if $\|x - x_0\| < \delta_2$, then

$$\|f(x) - u\| < \frac{\epsilon}{2(1 + \|v\|)},$$

and there exists δ_3 such that if $\|x - x_0\| < \delta_3$, then

$$\|g(x) - v\| < \frac{\epsilon}{2(1 + \|u\|)}.$$

Let δ be the minimum of $\delta_1, \delta_2, \delta_3$. If $\|x - x_0\| < \delta$, then

$$
\begin{aligned}
\|f(x)g(x) - uv\| &= \|f(x)g(x) - ug(x) + ug(x) - uv\| \\
&= \|(f(x) - u)g(x) + u(g(x) - v)\| \\
&\leq \|f(x) - u\| \, \|g(x)\| + \|u\| \, \|g(x) - v\| \\
&< \frac{\epsilon}{2(1 + \|v\|)} (1 + \|v\|) + \|u\| \frac{\epsilon}{2(1 + \|u\|)} \\
&< \epsilon,
\end{aligned}
$$

as was to be shown.

In dealing with vectors, we considered maps into $\mathbf{R}^n$. Such a map F is given by coordinate functions $(f_1, \ldots, f_n)$. Let us use the sup norm on $\mathbf{R}^n$. Then we can prove:

Let V be a normed vector space, and S a subset of V. Let $F: S \to \mathbf{R}^n$ be a mapping, and let $(f_1, \ldots, f_n)$ be its coordinate functions, i.e.

$$F(v) = (f_1(v), \ldots, f_n(v)),$$

where $f_i(v)$ is a number. Let $w = (w_1, \ldots, w_n)$ be an element of $\mathbf{R}^n$. Let v be arbitrarily close to S. Then

$$\lim_{x \to v} F(x) = w$$

if and only if, for every $i = 1, \ldots, n$, we have

$$\lim_{x \to v} f_i(x) = w_i.$$

Proof. Assume first that

$$\lim_{x \to v} F(x) = w.$$

Given ϵ, there exists δ such that if $\|x - v\| < \delta$ then $\|F(x) - w\| < \epsilon$. This means that $|f_i(x) - w_i| < \epsilon$, and hence we conclude that

$$\lim_{x \to v} f_i(x) = w_i$$

for all i.

Conversely, assume that

$$\lim_{x \to v} f_i(x) = w_i \qquad \text{for all } i.$$

Given ϵ, for each i there exists δ_i such that whenever $\|x - v\| < \delta_i$ then $\|f_i(x) - w_i\| < \epsilon$. Let δ be the minimum of all δ_i. Then when $\|x - v\| < \delta$ it follows that $\|F(x) - w\| < \epsilon$, as was to be shown.

In the text, instead of using the sup norm, we used the Euclidean norm. However, Exercise 1 shows that this is irrelevant when dealing with the theory of limits.

Finally, in considering the chain rule for mappings, we needed a theorem for the limit of composite maps, as follows:

Let U, V, W be normed vector spaces. Let S be a subset of U, and T a subset of V. Let

$$f: S \to T \qquad and \qquad g: T \to W$$

be maps. Let u be arbitrarily close to S and v arbitrarily close to T. Assume that

$$\lim_{x \to u} f(x) = v \qquad and \qquad \lim_{y \to v} g(y) = w.$$

Then

$$\lim_{x \to u} f(g(x)) = w.$$

Proof. Given ϵ, there exists δ_1 such that whenever $\|y - v\| < \delta_1$ then $\|g(y) - w\| < \epsilon$. With the δ_1 just found being given, there exists δ such that whenever $\|x - u\| < \delta$ then $\|f(x) - v\| < \delta_1$. Hence

$$\|g(f(x)) - w\| < \epsilon,$$

as was to be shown.

As usual, these properties of limits apply to the definition of continuous maps. Let $f: S \to W$ be a map as before. Let v be an element of S. We say that f is *continuous* at v if

$$\lim_{x \to v} f(x) = f(v).$$

Equivalently, this means: Given ϵ, there exists δ such that whenever $\|x - v\| < \delta$ then $\|f(x) - f(v)\| < \epsilon$.

The theorems concerning sums and products of limits now show that the sum and product of continuous functions are continuous. Furthermore, a map into $\mathbf{R}^n$ is continuous if and only if each coordinate function is continuous. Finally, our last statement concerning limits of composite maps shows that a composite of continuous maps is continuous.

It is not our purpose here to develop the theory of ϵ, δ any further, but merely to give an introduction to the basic definitions and properties, to acquaint the reader with them before he deals with them systematically in a course on analysis.

EXERCISES

1. Let S be a subset of a normed vector space V and let $f: S \to W$ be a map into a normed vector space W. Show that if one is given an equivalent norm on V, then the existence of a limit

   $$\lim_{x \to v} f(x) = w$$

   with respect to the new norm is equivalent to the existence of the same limit under the other norm. Do the same thing if the norm on W is changed into an equivalent norm. This shows that for limiting purposes, it is irrelevant whether one uses the sup norm or the Euclidean norm on $\mathbf{R}^n$. In fact, the sup norm is often much more convenient.

2. Let V, W be a normed vector space and let S be an open ball centered at 0 in V. Let $f: S \to W$ be a map. We say that f is $o(v)$ for $v \to 0$ if

   $$\lim_{v \to 0} \frac{f(v)}{\|v\|} = 0.$$

   Prove the following statements:

   (a) If f_1, f_2 are $o(v)$ for $v \to 0$ then so is $f_1 + f_2$.

(b) If f is $o(v)$ for $v \to 0$ and if g is a bounded function on S (that is there exists a number C such that $|g(v)| \leq C$ for all v in S), then gf is $o(v)$ for $v \to 0$.

By gf we mean of course the map such that $(gf)(v) = g(v)f(v)$.

(c) If f is $o(v)$ for $v \to 0$ and if f_1 is a map such that $\|f_1(v)\| \leq \|f(v)\|$ for all v in S, then f_1 is also $o(v)$ for $v \to 0$.

3. Let V be a normed vector space and let $L: \mathbf{R}^n \to V$ be a linear map. Show that there exists a number $C > 0$ such that for all X in $\mathbf{R}^n$ we have $\|L(X)\| \leq C\|X\|$. [*Hint:* Write $X = x_1 E_1 + \cdots + x_n E_n$ where $E_1, \ldots, E_n$ are the unit vectors. Use the sup norm if you wish.]

4. Show that a linear map as in Exercise 3 is continuous.

Answers to Exercises

Answers to Exercises

I am much indebted to Mr. I. Schochetman and Mr. J. Hennefeld for the answers to the exercises.

Chapter I, §1

	$A + B$	$A - B$	$3A$	$-2B$
1.	$(1, 0)$	$(3, -2)$	$(6, -3)$	$(2, -2)$
2.	$(-1, 7)$	$(-1, -1)$	$(-3, 9)$	$(0, -8)$
3.	$(1, 0, 6)$	$(3, -2, 4)$	$(6, -3, 15)$	$(2, -2, -2)$
4.	$(-2, 1, -1)$	$(0, -5, 7)$	$(-3, -6, 9)$	$(2, -6, 8)$
5.	$(3\pi, 0, 6)$	$(-\pi, 6, -8)$	$(3\pi, 9, -3)$	$(-4\pi, 6, -14)$
6.	$(15 + \pi, 1, 3)$	$(15 - \pi, -5, 5)$	$(45, -6, 12)$	$(-2\pi, -6, 2)$

Chapter I, §3

1. $5, 10, 30, 14, 10 + \pi^2, 245$ **2.** $-3, 12, 2, -17, 2\pi^2 - 16, 15\pi - 10$
4. (b) and (d)   **6.** $\frac{2}{3}, \frac{2}{5}, 0$

Chapter I, §4

1. $\sqrt{5}, \sqrt{10}, \sqrt{30}, \sqrt{14}, \sqrt{10 + \pi^2}, \sqrt{245}$
2. $\sqrt{2}, 4, \sqrt{3}, \sqrt{26}, \sqrt{4\pi^2 + 58}, \sqrt{\pi^2 + 10}$
3. $(\frac{3}{2}, -\frac{3}{2}), (0, 3), \frac{2}{3}(-1, 1, 1), \frac{17}{26}(1, -3, 4),$

$$\frac{\pi^2 - 8}{2\pi^2 + 29} (2\pi, -3, 7), \qquad \frac{15\pi - 10}{\pi^2 + 10} (\pi, 3, -1)$$

4. $\frac{3}{5}(-2, 1), \frac{6}{5}(-1, 3), \frac{1}{5}(2, -1, 5), \frac{17}{14}(1, 2, -3),$

$$\frac{2\pi^2 - 16}{\pi^2 + 10} (\pi, 3, -1), \qquad \frac{3\pi - 2}{49} (15, -2, 4)$$

5. $0, 0$ **6.** $\sqrt{\pi}, \sqrt{\pi}$ **7.** $\sqrt{2\pi}$ **8.** $\sqrt{2}$

Chapter I, §5

1. $X = (1, 1, -1) + t(3, 0, -4)$ **2.** $X = (-1, 5, 2) + t(-4, 9, 1)$
3. $y = x + 8$ **4.** $4y = 5x - 7$ **6.** (c) and (d)
7. (a) $x - y + 3z = -1$ (b) $3x + 2y - 4z = 2\pi + 26$
(c) $x - 5z = -33$
8. (a) $2x + y + 2z = 7$ (b) $7x - 8y - 9z = -29$
(c) $y + z = 1$
9. $(3, -9, -5), (1, 5, -7)$ (Others would be constant multiples of these.)
10. (a) $2(t^2 + 5)^{1/2}$ **11.** $(15t^2 + 26t + 21)^{1/2}, \sqrt{146/15}$
12. $(-2, 1, 5)$ **13.** $(11, 13, -7)$
14. (a) $X = (1, 0, -1) + t(-2, 1, 5)$ (b) $X = (1, 0, 0) + t(11, 13, -7)$
15. (a) $-\frac{1}{3}$ (b) $-2/\sqrt{42}$ (c) $4/\sqrt{66}$ (d) $-\sqrt{2}/3$
16. $t = \dfrac{P \cdot N - Q \cdot N}{N \cdot N}$ **17.** $(1, 3, -2)$ **18.** $2/\sqrt{3}$

19. $(-4, \frac{11}{2}, \frac{15}{2})$ **20.** $\dfrac{\sqrt{2240}}{35}$

21. (a) $\frac{1}{2}(-3, 8, 1)$ (b) $(-\frac{2}{3}, \frac{11}{3}, 0), (-\frac{7}{3}, \frac{13}{3}, 1)$ **22.** $\dfrac{P + Q}{2}$

Chapter I, §6

1. $(-4, -3, 1)$ **2.** $(-1, 1, -1)$ **3.** $(-9, 6, -1)$
4. 0 **5.** E_3, E_1, E_2 in that order.

Chapter II, §1

1. $(e^t, -\sin t, \cos t)$ **2.** $\left(2 \cos 2t, \dfrac{1}{1+t}, 1\right)$

3. $(-\sin t, \cos t)$ **4.** $(-3 \sin 3t, 3 \cos 3t)$
7. B **8.** $y = \sqrt{3}x$ and $y = 0$
9. $ex + y + 2z = e^2 + 3$ **10.** $x + y = 1$
11. $[(X(t) - Q) \cdot (X(t) - Q)]^{1/2}$ **12.** $\sqrt{2}$ **13.** $2\sqrt{13}$

16. (a) $\left(0, 1, \dfrac{\pi}{8}\right) + t(-4, 0, 1)$ (b) $(1, 2, 1) + t(1, 2, 2)$

   (c) $(e^3, e^{-3}, 3\sqrt{2}) + t(3e^3, -3e^{-3}, 3\sqrt{2})$ (d) $(1, 1, 1) + t(1, 3, 4)$

17. (a) $\dfrac{\pi\sqrt{17}}{8}$ (b) $\frac{3}{2}(\sqrt{41} - 1) + \dfrac{5}{4}\left(\log \dfrac{6 + \sqrt{41}}{5}\right)$ (c) $\frac{3}{2}e^2 - \frac{3}{2}e^{-2} + 6$

18. $\pi/2$ **19.** $(2, 0, 4)$ and $(18, 4, 12)$

Chapter II, §2

1. (a) $x + 4z = \pi/2$ (b) $y = 2x$ (c) $-x + e^6y + \sqrt{2}\, e^3z = 6e^3$
   (d) $2x - 2y + z = 1$

3. $r/(r^2 + c^2)$ **4.** (a) $\sqrt{266}/98$

9. $\frac{1}{2}(1 + 4x^2)^{3/2}$ **10.** $\dfrac{(a^2 \sin^2 t + b^2 \cos^2 t)^{3/2}}{ab}$

11. $\sqrt{t}$ **12.** πs

Chapter III, §2

	$\partial f/\partial x$	$\partial f/\partial y$	$\partial f/\partial z$
1.	y	x	1
2.	$2xy^5$	$5x^2y^4$	0
3.	$y \cos(xy)$	$x \cos(xy)$	$-\sin(z)$
4.	$-y \sin(xy)$	$-x \sin(xy)$	0
5.	$yz \cos(xyz)$	$xz \cos(xyz)$	$xy \cos(xyz)$
6.	yze^{xyz}	xze^{xyz}	xye^{xyz}
7.	$2x \sin(yz)$	$x^2z \cos(yz)$	$x^2y \cos(yz)$
8.	yz	xz	xz
9.	$z + y$	$z + x$	$x + y$
10.	$\cos(y - 3z)$ $+ \dfrac{y}{\sqrt{1 - x^2y^2}}$	$-x \sin(y - 3z)$ $+ \dfrac{x}{\sqrt{1 - x^2y^2}}$	$3x \sin(y - 3z)$

11. (1) (2, 1, 1) (2) (64, 80, 0) (6) $e^6(6, 3, 2)$ (8) (6, 3, 2) (9) (5, 4, 3)
12. (4) (0, 0, 0) (5) $\pi \cos (\pi^2)(\pi, 1, 1)$ (7) $(2 \sin \pi^2, \pi \cos \pi^2, \pi \cos \pi^2)$
13. $(-1, -2, 1)$ **14.** $yx^{y-1}, x^y \log x$

Chapter III, §3

6. $\lim_{h \to 0} g(h, k) = -1$, $\lim_{k \to 0} g(h, k) = 1$, $\lim_{k \to 0} \lim_{h \to 0} g(h, k) = -1$,

$\lim_{h \to 0} \lim_{k \to 0} g(h, k) = 1$

Chapter IV, §1

1. $\dfrac{\partial z}{\partial r} = \dfrac{\partial f}{\partial x} \dfrac{\partial u}{\partial r} + \dfrac{\partial f}{\partial y} \dfrac{\partial v}{\partial r}$ and $\dfrac{\partial z}{\partial t} = \dfrac{\partial f}{\partial x} \dfrac{\partial u}{\partial t} + \dfrac{\partial f}{\partial y} \dfrac{\partial v}{\partial t}$

2. (a) $\dfrac{\partial f}{\partial x} = 3x^2 + 3yz$, $\dfrac{\partial f}{\partial y} = 3xz - 2yz$

$\dfrac{\partial f}{\partial s} = 3x^2 + (3 + 2s)yz - 3xz + 6sxy - 2sy^2$

$\dfrac{\partial f}{\partial t} = 6x^2 + 8yz - 3xz + 6txy - 2ty^2$

(b) $\dfrac{\partial f}{\partial x} = \dfrac{y^2 + 1}{(1 - xy)^2}$, $\dfrac{\partial f}{\partial y} = \dfrac{x^2 + 1}{(1 - xy)^2}$

$\dfrac{\partial f}{\partial s} = \dfrac{(x^2 + 1) \sin(3t - s)}{(1 - xy)^2}$

$\dfrac{\partial f}{\partial t} = \dfrac{2(y^2 + 1) \cos 2t - 3(x^2 + 1) \sin(3t - s)}{(1 - xy)^2}$

3. $\dfrac{\partial f}{\partial x} = \dfrac{x}{(x^2 + y^2 + z^2)^{1/2}}$, $\dfrac{\partial f}{\partial y} = \dfrac{y}{(x^2 + y^2 + z^2)^{1/2}}$

4. $\dfrac{\partial r}{\partial x_i} = \dfrac{x_i}{r}$

9. (a) $-X/r^3$ (b) $2X$ (c) $-3X/r^5$ (d) $2e^{-r^2}X$ (e) $-X/r^2$
(f) $-4mX/r^{m+2}$

Chapter IV, §2

1.

	Plane	Line
(a)	$6x + 2y + 3z = 49$	$X = (6, 2, 3) + t(12, 4, 6)$
(b)	$x + y + 2z = 2$	$X = (1, 1, 0) + t(1, 1, 2)$
(c)	$13x + 15y + z = -15$	$X = (2, -3, 4) + t(13, 15, 1)$
(d)	$6x - 2y + 15z = 22$	$X = (1, 7, 2) + t(-6, 2, -15)$
(e)	$4x + y + z = 13$	$X = (2, 1, 4) + t(8, 2, 2)$
(f)	$z = 0$	$X = (1, \pi/2, 0) + t(0, 0, \pi/2 + 1)$

2. (a) (3, 0, 1) (b) $X = (\log 3, 3\pi/2, -3) + t(3, 0, 1)$
(c) $3x + z = 3 \log 3 - 3$
3. (a) $X = (3, 2, -6) + t(2, -3, 0)$ (b) $X = (2, 1, -2) + t(-5, 4, -3)$
(c) $X = (3, 2, 2) + t(2, 3, 0)$

4. Distance $= \sqrt{[X(t) - Q]^2}$

5. (a) $6x + 8y - z = 25$ (b) $16x + 12y - 125z = -75$

6. $x - 2y + z = 1$

Chapter IV, §3

1. (a) $\frac{5}{3}$ (b) max $= \sqrt{10}$, min $= -\sqrt{10}$

2. (a) $3/2\sqrt{5}$ (b) $\frac{48}{13}$ (c) $\sqrt{580}$

3. Increasing $\left(-\dfrac{9\sqrt{3}}{2}, -\dfrac{3\sqrt{3}}{2}\right)$, decreasing $(9\sqrt{3}/2, 3\sqrt{3}/2)$

4. (a) $\left(\dfrac{3}{4 \cdot 6^{3/4}}, \dfrac{3}{2 \cdot 6^{7/4}}, \dfrac{-3}{6^{7/4}}\right)$ (b) $(1, 2, -1, 1)$

Chapter IV, §4

1. $\log \|X\|$ **2.** $-1/2r^2$

Chapter V, §1

1. Yes   **2.** No   **3.** No   **4.** No

5. Yes   **6.** Yes

Chapter V, §3

1. No   **2.** No   **3.** No   **4.** No

5. (a) r (b) $\log r$ (c) $\dfrac{r^{n+2}}{n+2}$ if $n \neq -2$

6. $2x^2y$ **7.** $x \sin xy$ **8.** x^3y^2

9. $x^2 + y^4$ **10.** e^{xy} **11.** $g(r)$

12. Given the vector field $F = (f_1, \ldots, f_n)$ in n-space, defined on a rectangle, $[a_1, b_1] \times \cdots \times [a_n, b_n]$. Assume that

$$\frac{\partial f_i}{\partial x_j} = \frac{\partial f_j}{\partial x_i} \quad (\text{or} \quad D_j f_i = D_i f_j)$$

for all indices i, j. For $n = 3$, define $\varphi(x, y, z)$ to be

$$\int_{a_1}^{x} f_1(t, y, z)\,dt + \int_{a_2}^{y} f_2(a_1, t, z)\,dt + \int_{a_3}^{z} f_3(a_1, a_2, t)\,dt,$$

and similarly for n variables. Using the hypothesis and the fact that a partial derivative of parameters can be taken in and out of an integral, you will find easily that φ is a potential function for F.

Conversely, given a vector field $F = (f_1, \ldots, f_n)$ on an open set U, if there exists a potential function, and if the partial derivatives of the functions f_i exist and are continuous, then the relations

$$\frac{\partial f_i}{\partial x_j} = \frac{\partial f_j}{\partial x_i}$$

must be satisfied for all i, j, for the same reason as that given in the text for two variables. This generalizes Theorem 2.

Chapter V, §4

1. $-369/10$ **2.** $23/6$ **3.** 0   **4.** 0   **5.** 54
6. $\sqrt{3C/2}$ **7.** $4/3$ **8.** $-\pi - \frac{8}{3}$ **9.** $4/15$ **10.** 4π
11. $3\pi/4$ **12.** $-1/2$ **13.** -56

Chapter VI, §1

	$\partial^2 f/\partial x^2$	$\partial^2 f/\partial y^2$	$\partial^2 f/\partial x\,\partial y$
1.	$y^2 e^{xy}$	$x^2 e^{xy}$	$yx e^{xy} + e^{xy}$
2.	$-y^2 \sin xy$	$-x^2 \sin xy$	$-xy \sin xy + \cos xy$
3.	$2y^3$	$6x^2 y$	$6xy^2 + 3$
4.	0	2	2
5.	$2e^{x^2+y^2} + 4x^2 e^{x^2+y^2}$	$e^{x^2+y^2}(2 + 4y^2)$	$4xy e^{x^2+y^2}$
6.	$2\cos(x^2 + y)$ $-4x^2 \sin(x^2 + y)$	$-\sin(x^2 + y)$	$-2x \sin(x^2 + y)$
7.	$-(3x^2 + y)^2 \cos(x^3 + xy)$ $-6x \sin(x^3 + xy)$	$-x^2 \cos(x^3 + xy)$	$-(3x^2 + y)x \cos(x^3 + xy)$ $-\sin(x^3 + xy)$

8.
$$\frac{\partial^2 f}{\partial x^2} = \frac{2(1 + (x^2 - 2xy)^2) - (2x - 2y)^2(x^2 - 2xy)}{(1 + (x^2 - 2xy)^2)^2}$$

$$\frac{\partial^2 f}{\partial y^2} = \frac{-(1 + (x^2 - 2xy)^2) - 2y(x^2 - 2xy)}{(1 + (x^2 - 2xy)^2)^2}$$

$$\frac{\partial^2 f}{\partial x\,\partial y} = \frac{-2(1 + (x^2 - 2xy)^2) - (2x - 2y)(x^2 - 2xy)(-2y)}{(1 + (x^2 - 2xy)^2)^2}$$

9. All three $= e^{x+y}$ **10.** All three $= -\sin(x + y)$
11. 1   **12.** $2x$ **13.** $e^{xyz}(1 + 3xyz + x^2 y^2 z^2)$
14. $(1 - x^2 y^2 z^2)\cos xyz - 3xyz \sin xyz$
15. $\sin(x + y + z)$ **16.** $-\cos(x + y + z)$
17. $-\dfrac{48xyz}{(x^2 + y^2 + z^2)^4}$ **18.** $6x^2 y$

Chapter VI, §2

1. $9D_1^2 + 12D_1 D_2 + 4D_2^2$
2. $D_1^2 + D_2^2 + D_3^2 + 2D_1 D_2 + 2D_2 D_3 + 2D_1 D_3$
3. $D_1^2 - D_2^2$ **4.** $D_1^2 + 2D_1 D_2 + D_2^2$
5. $D_1^3 + 3D_1^2 D_2 + 3D_1 D_2^2 + D_2^3$
6. $D_1^4 + 4D_1^3 D_2 + 6D_1^2 D_2^2 + 4D_1 D_2^3 + D_2^4$
7. $2D_1^2 - D_1 D_2 - 3D_2^2$ **8.** $D_1 D_2 - D_3 D_2 + 5D_1 D_3 - 5D_3^2$
9. $\left(\dfrac{\partial}{\partial x}\right)^3 + 12\left(\dfrac{\partial}{\partial x}\right)^2 \dfrac{\partial}{\partial y} + 48\dfrac{\partial}{\partial x}\left(\dfrac{\partial}{\partial y}\right)^2 + 64\left(\dfrac{\partial}{\partial y}\right)^3$
10. $4\left(\dfrac{\partial}{\partial x}\right)^2 + 4\dfrac{\partial}{\partial x}\dfrac{\partial}{\partial y} + \left(\dfrac{\partial}{\partial y}\right)^2$
11. $h^2\left(\dfrac{\partial}{\partial x}\right)^2 + 2hk\dfrac{\partial}{\partial x}\dfrac{\partial}{\partial y} + k^2\left(\dfrac{\partial}{\partial y}\right)^2$

12. $h^3\left(\dfrac{\partial}{\partial x}\right)^3 + 3h^2 k\left(\dfrac{\partial}{\partial x}\right)^2 \dfrac{\partial}{\partial y} + 3hk^2\dfrac{\partial}{\partial x}\left(\dfrac{\partial}{\partial y}\right)^2 + k^3\left(\dfrac{\partial}{\partial y}\right)^3$

13. 8   **14.** 4   **15.** 4   **16.** 1

Chapter VI, §3

  1. xy **2.** 1   **3.** xy **4.** $x^2 + y^2$

  5. $1 + x + y + \dfrac{x^2}{2} + xy + \dfrac{y^2}{2}$ **6.** $1 - \dfrac{y^2}{2}$ **7.** x

  8. $y + xy$ **9.** $x + xy + 2y^2$ **10.** Yes, 0

  11. (a) Yes, 0   (b) Yes, 1   **12.** Yes, 0   **13.** Yes, 0

  14. $1 + x + \dfrac{x^2}{2} - \dfrac{y^2}{2} + \dfrac{x^3}{6} - \dfrac{xy^2}{2}$ **15.** 0

  17. Terms up to degree 2 given in text. Term of degree 3 is $\frac{1}{3}(x + 2y)^3$.
  20. (a) $X + t(Y - X), 0 \le t \le 1$
   (b) By the mean value theorem applied to the function

$$g(t) = f(X + t(Y - X)),$$

we get

$$f(Y) - f(X) = (\operatorname{grad} f(Z)) \cdot (Y - X)$$

for some Z on the line segment. Now use the Schwarz inequality.

Chapter VI, §4

  1. First observe that for each point X we have

$$f(X) - f(O) = \int_0^1 Df(tX)\, dt,$$

where $D = x_1 D_1 + \cdots + x_n D_n$. Assuming that $f(O) = 0$, and repeating the argument, assuming that $\nabla f(O) = 0$, we obtain

$$f(X) = \int_0^1 \int_0^1 t D^2 f(st X)\, ds\, dt.$$

Thus we find

$$f(X) = \sum_{i,j=1}^n h_{ij}(X) x_i x_j,$$

where

$$h_{ij}(X) = \int_0^1 \int_0^1 t D_i D_j f(st X)\, ds\, dt, \qquad \text{if } \ i \ne j,$$

$$h_{ij}(X) = \int_0^1 \int_0^1 \tfrac{1}{2} t D_i D_j f(st X)\, ds\, dt, \qquad \text{if } \ i = j.$$

We have $h_{ij} = h_{ji}$ because $D_i D_j = D_j D_i$.

Chapter VII, §1

  1. (2, 1), neither max nor min
  2. $((2n + 1)\pi, 1)$ and $(2n\pi, 1)$, neither max nor min

3. $(0, 0, 0)$, min, value 0

4. $(\sqrt{2}/2, \sqrt{2}/2)$, neither local max nor min. [*Hint:* Change variables, letting $u = x + y$ and $v = x - y$. Then the critical point is at $(\sqrt{2}, 0)$, and in the (u, v)-plane, near this point, the function increases in one direction, and decreases in the other.]

5. All points of form $(0, t, -t)$, neither max nor min.

6. All (x, y, z) with $x^2 + y^2 + z^2 = 2n\pi$ are local max, value 1.
   All (x, y, z) with $x^2 + y^2 + z^2 = (2n + 1)\pi$ are local min, value -1.

7. All points $(x, 0)$ and $(0, y)$ are mins, value 0.

8. $(0, 0)$, min, value 0

9. (t, t), min, value 0

10. $(0, n\pi)$, neither max nor min

11. $(1/2, 0)$, neither max nor min

12. $(0, 0, 0)$, max, value 1

13. $(0, 0, 0)$, min, value 1

Chapter VII, §2

1. $x^2 + 4xy - y^2$

2. At $((2n + 1)\pi, 1)$, $-xy$. At $(2n\pi, 1)$, $+xy$.

3. $x^2 + y^2 + z^2$

4. $\dfrac{1}{\sqrt{2}} e^{-1/2} \left(\dfrac{x^2}{2} + 3xy + \dfrac{y^2}{2} \right)$

5. $xy + xz$

6. At (a, b, c) such that $a^2 + b^2 + c^2 = 2n\pi$, the form is

$$-2(a^2x^2 + b^2y^2 + c^2z^2) - 4(abxy + acxz + bcyz).$$

At the point (a, b, c) such that $a^2 + b^2 + c^2 = (2n + 1)\pi$, the form is

$$2(a^2x^2 + b^2y^2 + c^2z^2) + 4(abxy + acxz + bcyz).$$

7. At points $(a, 0)$ we get a^2y^2. At points $(0, b)$, we get x^2b^2.

8. y^2 9. 0   10. $\pm xy$ 11. $x^2 + 2y^2$

2. $-x^2 - y^2 - z^2$ 13. $x^2 + y^2 + z^2$

Chapter VII, §3

1. Min $= -2$ at $(-1, -1)$, max $= 2$ at $(1, 1)$

2. None

3. Max $\frac{1}{2}$ at $(\sqrt{2}/2, \sqrt{2}/2)$ and $(-\sqrt{2}/2, -\sqrt{2}/2)$

4. Max at $(\frac{1}{2}, \frac{1}{3})$, no min

5. Min 0 at $(0, 0)$, max $2/e$ at $(0, \pm 1)$, rel. max at $(\pm 1, 0)$

6. Max $= 1$ at $(1, 0)$, min $= 1/9$ at $(3, 0)$

7. (a) max   (b) neither   (c) neither   (d) min

8. $t = (2n + 1)\pi$, so $(-1, 0, 1)$ and $(-1, 0, -1)$

Chapter VII, §4

1. $-1/\sqrt{2}$ 2. $1 + 1/\sqrt{2}$ 3. at $(\frac{5}{3}, \frac{2}{3}, \frac{1}{3})$ min $= 12$

4. $X = \frac{1}{3}(A + B + C)$, min value is $\frac{2}{3}(A^2 + B^2 + C^2 - AB - AC - BC)$

5. 45 at $\pm(\sqrt{3}, \sqrt{6})$ 6. $(\frac{2}{3})^{3/2}$ at $\sqrt{\frac{2}{3}}\,(1, 1, 1)$ 7. Min 0, max 0

8. Max at $(\pi/8, -\pi/8)$, value $2\cos^2(\pi/8)$; min at $(5\pi/8, 3\pi/8)$ value $\cos^2(5\pi/8) + \cos^2(3\pi/8)$

9. $(0, 0, \pm 1)$ **10.** No min, max $= \frac{1}{4}$ at $(\frac{1}{2}, \frac{1}{2})$ **11.** 1

12. Max $= \sqrt{3}$ at $\sqrt{3}/3(1, 1, 1)$, min $= -\sqrt{3}$ at $-\sqrt{3}/3(1, 1, 1)$.

17. 25/52 **18.** $d^2/(a^2 + b^2 + c^2)$

19. Closest: $(\pm\frac{1}{2}\sqrt{2}, \pm\frac{1}{2}\sqrt{2})$, farthest: $(\pm\sqrt{2}, \mp\sqrt{2})$

Chapter VIII, §2

2. (a) $A - B$, $(1, -1)$ (b) $\frac{1}{2}A + \frac{3}{2}B$, $(\frac{1}{2}, \frac{3}{2})$
(c) $A + B$, $(1, 1)$ (d) $3A + 2B$, $(3, 2)$

3. (a) $(\frac{1}{3}, -\frac{1}{3}, \frac{1}{3})$ (b) $(1, 0, 1)$ (c) $(\frac{1}{3}, -\frac{1}{3}, -\frac{2}{3})$

7. $(3, 5)$ **8.** $(-5, 3)$

Chapter IX, §1

1. $A + B = \begin{pmatrix} 0 & 7 & 1 \\ 0 & 1 & 1 \end{pmatrix}$, $\qquad 3B = \begin{pmatrix} -3 & 15 & -6 \\ 3 & 3 & -3 \end{pmatrix}$

$-2B = \begin{pmatrix} 2 & -10 & 4 \\ -2 & -2 & 2 \end{pmatrix}$, $\quad A + 2B = \begin{pmatrix} -1 & 12 & -1 \\ 1 & 2 & 0 \end{pmatrix}$

$2A + B = \begin{pmatrix} 1 & 9 & 4 \\ -1 & 1 & 3 \end{pmatrix}$, $\quad A - B = \begin{pmatrix} 2 & -3 & 5 \\ -2 & -1 & 3 \end{pmatrix}$

$A - 2B = \begin{pmatrix} 3 & -8 & 7 \\ -3 & -2 & 4 \end{pmatrix}$, $\quad B - A = \begin{pmatrix} -2 & 3 & -5 \\ 2 & 1 & -3 \end{pmatrix}$

2. $A + B = \begin{pmatrix} 0 & 0 \\ 2 & -2 \end{pmatrix}$, $\qquad 3B = \begin{pmatrix} -3 & 3 \\ 0 & -9 \end{pmatrix}$

$-2B = \begin{pmatrix} 2 & -2 \\ 0 & 6 \end{pmatrix}$, $\qquad A + 2B = \begin{pmatrix} -1 & 1 \\ 2 & -5 \end{pmatrix}$

$A - B = \begin{pmatrix} 2 & -2 \\ 2 & 4 \end{pmatrix}$, $\qquad B - A = \begin{pmatrix} -2 & 2 \\ -2 & -4 \end{pmatrix}$

Chapter IX, §2

3. ${}^tA = \begin{pmatrix} 1 & -1 \\ 2 & 0 \\ 3 & 2 \end{pmatrix}$, $\quad {}^tB = \begin{pmatrix} -1 & 1 \\ 5 & 1 \\ -2 & -1 \end{pmatrix}$

4. ${}^tA = \begin{pmatrix} 1 & 2 \\ -1 & 1 \end{pmatrix}$, $\quad {}^tB = \begin{pmatrix} -1 & 0 \\ 1 & -3 \end{pmatrix}$

7. Same $\qquad\qquad$ **8.** $\begin{pmatrix} 0 & 2 \\ 0 & -2 \end{pmatrix}$, same

9. $A + {}^tA = \begin{pmatrix} 2 & 1 \\ 1 & 2 \end{pmatrix}, \qquad B + {}^tB = \begin{pmatrix} -2 & 1 \\ 1 & -6 \end{pmatrix}$

11. Rows of A: $(1, 2, 3)$, $(-1, 0, 2)$. Columns of A:

$$\begin{pmatrix} 1 \\ -1 \end{pmatrix}, \quad \begin{pmatrix} 2 \\ 0 \end{pmatrix}, \quad \begin{pmatrix} 3 \\ 2 \end{pmatrix}$$

Chapter IX, §3

1. mn; $\{E_{ij}\}$ where E_{ij} has component 1 at the (i, j) place and 0 otherwise

2. $n^2 - n$ **3.** $n(n + 1)/2$

Chapter IX, §4

1. $IA = AI = A$ **2.** 0

3. (a) $\begin{pmatrix} 3 & 2 \\ 4 & 1 \end{pmatrix}$ (b) $\begin{pmatrix} 1 & 0 \\ 1 & 4 \end{pmatrix}$ (c) $\begin{pmatrix} 3 & 3 & 37 \\ 1 & 1 & -18 \end{pmatrix}$

5. $AB = \begin{pmatrix} 4 & 2 \\ 5 & -1 \end{pmatrix}, \qquad BA = \begin{pmatrix} 2 & 4 \\ 4 & 1 \end{pmatrix}$

6. $AC = CA = \begin{pmatrix} 7 & 14 \\ 21 & -7 \end{pmatrix}, \qquad BC = CB = \begin{pmatrix} 14 & 0 \\ 7 & 7 \end{pmatrix}.$

    If $C = xI$, where x is a number, then $AC = CA = xA$.

7. $(3, 1, 5)$, first row   **8.** Second row, third row, i-th row

11. $A^2 = \begin{pmatrix} 0 & 0 & 1 \\ 0 & 0 & 0 \\ 0 & 0 & 0 \end{pmatrix}, \qquad A^3 = O$ matrix.   If $B = \begin{pmatrix} 0 & 1 & 1 & 1 \\ 0 & 0 & 1 & 1 \\ 0 & 0 & 0 & 1 \\ 0 & 0 & 0 & 0 \end{pmatrix}$ then

$B^2 = \begin{pmatrix} 0 & 0 & 1 & 1 \\ 0 & 0 & 0 & 1 \\ 0 & 0 & 0 & 0 \\ 0 & 0 & 0 & 0 \end{pmatrix}, \qquad B^3 = \begin{pmatrix} 0 & 0 & 0 & 1 \\ 0 & 0 & 0 & 0 \\ 0 & 0 & 0 & 0 \\ 0 & 0 & 0 & 0 \end{pmatrix}$ and $B^4 = O.$

12. (a) $\begin{pmatrix} 9 \\ 5 \end{pmatrix}$ (b) $\begin{pmatrix} 3 \\ 1 \end{pmatrix}$ (c) $\begin{pmatrix} x_2 \\ 0 \end{pmatrix}$ (d) $\begin{pmatrix} 0 \\ x_1 \end{pmatrix}$

13. (a) $\begin{pmatrix} 2 \\ 4 \end{pmatrix}$ (b) $\begin{pmatrix} 4 \\ 6 \end{pmatrix}$ (c) $\begin{pmatrix} 3 \\ 5 \end{pmatrix}$

14. (a) $\begin{pmatrix} 3 \\ 1 \\ 2 \end{pmatrix}$ (b) $\begin{pmatrix} 12 \\ 3 \\ 9 \end{pmatrix}$ (c) $\begin{pmatrix} 5 \\ 4 \\ 8 \end{pmatrix}$

15. Second column of A **16.** i-th column of A

Chapter X, §1

1. (a) $\cos x$ (b) e^x (c) $1/x$
2. (a) $e^x - 1$ (b) $\arctan x$ (c) $\sin x$
3. (a) 11   (b) 13   (c) 6
4. (a) $(e, 1)$ (b) $(1, 0)$ (c) $(1/e, -1)$
5. (a) $(e + 1, 3)$ (b) $(e^2 + 2, 6)$ (c) $(1, 0)$
6. (a) $(2, 0)$ (b) $(\pi e, \pi)$
7. (a) 1   (b) 11
8. Ellipse $9x^2 + 4y^2 = 36$ **9.** Line $x = 2y$
10. Circle $x^2 + y^2 = e^2$, circle $x^2 + y^2 = e^{2c}$
11. Cylinder, radius 1, z-axis = axis of cylinder
12. Circle $x^2 + y^2 = 1$

Chapter X, §2

1. All except (c), (g)
4. If u is one element such that $Tu = w$, then the set of all such elements is the set of elements $u + v$ where $Tv = 0$.
8. Only Ex. 8
9. If $F(A) = 0$, image = point $F(P)$.   If $F(A) \neq 0$, image is the line $F(P) + tF(A)$.
12. Parallelogram whose vertices are $B, 3A, 3A + B, 0$
13. Parallelogram whose vertices are $0, 2B, 5A, 5A + 2B$

Chapter X, §3

6. Constant functions
7. Ker D^2 = polynomials of deg ≤ 1, Ker D^n = polynomials of

$$\deg \leq n - 1$$

9. Constant multiples of e^x
10. Constant multiples of e^{ax}

Chapter XI, §1

1. (a) $(5, 3)$ (b) $(5, 0)$ (c) $(5, 1)$ (d) $(0, -3)$

Chapter XI, §2

1. (a) $\begin{pmatrix} 1 & 0 & 0 & 0 \\ 0 & 1 & 0 & 0 \end{pmatrix}$ (b) $\begin{pmatrix} 1 & 0 & 0 & 0 \\ 0 & 1 & 0 & 0 \\ 0 & 0 & 1 & 0 \end{pmatrix}$

(c) $3I$ (d) $7I$ (e) $-I$ (f) $\begin{pmatrix} 1 & 0 & 0 & 0 \\ 0 & 1 & 0 & 0 \\ 0 & 0 & 0 & 0 \\ 0 & 0 & 0 & 0 \end{pmatrix}$

2. (a) $\begin{pmatrix} 0 & -1 \\ 1 & 0 \end{pmatrix}$ (b) $\dfrac{1}{\sqrt{2}}\begin{pmatrix} 1 & -1 \\ 1 & 1 \end{pmatrix}$ (c) $\begin{pmatrix} -1 & 0 \\ 0 & -1 \end{pmatrix}$ (d) $\begin{pmatrix} -1 & 0 \\ 0 & -1 \end{pmatrix}$.

(e) $\dfrac{1}{2}\begin{pmatrix} 1 & \sqrt{3} \\ -\sqrt{3} & 1 \end{pmatrix}$ (f) $\dfrac{1}{2}\begin{pmatrix} \sqrt{3} & -1 \\ 1 & \sqrt{3} \end{pmatrix}$ (g) $\dfrac{1}{\sqrt{2}}\begin{pmatrix} -1 & 1 \\ -1 & -1 \end{pmatrix}$

3. $\begin{pmatrix} \cos\theta & \sin\theta \\ -\sin\theta & \cos\theta \end{pmatrix}$ 4. $\dfrac{1}{\sqrt{2}}(-1, 3)$ 5. $(-3, -1)$

Chapter XII, §3

1. (a) $x = -\tfrac{1}{3}, y = \tfrac{2}{3}, z = -\tfrac{1}{3}$
(b) $x = \tfrac{5}{12}, y = -\tfrac{1}{12}, z = \tfrac{1}{12}$

Chapter XII, §4

1. (a) -20 (b) 5 (c) 4 (d) 5 (e) -76
2. (a) -18 (b) 45 (c) 0 (d) 0
3. $a_{11}a_{22} \cdots a_{nn}$ 4. 1
6. $a_{11}a_{22} \cdots a_{nn}$ 7. 1 8. $t^2 + 8t + 5$

Chapter XII, §5

1. (a) 1 (b) 1 (c) -1 (d) 1 (e) 1 (f) 1

2. (a) $\begin{bmatrix} 1 & 2 & 3 \\ 3 & 1 & 2 \end{bmatrix}$ (b) $\begin{bmatrix} 1 & 2 & 3 \\ 2 & 3 & 1 \end{bmatrix}$ (c) $\begin{bmatrix} 1 & 2 & 3 \\ 3 & 2 & 1 \end{bmatrix}$ (d) $\begin{bmatrix} 1 & 2 & 3 & 4 \\ 3 & 1 & 2 & 4 \end{bmatrix}$

(e) $\begin{bmatrix} 1 & 2 & 3 & 4 \\ 2 & 1 & 4 & 3 \end{bmatrix}$ (f) $\begin{bmatrix} 1 & 2 & 3 & 4 \\ 4 & 2 & 1 & 3 \end{bmatrix}$

Chapter XII, §9

1. (a) $-\dfrac{1}{20}\begin{pmatrix} 4 & 1 & -7 \\ -4 & -6 & 2 \\ 12 & 2 & 6 \end{pmatrix}$ (b) $\dfrac{1}{5}\begin{pmatrix} 2 & 23 & -11 \\ 1 & 19 & -8 \\ 0 & -10 & 5 \end{pmatrix}$

(c) $\dfrac{1}{4}\begin{pmatrix} 3 & 2 & -9 \\ 1 & 2 & -3 \\ -2 & -4 & 10 \end{pmatrix}$ (d) $\dfrac{1}{5}\begin{pmatrix} 5 & -16 & 3 \\ 0 & 7 & -1 \\ 0 & -2 & 1 \end{pmatrix}$

$$(e) \ -\frac{1}{76} \begin{pmatrix} 0 & -19 & 0 \\ -32 & -14 & 12 \\ 28 & 17 & -20 \end{pmatrix}$$

3. $\dfrac{1}{ad-bc} \begin{pmatrix} d & -b \\ -c & a \end{pmatrix}$

Chapter XIII, §2

1. (a) $\begin{pmatrix} 1 & 1 \\ 2xy & x^2 \end{pmatrix}$ (b) $\begin{pmatrix} \cos x & 0 \\ -y\sin xy & -x\sin xy \end{pmatrix}$ (c) $\begin{pmatrix} ye^{xy} & xe^{xy} \\ 1/x & 0 \end{pmatrix}$

(d) $\begin{pmatrix} z & 0 & x \\ y & x & 0 \\ 0 & z & y \end{pmatrix}$ (e) $\begin{pmatrix} yz & xz & xy \\ 2xz & 0 & x^2 \end{pmatrix}$

(f) $\begin{pmatrix} yz\cos xyz & xz\cos xyz & yx\cos xyz \\ z & 0 & x \end{pmatrix}$

2. (a) $\begin{pmatrix} 1 & 1 \\ 4 & 1 \end{pmatrix}$ (b) $\begin{pmatrix} -1 & 0 \\ -\dfrac{\pi}{2}\sin\dfrac{\pi^2}{2} & -\pi\sin\dfrac{\pi^2}{2} \end{pmatrix}$ (c) $\begin{pmatrix} 4e^4 & e^4 \\ 1 & 0 \end{pmatrix}$

(d) $\begin{pmatrix} -1 & 0 & 1 \\ 1 & 1 & 0 \\ 0 & -1 & 1 \end{pmatrix}$ (e) $\begin{pmatrix} 1 & -2 & -2 \\ -4 & 0 & 4 \end{pmatrix}$ (f) $\begin{pmatrix} 8 & 4\pi & 2\pi \\ 4 & 0 & \pi \end{pmatrix}$

5. $x = 0$, y arbitrary; also all points with $x = 2y$

7. $\begin{pmatrix} \cos\theta & -r\sin\theta \\ \sin\theta & r\cos\theta \end{pmatrix}$, r; determinant vanishes only for $r = 0$.

8. $\begin{pmatrix} \sin\varphi\cos\theta & -r\sin\varphi\sin\theta & r\cos\varphi\cos\theta \\ \cos\varphi & 0 & -r\sin\varphi \\ \sin\varphi\sin\theta & r\sin\varphi\cos\theta & r\cos\varphi\sin\theta \end{pmatrix}$
Determinant $r^2\sin\varphi$

Chapter XIII, §4

1. Yes in all cases

5. Letting $y = \varphi(x)$, we have

$$\varphi''(x) = \frac{-1}{D_2 f(x, y)^2} \left[\begin{array}{l} D_2 f(x, y)(D_1^2 f(x, y) + D_2 D_1 f(x, y)\varphi'(x)) \\ - D_1 f(x, y)(D_1 D_2 f(x, y) + D_2^2 f(x, y)\varphi'(x)) \end{array} \right].$$

9. (a) We have $2x - y - xy' + 2yy' = 0$. This yields

$$\varphi'(1) = 0.$$

(e) $\varphi'(0) = -1$

10. (a) both -1 (c) both $\frac{1}{3}$

11. $3x^2 D_1\varphi(y, z) - 4y + 2z = 0$ so $D_1\varphi(1, 1) = \frac{1}{3}$

Chapter XIV, §2

1. (a) 12   (b) $\frac{11}{5}$ (c) $\frac{1}{10}$ (d) $2 + \pi^2/2$ (e) $\frac{5}{6}$ (f) $\pi/4$

3. (a) $-3\pi/2$ (b) $e - 1/e$ (c) $\pi^2 - \frac{40}{9}$ (d) $\frac{63}{32}$

4. $9\frac{3}{4} - \frac{28}{3}$

6. (a) $\frac{49}{20}$ (b) $e^{-3}/3 - e^{-2}/2 - e^3/3 + e^2/2$

    (c) $1 - \cos 2$ (d) 0   (e) 1   (f) $\frac{1}{6}$

7. $3\pi/8$

8. (a) $\log 2$ (b) $\frac{1}{3}$ (c) π (d) $-\frac{1}{3}$ (e) $\log \frac{27}{16}$

Chapter XIV, §3

1. $(e - 1)\pi$ **2.** $3\pi/2$ **3.** $\pi(1 - e^{-a^2})$ **4.** π

5. $2ka^4/3$ **6.** $3k\pi a^4/2$ **7.** $k\pi/4$ **8.** πa^2

9. $\pi a^4/8$ **10.** $a^3\sqrt{2}/6$ **11.** $a^2(\pi + 8)/4$

12. $a^3(15\pi + 32)/24$ **13.** $2a^2$

14. $(3\pi + 20 - 16\sqrt{2})2\sqrt{2}\, a^3/9$

Chapter XIV, §5

1. π **2.** (a) $\frac{128}{3}$ (b) 128

3. (a) 42   (b) 120   **4.** 2   **6.** πab **7.** $\frac{99}{2}$

8. 1500π **9.** $15\pi ab$ **11.** πab^2

Chapter XIV, §6

1. (a) $\begin{pmatrix} 1 & 0 & 0 \\ 0 & \rho\cos\varphi & \sin\varphi \\ 0 & -\rho\sin\varphi & \cos\varphi \end{pmatrix}$ and determinant is ρ.

    (b) $\displaystyle\iiint_A f(G(\theta, \varphi, \rho))\rho \, d\rho \, d\varphi \, d\theta = \iiint_{G(A)} f(\theta, r, z) \, dz \, dr \, d\theta$

2. 0   **3.** $ka^4\pi$ **4.** $2\pi k(b^2 - a^2)$ **5.** $\pi ba^4/4$

6. $k\pi a^4/2$ **7.** $\pi/8$ **8.** $2\pi\left[-\frac{1}{3}(1 - r_0^2)^{3/2} + \frac{1}{3} - \frac{r_0^4}{4} \right]$

$$\text{where } r_0^2 = \frac{-1 + \sqrt{5}}{2}$$

9. $\frac{2}{9}a^3(3\pi - 4)$ **10.** πa^3

11. (a) $\pi/3$ (b) $2\pi\sqrt{2}/3$ (c) $\pi/2$ (d) $\pi/32$

12. (a) 25   (b) 15/2   (c) $7a^2b^3/3$

13. $4\pi/3$ **14.** $abck$ **15.** $\frac{4}{3}\pi abc$ **16.** $\frac{4}{3}\pi a^3 \cdot 14$

17. (a) $\frac{1}{3}$ (c) $\frac{2}{3}$ (d) $\frac{2}{3}$ **18.** (a) $\frac{7}{3}$ (b) 3

Chapter XV, §1

1. (a) -4 (b) 4   (c) 4π (d) π (e) 8   (f) πab
3. 2π

Chapter XVI, §2

1. dim 4

2. (a) $\dfrac{1}{\sqrt{3}}(1, 1, -1)$ and $\dfrac{1}{\sqrt{2}}(1, 0, 1)$

(b) $\dfrac{1}{\sqrt{6}}(2, 1, 1),$ $\dfrac{1}{5\sqrt{3}}(-1, 7, -5)$

3. $\dfrac{1}{\sqrt{6}}(1, 2, 1, 0)$ and $\dfrac{1}{\sqrt{31}}(-1, -2, 5, 1)$

4. $\dfrac{1}{\sqrt{2}}(1, 1, 0, 0),$ $\tfrac{1}{2}(1, -1, 1, 1),$ $\dfrac{1}{\sqrt{18}}(-2, 2, 3, 4)$

5. $\sqrt{80}\,(t^2 - 3t/4), \sqrt{3}\,t$
6. $\sqrt{80}\,(t^2 - 3t/4), \sqrt{3}\,t, 10t^2 - 12t + 3$

Chapter XVI, §3

1. (a) 2 (b) 2 (c) 2 (d) 1
3. n **4.** (a) 1 (b) 2 (c) 1 (d) 0
5. (a) 1 (b) 1 (c) 0 (d) 2   **6.** $n - 1$

Chapter XVI, §4

1. $\left(\displaystyle\int_{-\pi}^{\pi} (f(x) + g(x))^2 \, dx \right)^{1/2} \leqq \left(\displaystyle\int_{-\pi}^{\pi} f(x)^2 \, dx \right)^{1/2} + \left(\displaystyle\int_{-\pi}^{\pi} g(x)^2 \, dx \right)^{1/2}$

4. (a) $\dfrac{x}{2} = \sin x - \dfrac{\sin 2x}{2} + \cdots + (-1)^n \dfrac{\sin nx}{n} + \cdots$

(b) $x^2 = \dfrac{\pi^2}{3} - 4\left(\cos x - \dfrac{\cos 2x}{2^2} + \cdots + (-1)^{n+1} \dfrac{\cos nx}{n^2} + \cdots \right)$

(c) $x = \dfrac{\pi}{2} - \dfrac{4}{\pi}\left(\cos x + \dfrac{\cos 3x}{3^2} + \cdots + \dfrac{\cos (2n + 1)x}{(2n + 1)^2} + \cdots \right)$

(f) $\cos x = \dfrac{4}{\pi}\left(\dfrac{1}{2} + \dfrac{\cos 2x}{3} + \cdots + (-1)^{n-1} \dfrac{\cos 2nx}{4n^2 - 1} + \cdots \right)$

(g) $\sin^3 x = \tfrac{3}{4} \sin x - \tfrac{1}{4} \sin 3x$

Index

I1

I2 INDEX